# A HISTORY OF
# INVENTION

The fixed aerial of the Radio Astronomy
Observatory, University of Cambridge.

# EGON LARSEN

## A HISTORY OF
## INVENTION

WITH 68 PHOTOGRAPHS AND
112 LINE ILLUSTRATIONS, INCLUDING
MANY ESPECIALLY DRAWN
BY GEORGE LANE

PHOENIX HOUSE · LONDON
ROY PUBLISHERS · NEW YORK

# Contents

# Illustrations

## PLATES

\* 7

TV camera without cameraman
*B.B.C.*
Automation at the Saratov glass factory
*'Soviet Weekly'*
An electronic process-control computer
*Sir W. G. Armstrong-Whitworth Aircraft Ltd*

# LINE DRAWINGS

# I

# Energy

# I

◇◇◇◇◇◇◇◇◇◇◇◇◇◇◇◇◇◇

# Slaves, Wind, and Water

SOMETIMES the zoo warders entertain the visitors who have come to see the apes by putting a banana or an apple in a position where even the best climbers with the longest arms cannot get it. After many unsuccessful attempts one or the other of the apes may find that the warder has left a stick lying about. Without fail the animal will eventually discover that it can use the stick as an extension of its own hand, and push the fruit down with it.

But this is about as far as our nearest relatives in the animal kingdom will go in the use of tools, and we may take it that the earliest ape-like men lived without them. Only as their brains developed the sheer necessity of survival made them look around for tools and weapons to increase the power, efficiency, and range of their own hands and teeth. From that age—we cannot tell how long ago it was, or how long it lasted—we may date the beginning of the rise of Man which set him apart from the rest of the animals, and made him master of our planet.

Tens of thousands of years ago, when he passed through the period now called the Old Stone Age, he was already using a variety of implements for hunting and food-gathering. He began by chipping suitable stones into shape and using them as axes, knives, spearheads, and the like. He invented the bow, which may be regarded as the first device for storing up energy, to be released at will. Later generations made flint tools with finely retouched edges, fishing tackle, needles, carpenter's tools, and even primitive surgical instruments. Man's hands and the tools he had invented entered an association which has never been broken until this day.

Prehistory, the study of the development of Man up to the

15

period of recorded historical events, is rather vague about the times when this or that invention or achievement made its first appearance. The reason is that the successive stages of development occurred at different times with the various human tribes— in one part of the world they were still in their stone-age phase while in others they had already entered the advanced periods of bronze and iron tools. But we only have to look around in our own present-day world to see enormous differences in technological development.

Moving a stone by leverage

We may safely assume that fundamental discoveries and inventions, such as the wheel and the utilization of fire, were made in a number of places and periods, and many times all over again. But the road to true civilization opened only when Man found out— in the Middle Eastern region some time during the later stone age, a few thousand years B.C.—that there was another possible way of life, and a better one, than that of the wandering hunter. He became a farmer. He learnt to till the ground and to make suitable tools: the plough and the hoe, the sickle and the flail. He built houses, and invented tools for the job. He tackled the problem of irrigation. He began to dig in the earth for metals. Slowly, the age of the stone tool came to an end.

At first the farmer himself dragged the plough through the soil.

Then he trained oxen to do it for him. He tamed the ass and much later the horse to pull his cart and to let him ride on their backs. In this way he achieved much relief for his own muscles. Laziness is certainly the mother of invention; there is good reason for believing that this eternal weakness was responsible for the creation of the first and simplest of all machines, the lever.

'Give me a fixed point outside the earth, and I will move it', said Archimedes, the greatest of Greek physicists and mathematicians, who lived in the third century B.C. and was among the first educated men who took an interest in technical problems—

Lifting water from a well by means of a pulley

such things were usually left to the working class of antiquity, the slaves. What did Archimedes mean with his famous sentence? He studied the mechanical laws underlying the lever, a long stick or strong branch of a tree, which had been used for ages to shift heavy weights by putting it on a stone or another piece of wood so that one 'arm', the one which was to move the weight, was very short and the other very long. If, for instance, the two 'arms' have a proportion of 1 to 5 in length, the men who have to move the weight will need only one-fifth of the strength they would require if they tried to move it directly; but in order to lift the weight, say, one foot, they will have to press the long lever arm down five feet. What they save in energy they lose in distance, because Nature does not give us something for nothing and requires a certain amount of labour if a certain result is to be obtained; but the lever translates the labour into a more practical form.

It was Archimedes who formulated the principle of the lever: the longer the arm the less need be the force that operates it. His often-quoted dictum about the earth and the fixed point, however, does not mention another essential requirement—the lever itself. It would have to be so long that its end would stick right out of our own galaxy into some other part of the universe.

The unknown inventors of antiquity supplied mankind with innumerable devices which, though in much more advanced forms, are still doing their jobs in many walks of life, and especially in industry. In building and transport, the pulley— probably invented in the early period of iron tools—is still one of the basic machines for moving heavy objects with a minimum of energy. An Assyrian relief of the eighth century B.C. shows that it must have been in fairly common use in the Middle Eastern civilizations in that period. The pulley, too, translates mechanical energy into a more efficient form: in its most primitive shape it is a combination of two grooved wheels, a fixed one and a loose one, with a rope running in the grooves; it permits heavy weights to be raised by pulling the rope downward, with less effort than if the weight were lifted directly—but again the saving of energy is offset by the greater distance over which the rope has to be pulled.

The same effect was achieved by another early invention, that of the cogged wheel: two interlocking cogged wheels, one of them small and the other large, provided the simplest form of driving gear. It is still incorporated in our modern motor-cars. Wheels appeared in all kinds of combinations—cranked wheels for raising water from wells, spinning-wheels, potter's wheels. But far more revolutionary than any of them was the water-wheel; for it was the first harnessing of the power of Nature (apart from the use of sailing ships) to carry out work for Man.

This 'prime mover', as we would call it today, seems to have been invented around 100 B.C. somewhere in the Roman Empire. The power of the flowing river—and later that of the waterfall— was transformed into usable energy by making it turn a large wheel with many small boards, or shovel-shaped blades, fixed to its outer rim. For many centuries it was used mainly for flour-milling; two cogged wheels, one vertical and one horizontal one, transmitted the power of the water to the grindstones. Here and there, the water-wheel was also fitted with buckets instead of boards so that the water from the river could be raised for irrigation. Around A.D. 200 the Romans operated what may be called the earliest power station: a combination of sixteen water-wheels near Arles in the south of France; the wheels drove thirty-two mills which produced thirty tons of flour per day.

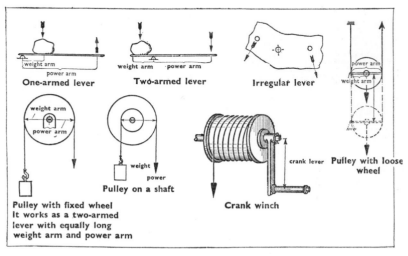

Lever, pulley, and winch

The mechanically minded Arabs made great use of the water-wheel, while Europe, as it entered the Middle Ages, forgot all about this invention. It returned to the Western world only between A.D. 800 and 1200 to become the great prime mover of the period and the first engine to raise industrial productivity by providing power for flour-mills, saw-mills, fulling-mills, sledge-hammers, foundries, and for pumping in mines. There was, of course, no way of 'sending' energy to where it was needed—it was available only on the spot. Not until towards the end of the last century did human inventiveness succeed in transmitting the energy of the flowing and falling water to any place where it was required—by the electric current. We shall hear a great deal more about this development later in our story.

But let us return to the days of the ancient Greeks. We may

Power from the water-wheel

wonder why that nation, which produced so many great philosophers, artists, and writers, did so little in the field of applied Science. The reason was a sociological and psychological one. Greece was a state based on slavery; all practical work had to be done by those hapless people who had the bad luck of being conquered and captured in a war, or of having been born to slave parents. Originally it was the stronger man, and the one with the more advanced arms, who forced the weaker one to serve him and labour for him. Later slaves were bought and sold, and the entire social system of antiquity developed into a society with sharp class divisions, with private and state-owned slaves providing by the labour of their hands a carefree, luxurious existence for the privileged minority of free men.

The Greek philosophers, studying and analysing all aspects of life, hardly ever questioned this state of affairs. It was generally accepted as the 'natural' or 'normal' condition of a large part of mankind that they must toil for the few. Therefore, a shortage of 'labour' or 'energy' in our modern sense was never a problem—when a job had to be done, the slaves just had to do it, and if they found it strenuous they were whipped until it was done. Human effort, life, or health was regarded as expendable as long as only the slaves were concerned. Why, then, should cultured and educated men rack their brains to invent labour-saving machines?

However, there must have been a few upper-class Greeks who were born with technical minds, and who just could not refrain from tinkering and experimenting and inventing. Archimedes, whom we have already mentioned in connection with the lever, was one of them. He discovered the fundamental law of hydro-statics, the equilibrium between a floating body and the pressure of the liquid in which it floats; according to tradition, Archimedes had been asked by the King of Syracuse to find out whether a golden crown made for him contained some proportion of the less precious silver, and Archimedes was at a loss—until one day he stepped into his bath and saw the water running over. This made him realize that a lump of gold placed into a container full of water would cause the overflow of less water than an equally heavy lump of silver—as the latter metal is lighter it must have more bulk. The story goes that Archimedes was so excited that he ran home without first putting on his clothes, shouting 'Eureka, eureka!' into the street.

His theory of the lever was one of the starting-points of the science of theoretical physics (which, however, lay dormant for many centuries after him). Whether he invented the famous screw which bears his name—a simple yet efficient machine for 'screw-ing up' water through a cylinder—is doubtful; however, his works on three-dimensional geometry are of fundamental importance. He also invented some military machines for the defence of his home town, Syracuse, against the Romans; when they conquered it after all, they killed him (212 B.C.).

Another exception to the rule that free men should not bother about labour-saving devices was Hero of Alexandria, who lived some time before the birth of Christ—the dates of his birth and death are not known and neither are the circumstances of his life. He may have been a surveyor by profession because among the variety of useful inventions which are ascribed to him were a kind of theodolite and a device for measuring distances. In his writings he describes lifting tackle, pumps and syringes, gear-wheels, screw-threads, fire-engines, a mechanical fountain, a slot machine for dispensing holy water, stopcocks, automatic puppet theatres, mechanical birds that could flap and whistle, automatically opening temple gates, and similar showpieces and toys.

Some of his inventions, however, were more important than that, because they kindled the imagination of generations of mechanics after him. In his essay, *Pneumatica*, he describes a

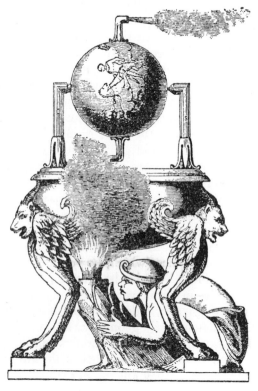

Hero's steam-engine

spherical boiler in which water is heated by a fire from below. The sphere hangs in two brackets so that it can turn, and it has two nozzles through which the steam can escape, making it revolve. It is, in fact, the first reaction turbine driven by a steam jet. It was never put to any practical use, but it proved that the power of steam could carry out mechanical work—in other words, that fire could provide energy for moving objects.

Another of Hero's gadgets was the ball which bears his name

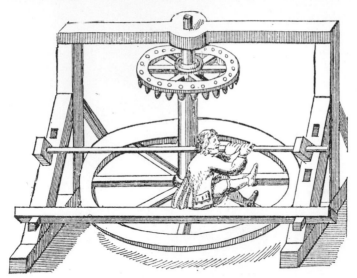

Horizontal treadmill

Vertical treadmill

Ancient windmill

and is still being used as a washing-bottle in chemical laboratories: by squeezing air into a water-filled container you squeeze the water out of a nozzle. Hero's ball is therefore also the ancestor of the perfume 'atomizer'.

One of the many toys described, and probably built, by Hero was a windmill adapted to driving the bellows of an organ. Here again, a prime mover makes its appearance in antiquity: a machine whose origins go back far into the past, but which has been revived in recent times, though in a different form. It may yet have a prosperous future.

The windmill is a combination of the sail, as used in sailing ships, and the treadmill, powered by slaves or animals and used for milling flour. It may have been brought to Europe by the Arabs (at the time of Cervantes's *Don Quixote* there seem to have been a number of windmills in Spain); or it could have been

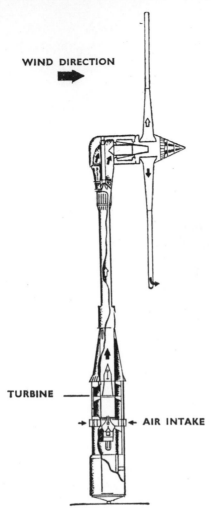

WIND DIRECTION

TURBINE

AIR INTAKE

Modern wind-driven electric generator

invented, or rather reinvented, in Germany. At any rate, the
construction and use of windmills spread from the twelfth to the
eighteenth century all over the Western world, mostly for flour-
milling and water-raising. Therefore, Holland—where strong
sea winds are blowing most of the time—became Europe's windmill country; it needed the free energy of the moving air to pump
water through its irrigation systems. In England, about ten
thousand mills were in operation at the beginning of the nineteenth century. As the steam-engine and other prime movers were

developed their number decreased rapidly, but in our energy-hungry age the scientists and technicians have taken another look at Don Quixote's 'giants'.

The modern wind generator, which has made its appearance in a number of countries, does not use sail-covered wings to drive mill-stones or pumps. It works on the 'depression' principle. It has a propeller with two or more aluminium blades whose pitch is adjusted automatically to the speed of the wind. The blades are hollow and have slits at their tips; as the wind turns them, air is sucked from these slits; the propeller is mounted on top of a hollow steel tower with an air turbine at the bottom, and the turbine is set in motion as a result of the pressure difference between the outside air and the 'depression' in the hollow tower, caused by the air being sucked out of the blade slits. An electric generator is geared to the turbine and produces current.

Today, we can even store the energy of the wind—by using the current (generated during the hours of low consumption) for the electrolysis of water. The hydrogen and oxygen thereby produced are stored in separate cylinders, and when they are brought together again in a so-called fuel cell they produce current, which can be fed to the consumer when there is no wind to drive the turbo-generator. (We shall deal with the fuel cell in greater detail in Part II.)

Thus one of the oldest prime movers has not only stood the test of time, but is now making a come-back two thousand years after Hero's invention.

# 2

◇◇◇◇◇◇◇◇◇◇◇◇◇◇◇◇◇◇◇◇◇◇◇◇

# Steam and Industry

THE slave societies of antiquity withered away and were replaced, at least in the Western world, by the feudal states of the Middle Ages. The effect of this change on technological development was at first negligible. Nearly all the energy available was that of human and animal muscles, later to be supplemented by some wind and water power in the more advanced civilizations. But there were enough poor people everywhere who could be made to work for the rich and mighty, providing amply for their needs. The peasants and artisans toiled throughout their lives, never achieving a high standard of existence as the fruits of their labours went into keeping a thin upper crust of society in comfort. Church and State did their best to keep the common man in his lowly place.

We must try to visualize these circumstances if we want to understand why Science and engineering did not develop very much during the Middle Ages—why, for instance, the steam-engine was not invented, and electricity discovered, a thousand years earlier. Certainly many creative minds turned to the problem of harnessing the forces of Nature for the benefit of Man in those 'dark' centuries; but there seemed to be no need for such devices, and even if they had been invented no one would have dared to suggest how they might have been used. Life on earth, except for the chosen few, was to be a valley of tears, toil, and sweat, and any attempt at making it easier could only have been a temptation by the Devil. Savants who dared to find out some scientific truth—for instance, that the earth is not the centre of the Universe—were made to recant, or burnt at the stake if they stuck to their 'heresies'.

Thus there was little incentive for discovery and invention, and it is no mere chance that some of the very few medieval scientists were monks and clerics, and therefore less suspect of being in league with the Evil One: Roger Bacon, the thirteenth-century natural philosopher, joined the Franciscans, and his contemporary, Berthold Schwarz, the German inventor of gunpowder, belonged to the same Holy Order, to mention only two of them. To the medieval mind, Science was more or less confined to alchemy, and alchemy was mainly the quest for the legendary 'Philosophers' Stone', some magic substance which would convert all baser metals into gold. Many rulers retained their court alchemists in the hope that they would discover the secret, and make them the richest princes in the world. A few useful discoveries were achieved as 'by-products' of that futile quest: Böttger, a Dresden alchemist, stumbled on the secret of how to make porcelain, Dr Glauber found the 'salts' which still bear his name, and the properties of acids and gases were discovered in the same roundabout way.

Technical achievements do not appear out of the blue. Apart from the incentive to the inventor and the possibility of putting his inventions to some practical use, there is the development of craftsmanship which plays a decisive part. For instance, the invention of the steam-engine depended on a high standard of boiler-making, which in turn meant that the craft of riveting had to be well developed. Or, to quote another example: the main achievement of Peter Henlein, the Nuremberg locksmith who lived at the beginning of the sixteenth century, was not that he 'invented the watch', as the textbook tells us, but that he was able to produce springy strips of steel, elastic enough to bend them tightly into coils. Anyone could have thought of making a pocket model of a clock, but it was the craftsmanship of Henlein the locksmith which provided the essential part, the mainspring.

The frustration which an inventor must have felt when he discovered that the technological development of his time was far behind his own flight of ideas can be guessed from Leonardo da Vinci's famous notebooks. It was only late in the eighteenth century, three hundred years after Leonardo's lifetime, that his manuscripts became generally known; until then he had ranked as a great artist, but few had any idea of his importance as an engineer and inventor. From these five thousand pages he

emerges as a mechanical genius—but so far ahead of his time
that most of his inventions were impossible to execute with the
technological means and the craftsmanship available around A.D.
1500. However, the notebooks seem to have circulated among
his contemporaries, and his ideas influenced many of them. It was
the time of the Renaissance, that is, of the revival of classic art and
Science, which marks the end of the Middle Ages and the beginning of modern times. Medieval society began to break up; a new
class—that of the merchants—rose between the upper and the
lower classes, and stimulated inventive thought, exploration, and
expansion.

Among the technical ideas which Leonardo described in words
and drawings in his notebooks, and which had to remain dreams
for a few more centuries because there was no practical possibility
of realizing them, were among other things a power loom, a
wheel-lock pistol, a flying-machine, a revolving stage, a pendu-
lum-driven pump, and several devices to use the motive power of
steam, for instance for firing cannon and turning a spit. However,
he carried out the construction of canals, harbours, and fortifica-
tions as chief engineer to the power-loving Cesare Borgia.

Throughout the seventeenth and eighteenth centuries numerous attempts were made at utilizing the power of steam. It was
an odd succession of scientists and inventors who took up the idea
every few years, now in this country, now in that: the idea of
using the expanding force of water, gasified by boiling, to drive
some kind of machine. There was the French architect, Salomon
de Caux, whom Cardinal Richelieu sent to a madhouse because of
the 'lunacy' of his plans; there he died after thirty years of
captivity. One of his visitors at that dismal place was the Marquis
of Worcester, himself a man with an inventive mind, who was
also to spend a number of years behind bars. He acted as a secret
agent of the exiled King Charles II until he was caught by
Cromwell's men and imprisoned in the Tower of London. There
he compiled his famous *Century of Inventions*, a collection of
technical ideas, many of which were carried out long after his
time: telegraph, automatic pistol, airplane, stenography, ship-
lifting crane, light-metal gun, megaphone, combination lock,
horseless carriage, and sailless ship. Only one of his inventions—
No. 68 in the *Century*—reached the model stage during the
Marquis's lifetime, a machine for raising water 40 feet by steam

pressure in mines. Freed from the Tower by the Restoration in 1660, he was granted a patent by Parliament. The machine was exhibited as a model in Vauxhall, but it was never executed in full size. The Marquis used a cylinder into which steam was blown

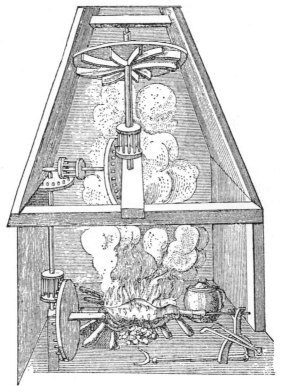

Leonardo's hot-air-driven automatic spit

and then condensed; the resulting vacuum would suck the cylinder full of water after a valve had been opened. By blowing in some more steam the water could be forced out of the cylinder, and the cycle restarted.

It may seem surprising that even in the seventeenth century, when the superstitious and reactionary forces of medieval society had lost much of their hold over the minds of men, technical progress was so slow and inventive ideas so rare. But there still seems to have lingered some doubt whether it was 'right' to use the powers of Nature for the purpose of making the lot of man-kind a little easier—of saving the common man some of the toil to which he had been condemned when the Cherubim and the flaming sword drove him out of Eden. Even the Marquis of Worcester must have suffered from some feeling of guilt; he wrote, in connection with his water-raising machine, that he prayed to Providence to punish him for his arrogance and for yielding to evil temptations if his insight into the workings of Nature had made him conceited.

No doubt, the power of steam had something awe-inspiring to the good people in past centuries, much as the energy of the split atom has to us. The ancient Teutons even used it as a machine to impress the faithful and scare their enemies: they built an idol called *püsterich* with a metal head filled with water; the mouth of the figure was stopped up with a wooden plug, and when the water was heated by a charcoal fire the plug shot out, followed by a jet of steam.

It was something like the *püsterich* which another seventeenth-century inventor, the Italian architect Giovanni Branca, had in mind when he designed a head-shaped boiler from whose mouth issued a jet of steam, directed against the blades of a wooden wheel—in fact, an early model of the steam turbine. At about the same time, in 1630, the Englishman David Ramsey received a patent for a similar machine, but his technical specifications were too woolly for a practical execution of the invention.

Perhaps the most interesting personality among the seven-teenth-century steam-engine inventors was Denis Papin, a French Huguenot, who studied medicine and physics as a young man. He met the great Dutch scientist Christian Huygens, inventor of the pendulum clock and author of the wave theory of light, in Paris and went with him to The Hague. They worked together for eight years, and then Huygens recommended the young Frenchman to Robert Boyle, the famous English physicist, whose special field was the pressure of gases.

From 1675, Papin lived in Boyle's house in Pall Mall, London, and here he made an invention which has only recently become popular in the kitchens of the world—the pressure cooker. It was the outcome of his investigations into the nature of steam.

Papin's 'bone-digester', as he called his machine, worked on the principle that when water or juice is boiled in a hermetically

B

closed vessel so that the steam cannot escape, the pressure increases so much that the steam is heated far beyond the boiling-point of water. The superheated steam helps to cook the food much faster and more thoroughly than is possible in ordinary saucepans. 'I took beef bones that had never been boiled, but kept dry a long time', Papin wrote in the description of his first experiment, 'and of the hardest part of the leg; these being put

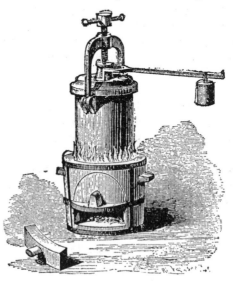

Papin's 'bone digester', forerunner of the pressure cooker

into a little glass pot, with water, and inserted in the engine.' He also invented the safety-valve, a little stopper with a weight attached, which closed a hole in the pot so long as the pressure did not increase beyond a certain point; when it became too great it forced the stopper out, and some steam escaped. This invention alone would have established his fame in the annals of technical history, for it was the first automatic control device.

Papin introduced his bone-digester to the savants of the Royal Society by cooking a meal for them. It was excellent, and they enjoyed this 'scientific dinner', as Papin called it, very much. But he made it plain to them that he regarded his bone-digester merely as a stepping stone to the steam-engine which he hoped to build one day.

A political event of great importance interfered with Papin's plan to return to his native country and continue his work there. Louis XIV revoked the Edict of Nantes, that solemn guarantee assuring the Huguenots of religious freedom. Denis Papin had become an exile.

At this turning-point in his life, a German Protestant prince, the Landgrave of Hesse, offered him a chair at the University of

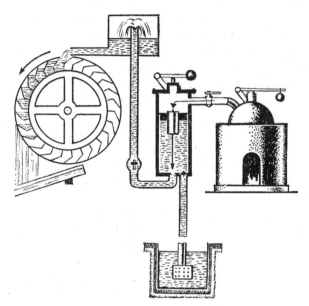

Papin's water-lifting machine

Marburg. Papin accepted, hoping that under the protection of an enlightened ruler he would be able to develop his steam-engine; his pet idea was that of driving a ship with it 'against the wind'.

He built an experimental model at Marburg. It was a complicated and rather clumsy machine whose energy derived more from atmospheric pressure than from the power of the expanding steam; a workman had to shove a fire-box under it at certain intervals to produce the steam, and remove it again to cause condensation. But it had one ingenious feature which pointed the way to a really efficient prime mover: Papin used the cylinder and piston of a pump in his design. This, above all, was Papin's most valuable contribution to the development of the steam-engine.

He described his invention in a pamphlet published in 1690, hopeful that the whole world would acclaim him as its benefactor. But the world seemed to have little use for the steam-engine; only one inventor, an English captain by the name of Thomas Savery, carried out some of Papin's ideas and took out a patent for a water-lifting machine. Even the Hessian landgrave had lost interest in Papin's work; the experimental prototype was made to drive a flour-mill, but the idea of backing a steam-engine for ships did not appeal to the prince. So Papin decided to return to England, where he hoped to find more support.

He bought a boat and fitted it with paddle-wheels, later to be driven by steam power; but as a kind of propaganda stunt Papin intended to propel it by means of hand-cranks from Marburg all the way to England, with his wife and his numerous children on board.

He did not get very far. A few miles down the river, at the next town, the watermen's guild barred the way to the strange vessel full of foreigners. There was a tussle, the irate scientist tried to push on, but the watermen pulled the boat on land and cut it to pieces with their pickaxes.

Desperate and without a penny to his name Papin arrived back in London. In vain he tried to get the Royal Society to help him build his steam-engine, or at least compare his designs with those of Savery. In the end he had to struggle for a bare livelihood. His traces are lost in the slums of London; the last document in his handwriting, a letter to a friend, dated June 1712, closes thus:

'I am in a melancholy situation; in spite of all my effort I only bring down enmity on myself. But I have no fear, and trust in Almighty God.'

In the same year an ironmonger and Baptist preacher from Dartmouth, Thomas Newcomen, completed his own steam-engine after years of experimenting with Savery's pumps. The only place where such an engine was urgently needed was in Britain's mines, which filled with water faster than it could be cleared out. Savery had used the method of creating a partial vacuum in the cylinder by dashing cold water on its outside, thus causing the steam inside to condense; Newcomen, however, sprayed the cold water directly into the steam-filled cylinder to create a vacuum so that the atmospheric pressure forced the piston down. From the time of Savery's death in 1715, Newcomen

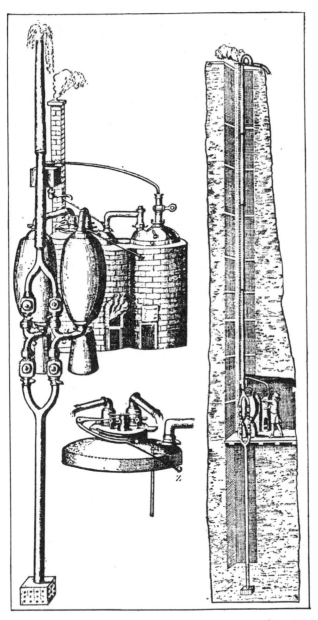

Savery's 'Engine to raise Water by Fire'—a pump for mines

controlled the manufacture of steam pumps in Britain for a good many years. Some were exported to the Continent although they wasted an enormous amount of coal and had to have constant attention. The valves, for instance, had to be opened and closed by so-called cock boys.

One of these, Humphrey Potter, got so bored with the job, which he had to do all day long in a Cornish mine, that he achieved a brilliant invention which made the machine almost automatic. He connected the valve rods, which he was meant to operate, to the big working-beam of the engine so that they opened and shut as it swung up and down. It was a major improvement.

Newcomen machines were the only practical steam-engines from the early to the late eighteenth century; a few improvements were made by a Leeds engineer, John Smeaton, at the Carron ironworks in Scotland. One of his largest Newcomen engines went to Russia in 1775 to pump out the dry docks at Kronstadt.

By that time, however, the childhood of the steam-engine was already drawing to an end. A young Scotsman by the name of James Watt, the fifth son of a ship's carpenter from Greenock, gave the machine its most efficient form—and thereby helped to revolutionize the British way of life.

He was a weakly child, suffering from headaches and unable to go to school. His mother taught him, and as soon as James could read he began to devour books. At the age of 15 he had learnt most of what was then known about physics, and his father sent him to Glasgow to study advanced mechanics. Later, his professor helped him to set himself up as an instrument-maker and 'machine-doctor' in a shop in the University building.

One day in 1763—Watt was 27 years old—he was asked to repair a small model of a Newcomen engine, which was needed for the natural-science lectures. The little machine refused to work properly, stopping again and again after a few strokes of the piston.

Watt examined it carefully. It had a boiler in which the steam was produced. At the bottom of the cylinder were two valves, one to admit the steam and the other to let a jet of cold water cool the cylinder when the piston had reached its highest point. This caused the steam to condense—and as steam takes up 1,700 times more space than water a vacuum was created under the piston, and it was forced down by the pressure of the atmosphere.

It was clear to Watt's inquisitive mind that this machine, even when in perfect working order, used the steam not nearly efficiently enough. Was there, he asked himself, some better way of making the piston move? The cold-jet injection seemed too clumsy to him.

For two years he tried to find a solution to the problem. 'One Sunday afternoon in 1765', he recalled later, 'I had gone for a walk and my thoughts turning naturally to the experiments I had been engaged in for saving heat in the cylinder, the idea occurred to me that, as steam was an elastic vapour, it would expand, and rush into a previously exhausted space; and that if I were to produce a vacuum in a separate vessel, and open a communication between this and the steam in the cylinder, such would be the result.'

It was this idea of the separate condenser which made the steam-engine the first great prime mover in modern times. Now the cylinder could remain hot, without having to be cooled and reheated with each cycle; he even put a steam jacket around it to preserve the heat. The result was that he saved 75 per cent of the fuel which the Newcomen engine needed. He also closed the upper end of the cylinder, which was open in the Newcomen engine, and built around the piston rod what is now called a stuffing-box; instead of making the air push the piston down he used steam for this purpose too, introducing it above the piston as well as below in the cylinder. The fourth of his improvements was an air pump to maintain the vacuum in his condenser by pumping out the condensed water and air from it.

Watt's first model was single acting and could be used only for pumping. But a great many tasks were awaiting the steam-engine. New machines in various branches of industry needed power; goods were to be moved, people transported.

A manufacturer from Soho, near Birmingham, Matthew Boulton, made James Watt his partner in the world's first steam-engine factory. Soon the firm of Boulton & Watt became one of the wonders of the age: here the visitors, who turned up from all over Europe and even America, could see the shape of things to come.

Boulton badgered Watt to think of ways and means to convert

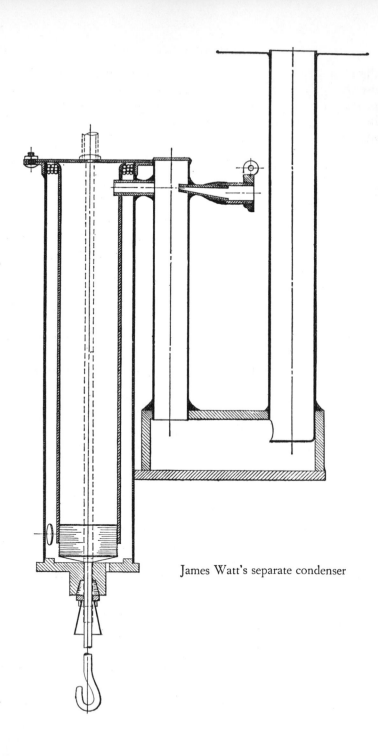

James Watt's separate condenser

the reciprocating movement of the engine into a rotary one for use in factories and, later perhaps, for vehicles and ships. Watt produced no less than five different solutions, the best of them being the 'sun-and-planet' system—we are so familiar with it that we hardly realize what an excellent solution to a tricky problem it is. Watt also adopted an old invention, the fly-wheel, for the important purpose of turning the irregular motion of the piston into a regular, rotary one. The fly-wheel is, in fact, a reservoir of energy, which it 'stores up' during the working stroke of the engine, to release it as the crank passes through the dead centre. Watt does not seem to have known the mechanics of the fly-wheel, but he realized that it was the answer to the problem of how to overcome the dead centre.

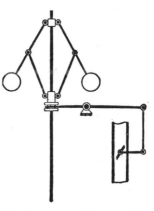

Watt's 'governor', an eighteenth-century 'feed-back' device for controlling the speed of a steam-engine

Neither could he have known that he invented one of the major 'feedback' devices—which play such a vital part in automation, where they act as automatic controls. This is the 'governor', whose task it is to keep the engine speed constant, detect an unnecessary or dangerous increase of engine power, and to reduce it by closing the throttle or steam-valve. The Watt governor works simply by using centrifugal force: a vertical shaft, carrying two heavy metal balls at the ends of arms, is rotated by the engine, and centrifugal force moves the balls outwards as the engine speed increases, or allows them to sink as the speed decreases. The arms to which the balls are fixed move therefore up or down, raising or lowering a 'collar' around the vertical shaft. This is connected to the throttle or steam-valve, closing or opening it if the engine speed becomes too great or too low. Thus the steam-engine controls itself.

'The people of London, Manchester, and Birmingham are steam-mill mad', Boulton told Watt in 1781. The Soho factory turned out as many steam-engines as possible, yet the demand surpassed by far its production capacity, and other manufacturers

* B

were permitted to build them under Watt's licence. Why was there now such an enormous demand for energy, after centuries of indifference and even hostility towards the idea of using the forces of Nature for the benefit of mankind?

Slowly, the medieval system of the individual craftsman had begun to crumble. In England a new form of industry appeared, timidly at first: groups of men banded together to use machines which were too costly and too heavy for the independent artisan. Merchants who needed wares to sell provided the money and organized the manufacture, or 'factory'. These 'capitalists' employed the workers for wages. They appeared first in those trades where heavy machinery and capital was most necessary: mainly in coal-mining, where the early steam pumps saved many pits from ruin through flooding, and in textile production, where a number of inventions were revolutionizing spinning and weaving.

It was through the impact of these new machines that Britain, hitherto a nation of farmers, turned into an industrial state—and that Englishmen left the countryside by their many thousands to crowd into the towns and seek employment in the factories which seemed to promise work and livelihood for all. Spinning and weaving, a most important industry in a cold, northern climate, had been carried out in the villages with spinning-wheels and hand looms; but although the cloth produced in this way was expensive, the men and women who made it lived in poverty from the cradle to the grave. Only a substantial rise in the level of production could have increased the country's standard of living. Tolls and taxes took away much of the people's earnings, and feudal restrictions prevented a free exchange of goods and services.

The new machines broke through this barrier, changing an old-fashioned handicraft to modern mass production. John Kay, a poor clockmaker from Bury in Lancashire, made the beginning with his 'fly shuttle', a little box on either side of the loom, where the shuttle remained between its journeys across the warp threads. Each box had a little rod, one end of which was fastened to a cord, and when the cord was pulled the rod hit the shuttle and shot it across the loom into the little box on the other side. Then the cord on the other side was pulled, and the shuttle flew back again. Thus the weaver—instead of throwing the shuttle across and back again by hand—could work much faster, and the width of the cloth could be doubled.

John Kay made his invention in 1733. Thirty-five years later, a weaver, James Hargreaves of Blackburn, invented a spinning machine—which he called 'Spinning Jenny' after his wife—with eight spindles operated by a single wheel. Later he built a machine with thirty spindles. Richard Arkwright, a barber by profession, heard the weavers in his home town, Bolton, complain that the yarn produced by the new spinning-jenny was not as fine and smooth as that spun by the old method. With the help of a watch-maker he built a new machine which squeezed the wool or cotton

Hargreaves's 'Spinning Jenny'

into long, flat strands and then twisted them into smooth threads. The machine was good but heavy and could be worked only by power; as it was first worked by water power it became known as the 'water frame'.

Next came Samuel Crompton, also from Bolton, but a farmer's son. He invented the 'mule', a cross between the spinning-jenny and the water frame. His biggest model had 20 spindles; a modern 'mule' may work with up to 1,350 spindles. In the 1780's, a clergyman by the name of Dr Edmund Cartwright, who at first knew nothing at all about weaving, built a most efficient weaving machine that could work only with the help of an equally efficient prime mover—the steam-engine.

At the turn of the century a young university graduate from Massachusetts, Eli Whitney, revolutionized cotton harvesting by his invention of the 'cotton gin'. Negro slaves had been used in the southern states of the U.S.A. to separate the fibre from the seeds by hand; the gin did it mechanically. It was this machine which influenced the development of the whole of the United States more than any other; cotton became the country's great source of wealth. When Whitney first introduced his machine, the U.S.A. produced no more than 140,000 lb. of cotton per year; in 1800, only a few years later, the figure was 35 million pounds, and today it is 7,000 million pounds.

All these inventors had to struggle hard against prejudice and fear, most of all among the workers, who were worried about losing their jobs when those new machines would start to produce more and more goods. There were riots, some inventors were driven out of the country, others died penniless. But the men who built the new factories saw that these machines could offer them enormous profits. They installed them, bought steam-engines to power them, and the workers had to come willy-nilly to ask for jobs in the factories if they wanted to make a living. Wages were low, conditions in the 'dark satanic mills' usually deplorable, working hours long—up to fourteen hours per day—and many children went into factories to toil with their parents so that the family would have enough to eat.

When James Watt retired from the firm of Boulton & Watt at the age of 64 in 1800, steam-engines were already puffing and hissing all over Europe, and even in America. For the first time in human history, the immense storehouse of the earth's mineral wealth had been unlocked to provide its inhabitants with mechanical power. The consequences were far-reaching. Not only because the steam-engine was a British invention but also because Britain was particularly rich in coal, this country was the first to undergo an industrial revolution which changed the whole way of life completely within the short span of two or three generations. As agricultural Britain became industrial Britain, the power of the landowning class began to wane, and the middle classes— the producers and distributors of goods—rose in importance and wealth. In her quickly growing Empire, England found many sources of new materials for her factories—and cheap labour to reap a rich harvest; until the 1830's, tobacco, sugar, and cotton were almost exclusively produced by coloured slaves.

As the use of steam power became general it was found necessary to set a standard for determining the capacity of engines. People were still familiar with the horse as a source of power, and so it was natural to compare the power of a steam-engine with that of a horse. Boulton & Watt standardized one horsepower at 33,000 foot-pounds per minute, or 550 foot-pounds per second—i.e. the power necessary to lift 550 lb. one foot per second (or 1 lb. 550 ft per second). Later, when electricity became important for the transmission of energy, James Watt's name was honoured by the acceptance of the watt as a unit of electrical power. The relationship between horsepower and watt is that 746 watts are 1 h.p., and 1 kW (1,000 W) = 1·36 h.p.

Eli Whitney, the inventor of the cotton gin, was also responsible for the first application of mass production methods. The United States Army needed muskets because there was some danger that there might be a war with France. Eli Whitney accepted, in 1798, a contract for the delivery of 10,000 muskets within fifteen months. They could never have been made by the traditional methods, with one gunsmith making the complete musket from start to finish. So Whitney had the idea of dividing up the work into a great number of small jobs, as a result of which all the component parts of the musket would be made so accurate as to be interchangeable. It was a completely new system.

First he designed the tools to make the parts with utmost precision, uniformly, and quickly. Then he trained his workers to use these hand and machine tools (he also invented the milling machine at a later date): the 'filing jigs' which guided the workman's file; the stencils with up to a dozen holes, which enabled the mechanic to bore the holes in the workpiece in exactly the right places; the mechanical stops fixed to the lathe, which prevented the worker from turning the piece too little or too much; and the dies and moulds for various components.

He brought his first batch of ten muskets to the United States Treasury officials in Philadelphia, but he did not show them the complete weapons—he brought parcels with the component parts, and asked them to pick the parts from each batch at random. From these components he assembled the muskets before their eyes. It was the first demonstration of the system of interchangeable parts, made by semi-skilled workers in mass production.

Whitney carried out his contract with the help of a small number of men. But he used a water-mill as his main source of power in the factory which he built near New Haven. Legal battles and troubles concerning his cotton gin as well as increasing ill health sapped his energy and shortened his life; otherwise he would certainly have become America's first industrial king, ruling over an empire of steam-powered engineering works.

During the comparatively short time of thirty-five years the genius of James Watt improved the reciprocating steam-engine so much that throughout the nineteenth century this prime mover remained basically as he had shaped it—although it increased a great deal in size, performance, and accuracy of construction. There was only one significant advance achieved by a rival, the compound engine, invented by another British engineer, Jonathan Carter Hornblower. He added another, larger cylinder to Watt's one-cylinder engine; this received the exhaust from the first cylinder, which operated under high pressure, and, like it, was connected to the crankshaft. In this way the steam was made to perform additional work in the second cylinder. Watt felt that his patent had been infringed; he and Boulton sued Hornblower, who had to stop making steam-engines, and died in frustration and poverty.

Arthur Woolf, a millwright who had worked with him, took up the idea of the compound engine after Watt's patent had expired, and this type was widely introduced. Other improvements came with the application of steam power for transport (see Part II). Only at the end of the nineteenth century did the reciprocating steam-engine meet its greatest challenge, that of the steam-turbine, with which we shall deal in the next chapter.

# 3

◇◇◇◇◇◇◇◇◇◇◇◇◇◇◇◇◇◇◇◇◇◇

# The Story of Electricity

THERE is electricity everywhere in the world. It is present in the atom, whose particles are held together by its forces; it reaches us from the most distant parts of the universe in the form of electro-magnetic waves. Yet we have no organs that could recognize it as we see light or hear sound. We have to make it visible, tangible, or audible, we have to make it perform work (or give us a shock) to become aware of its presence. There is only one natural phenomenon which demonstrates it unmistakably to our senses of seeing and hearing—thunder and lightning; but we recognize only the effects—not the force which causes them.

Small wonder, then, that Man lived for aeons on this earth without knowing anything about electricity. He tried to explain the phenomenon of the thunderstorm to himself by imagining that some gods or other supernatural creatures were giving vent to their heavenly anger, or were fighting battles in the sky. Thunderstorms frightened our primitive ancestors; they should have been grateful to them instead because lightning gave them their first fires, and thus opened to them the road to civilization. It is a fascinating question how differently life on earth would have developed if we had an organ for electricity.

We cannot blame the ancient Greeks for failing to recognize that the force which causes a thunderstorm is the same which they observed when rubbing a piece of amber: it attracted straw, feathers, and other light materials. Thales of Miletos, the Greek philosopher who lived about 600 B.C., was the first who noticed this. The Greek word for amber is *elektron*, and therefore Thales called that mysterious force 'electric'. For a long time it was thought to be of the same nature as the magnetic power of the lodestone since the effect of attraction seems similar, and in fact there are many links between electricity and magnetism.

There is just a chance, although a somewhat remote one, that the ancient Jews knew something of the secret of electricity. Georg Christoph Lichtenberg, the famous eighteenth-century physicist at Göttingen, and a friend of Hogarth, came to the conclusion that the Ark of the Covenant was an electrical machine. This sacred shrine of the Children of Israel, which they carried about during their desert wanderings, contained two stone tables with the Ten Commandments; it was built of dry acacia wood clad inside and outside with thin sheets of gold—in modern technical language, the framework consisted of two layers of conducting metal with a layer of insulating material between them. The entire Tabernacle, whose innermost sanctuary the Ark was, held a great deal of gold, silver, and brass, which may have attracted atmospheric electricity, and this could have charged the 'battery', the Ark; in the Fifth Book of Moses we read a good deal about the cloud that used to gather above the Tabernacle. The priests might have used this 'magic' to impress their people. Anyone not 'in the know' could have been electrocuted by drawing an electric discharge upon himself, and in Leviticus x. 2 we are told that two of Aaron's sons brought a censer (a metal vessel for burning incense) to the Ark, although they had not been commanded to do so, 'and there came forth fire from before the Lord, and devoured them, and they died'.

Perhaps the Israelites did know something about electricity; this theory is supported by the fact that the Temple at Jerusalem had metal rods on the roof which must have acted as lightning-conductors. In fact, during the thousand years of its existence it was never struck by lightning although thunderstorms abound in Palestine.

There is no other evidence that electricity was put to any use at all in antiquity, except that the Greek women decorated their spinning-wheels with pieces of amber: as the woollen threads rubbed against the amber it first attracted and then repelled them —a pretty little spectacle which relieved the boredom of spinning.

More than two thousand years passed after Thales's discovery without any research work being done in this field. It was Dr William Gilbert, Queen Elizabeth I's physician-in-ordinary, who set the ball rolling. He experimented with amber and lodestone and found the essential difference between electric and magnetic attraction. For substances which behaved like amber—such as glass, sulphur, sealing-wax—he coined the term 'electrica', and for the phenomenon as such the word 'electricity'. In his famous work, *De magnete*, published in 1600, he gave an account of his studies. Although some sources credit him with the invention of

Von Guericke's demonstration of atmospheric pressure with two hemispheres from which the air has been pumped out

the first electric machine, this was a later achievement by Otto von Guericke, Burgomaster of Magdeburg and inventor of the air pump—which he demonstrated most impressively before the Emperor and an assembly of notables at Ratisbon, Bavaria, in 1654 by showing that two teams of eight strong horses each were unable to pull two hemispheres apart once a vacuum had been created in them.

Von Guericke's electric machine consisted of a large disc spinning between brushes; this made sparks leap across a gap between two metal balls. It became a favourite toy in polite society but nothing more than that. In 1700, an Englishman by the name of Francis Hawksbee produced the first electric light: he exhausted a glass bulb by means of a vacuum pump and rotated it at high speed while rubbing it with his hand until it emitted a faint glow of light.

A major advance was the invention of the first electrical condenser, now called the Leyden jar, by the Dutch scientist, Pieter van Musschenbroek of Leyden: a water-filled glass bottle coated inside and out with metallic surfaces, separated by the non-conducting glass; a metal rod with a knob at the top reached down into the water. When charged by an electric machine it stored enough electricity to give anyone who touched the knob a powerful shock.

More and more scientists took up electric research; three clerics, Dean von Kleist of Cammin in Pomerania, Father Franz, a Jesuit from Prague, and Prokop Diwisch, a village priest from Moravia, were among them. The last invented a lightning-conductor in 1756, but his superiors discouraged him from using it. A Russian scientist, Professor Richmann of St Petersburg, was killed when he worked on the same problem. It was left to an American to save the world from the destructive heavenly fire.

Benjamin Franklin, born in Boston, Massachusetts, was the fifteenth child of a poor soap-boiler from England. He was well over 30 when he took up the study of natural phenomena, and over 40 when he accepted the theory put forward by a Leipzig professor, J. H. Winkler, that the discharge of an electric machine and thunder and the flash of lightning are basically the same thing.

'We had for some time been of opinion, that the electrical fire was not created by friction, but collected, being really an element diffused among, and attracted by other matter, particularly by water and metals', wrote Franklin in 1747. Here was at last a plausible theory of the nature of electricity, namely, that it was some kind of 'fluid'. It dawned on him that thunderstorms were merely a discharge of electricity between two objects with different electrical potentials, such as the clouds and the earth. He saw that the discharging spark, the lightning, tended to strike high buildings and trees, which gave him the idea of trying to attract the electrical 'fluid' deliberately to the earth in a way that the discharge would do no harm.

In order to work this idea out he undertook his famous kite-and-key experiment in the summer of 1752. It was much more dangerous than he realized. During the approach of a thunder-storm he sent up a silken kite with an iron tip; he rubbed the end of the kite string, which he had soaked in water to make it a good conductor of electricity, with a large iron key until sparks sprang from the string—which proved his theory. Had the lightning struck his kite he, and his small son whom he had taken along, might have lost their lives.

In his next experiment he fixed an iron bar to the outer wall of his house, and through it charged a Leyden jar with atmospheric electricity. Soon after this he was appointed Postmaster General of Britain's American colonies, and had to interrupt his research work. Taking it up again in 1760, he put up the first effective lightning-conductor on the house of a Philadelphia business man.

His theory was that during a thunderstorm a continual radiation of electricity from the earth through the metal of the lightning-conductor would take place, thus equalizing the different potentials of the air and the earth so that the violent discharge of the lightning would be avoided. The modern theory, however, is that the lightning-conductor simply offers to the electric tension a path of low resistance for quiet neutraliza-tion. At any rate—even if Franklin's theory was wrong—his invention worked.

Yet its general introduction in America and Europe was delayed by all kinds of superstitious and pious objections: if God wanted to punish someone by making the lightning strike his house, how could Man dare to interfere? By 1782, however, all the public buildings in Philadelphia, first capital of the U.S.A., had been equipped with Franklin's lightning-conductors, except the French Embassy. In that year this house was struck by light-ning and an official killed. Franklin had won the day.

It was he who introduced the idea of 'positive' and 'negative' electricity, based on the attraction and repulsion of electrified objects. A French physicist, Charles Augustin de Coulomb, studied these forces between charged objects, which are pro-portional to the charge and the distance between the objects; he invented the torsion balance for measuring the force of electric and magnetic attraction. In his honour, the practical unit of quantity of electricity was named after him.

To scientists and laymen alike, however, this phenomenon of 'action at a distance' caused by electric and magnetic forces was still rather mysterious. What was it really? In 1780, one of the greatest scientific fallacies of all times seemed to provide the answer. Aloisio Galvani, professor of medicine at Bologna, was lecturing to his students at his home while his wife was skinning frogs, the professor's favourite dish, for dinner with his scalpel in the adjoining kitchen. As she listened to the lecture the scalpel fell from her hand on to the frog's thigh, touching the zinc plate at the same time. The dead frog jerked violently as though trying to jump off the plate.

The *signora* screamed. The professor, very indignant about this interruption of his lecture, strode into the kitchen. His wife told him what had happened, and again let the scalpel drop on the frog. Again it twitched.

No doubt the professor was as much perplexed by this occurrence as his wife. But there were his students, anxious to know what it was all about. Galvani could not admit that he was unable to explain the jerking frog. So, probably on the spur of the moment, he explained: 'I have made a great discovery—animal electricity, the primary source of life!'

'An intelligent woman had made an interesting observation, but the not-so-intelligent husband drew the wrong conclusions', was the judgment of a scientific author a few years later. Galvani made numerous and unsystematic experiments with frogs' thighs, most of which failed to prove anything at all; in fact, the professor did not know what to look for except his 'animal electricity'. These experiments became all the rage in Italian society, and everybody talked about 'galvanic electricity' and 'galvanic currents'—terms which are still in use although Professor Galvani certainly did not deserve the honour.

A greater scientist than he, Alessandro Volta of Pavia, solved the mystery and found the right explanation for the jerking frogs. Far from being the 'primary source of life', they played the very modest part of electric conductors while the steel of the scalpel and the zinc of the plate were, in fact, the important things. Volta showed that an electric current begins to flow when two different metals are separated by moisture (the frog had been soaked in salt water), and the frog's muscles had merely demonstrated the presence of the current by contracting under its influence.

Professor Volta went one step further—a most important step, because he invented the first electrical battery, the 'Voltaic pile'.

He built it by using discs of different metals, separated by layers of felt which he soaked in acid. A 'pile' of these elements produced usable electric current, and for many decades this remained the only practical source of electricity. From 1800, when Volta announced his invention, electrical research became widespread among the world's scientists in innumerable laboratories; here was a new kind of current electricity which did not spend itself in

Eighteenth-century frog experiments à la Galvani

a flash or a shock, but flowed steadily like water, and which could be conducted from one place to another by wire.

It is at this important juncture in the history of electrical research that we see the first, groping attempts to make this force of Nature do some work. We shall follow the course of electrical engineering in the field of communications in another part of this book; for the time being, however, we are concerned with the development of electricity for the transmission of energy.

One day in 1819 a Danish physicist, Hans Christian Oersted, was lecturing at the University of Kiel, which was then a Danish town. Demonstrating a galvanic battery, he held up a wire leading from it when it suddenly slipped out of his hand and fell on the

table across a mariner's compass that happened to be there. As he
picked up the wire again he noticed to his astonishment that the
needle of the compass no longer pointed north, but had swung
completely out of position. He switched the current off, and the
needle pointed north again.

For a few months he mused over this incident, and eventually
wrote a short report on it. No one could have been more surprised
than Oersted at the extraordinary impact which his discovery

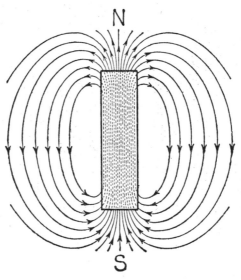

Lines of force active in a bar magnet

made on physicists all over Europe and America. At last the long-
sought connection between electricity and magnetism had been
found! Yet neither Oersted nor his colleagues could foresee the
paramount importance of this phenomenon, for it is the connection between electricity and magnetism on which the entire
practical use of electricity in our time is founded.

What was it that Oersted had discovered? Nothing more than
that an electrically charged conductor, such as the wire leading
from a battery, is the centre of a magnetic 'field', and this has the
effect of turning a magnetic needle at a right angle with the
direction in which the current is flowing; not quite at a right
angle, though, because the magnetism of the earth also influences

the needle. Now the physicists had a reliable means of measuring the strength of a weak electric current flowing through a conductor; the galvanoscope, or galvanometer, is such a simple instrument consisting of a few wire loops and a magnetic needle whose deflection indicates the strength of the current.

Prompted by the research work of André-Marie Ampère, the great French physicist whose name has become a household word as the unit of the electric current, the Englishman Sturgeon experimented with ordinary, non-magnetized iron. He found that any piece of soft iron could be turned into a temporary magnet by putting it in the centre of a coil of insulated wire and making an electric current flow through the coil. As soon and as long as the current was turned on the iron was magnetic, but it ceased to be a magnet when there was no more current. Sturgeon built the first large electro-magnet, and with this achievement there began the development of the electrical telegraph and later the telephone, which we shall describe in Part III of this book.

But there was yet another, and perhaps even more important, development which began with the electro-magnet. Michael Faraday, the son of a blacksmith, who began his career as a book-binder's apprentice near London before Sir Humphry Davy made him his assistant at the Royal Institution in Piccadilly, repeated the experiments of Oersted, Sturgeon, and Ampère. His brilliant mind conceived this idea: if electricity could produce magnetism, perhaps magnetism could produce electricity!

But how? For a long time he searched in vain for an answer. Every time he went for a walk in one of London's parks he carried a little coil and a piece of iron in his pocket, taking them out now and then to look at them. It was on such a walk that he found the solution. Suddenly, one day in 1830, in the midst of Green Park (so the story goes), he knew it: the way to produce electricity by magnetism was—by motion. He hurried to his laboratory and put his theory to the test. It was correct.

A stationary magnet does not produce electricity. But when a magnet is pushed into a wire coil current begins to flow in the coil; when the magnet is pulled out again, the current flows in the opposite direction. This phenomenon confirms the basic fact that the electric current cannot be produced out of nothing—some work must be done to produce it. Electricity is only a form of energy; it is not a 'prime mover' in itself.

What Faraday had discovered was the technique of electro-magnetic induction, on which the whole edifice of electrical engineering rests. He soon found that there were various ways of transforming motion into electric current. Instead of moving the magnet in and out of the wire coil you can move the coil towards and away from the magnet; or you can generate electricity by changing the strength of a stationary magnet; or you can produce

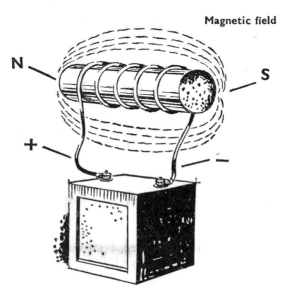

Faraday's experiments with the electro-magnet

a current in one of two coils by moving them towards and away from each other while a current is flowing in the second coil. Faraday then substituted a magnet for the second coil and observed the same effect. Using two coils wound on separate sections of a closed iron ring, with one coil connected to a galvanometer and the other to a battery, he noticed that when the circuit of the second coil was closed the galvanometer needle pointed first in one direction and then returned to its zero position. When he interrupted the battery circuit, the galvanometer jerked into the opposite direction. Eventually, he made a 12-inch-wide copper disc which he rotated between the poles of a strong horse-shoe magnet; the electric current which was generated in the copper disc could be obtained from springs or wire brushes touching the edge and axis of the disc.

Thus Faraday demonstrated quite a number of ways in which motion could be translated into electricity. His fellow-scientists at the Royal Institution and in other countries were amazed and impressed—yet neither he nor they proceeded to make practical use of his discoveries, and nearly forty years went by before the first electric generator, or dynamo, was built.

Meanwhile, fundamental research into the manifold problems of electricity continued. In America, Joseph Henry, professor of mathematics and natural science, also starting from Oersted's and Sturgeon's observations, used the action of the electric current upon a magnet to build the first primitive electric motor in 1829. At about the same time, Georg Simon Ohm, a German school-teacher who had begun his career as a locksmith's apprentice, found the important law of electric resistance: that the amount of current in a wire circuit decreases with the length of the wire, which acts as resistance. Ohm's excellent research work remained almost unnoticed during his lifetime, and he died before his name was accepted as that of the unit of electrical resistance.

It was only in the last quarter of the nineteenth century that electricity began to play its part in modern civilization, and the man who achieved more in this field of practical engineering than any of his contemporaries was the American inventor, Thomas Alva Edison. His dramatic career is too well known, and has been described too often, to be told again; it may suffice to recall that he became interested in the problem of electric lighting in 1877, and began to tackle it with the systematic energy which distinguished him from so many other inventors of his time. Edison was no scientist and never bothered much about theories and fundamental laws of Nature; he was a technician pure and simple, and a very good business man as well.

He knew what had been done in the field of electric lighting before his time, and he had seen some appliances of his contemporaries, such as the arc-lamp illuminations which had been installed here and there. Two sticks of carbon, nearly touching, can be made to produce an electric arc which closes the circuit. Humphry Davy had done this for the first time in the early 1800's. But these lights were too dazzling and uneconomical for ordinary rooms, and they needed constant adjustment. Many scientists and inventors who tried to tackle the problem were therefore convinced that only incandescent electric light—produced by some substance glowing in a vacuum so that it cannot burn up—could ever replace gas lighting, then the universal system of illumination in Europe and America. One of the more successful attempts was that of an Englishman, Joseph Wilson Swan, who developed a number of lamp types. But they were not suitable for mass production, and Swan did not have enough business sense to introduce his invention to a sceptical world.

Edison's first electric lamp with carbon filament

Edison put his entire laboratories at Menlo Park to the task of developing such a lamp. The most important question was that of a suitable material for the filament. He experimented with wires of various metals, bamboo fibre, human hair, paper; everything was carbonized and tried out in glass bulbs from which the air had been exhausted. In the end—it is said that a button hanging loose from its thread on his jacket gave him the idea—he found that ordinary sewing thread, carefully carbonized and inserted in the airless bulb, was the most suitable material. His first experimental lamp of 1879 shed its soft, yellowish light for forty hours: the incandescent electric lamp was born.

It was, no doubt, one of the greatest achievements in the history of modern invention. Yet Edison was a practical man who knew quite well that the introduction of this revolutionary system of illumination must be properly prepared. He worked out methods for mass-producing electric bulbs at low cost, and devised circuits for feeding any number of bulbs with current. He found that 110/220 volts was the most suitable potential difference and would reduce transmission losses of current to a minimum— he could not have foreseen that the introduction of that voltage was to set the standard for a century of electric lighting. But most important of all 'accessories' of the lamp was the generator that could produce the necessary high-tension current.

Since Faraday's ingenious discovery of the way in which movement could be transformed into electricity, only a small number of engineers had tried to build generators based on this principle, the most tireless of them being a Belgian-born inventor, Zénobe Théophile Gramme. His first hand-driven generator was ready in 1871, and two years later he installed improved models in some French lighthouses, powered by steam-engines. This was a great advance on the generator invented by an Italian, Antonio Pacinotti, in the 1860's, and on the models built by the Siemens brothers in Berlin at about the same time. But none of these machines answered the particular requirements of Edison's electric light; so he had to design his own generator, which he did so well that his system—apart from minor improvements and of course the size of the machines—is still in general use today.

It is little known that the first application of Edison's lighting system was on board an arctic-expedition steamer, the *Jeannette*, which the inventor himself equipped with lamps and a generator only a few weeks after his first lamp had lit up at Menlo Park. The installation worked quite satisfactorily until the ship was crushed in the polar ice two years later.

Edison, a superb showman as well as a brilliant inventor, introduced his electric lamps to the world by illuminating his own laboratories at Menlo Park with 500 bulbs in 1880. It caused a sensation. From dusk to midnight, visitors trooped around the laboratories, which Edison had thrown open for the purpose, regarding the softly glowing lamps with boundless admiration. Extra trains were run from New York, and engineers crossed the Atlantic from Europe to see the new marvel. There was much talk about the end of gas-lighting, and gas shares slumped on the stock exchanges of the world. Edison was even accused of having put up his 'Yankee bluff' only to get in cheap on the gas shares market, and a famous Berlin engineer—none other than Werner von Siemens, who later became Edison's great rival in central Europe—pronounced that electric light would never take the place of gas. When Edison showed his lamps for the first time in Europe, at the Paris Exhibition of 1881, a well-known French industrialist said that this would also be the last time.

Meanwhile, however, Edison staked his money and reputation

on a large-scale installation in the middle of New York. He bought a site on Pearl Street, moved into it with a small army of technicians, and built six large direct-current generators, altogether of 900 h.p., powered by steam-engines. Several miles of streets were dug up for the electric cables—also designed and manufactured

From Edison's order book: the order for the electric lamps to be installed in S.S. *Columbia*

by Edison—to be laid, and eighty-five buildings were wired for illumination. On 4 September 1882 New Yorkers had their first glimpse of the electric age when 2,300 incandescent lamps began to glow at the throwing of a switch in the Pearl Street power station. Electric lighting had come to stay. And what was most important: Edison had finally established a practical method of supplying electricity to the homes of the people.

Pearl Street was not the first generator station to be built. A 1-h.p. generator for the supply of current for Edison lamps was built in Appleton, Wisconsin, and another one—England's first —in Godalming, Surrey, in 1881. In Germany, Werner von Siemens did more than any other engineer for the introduction of electric lighting, in which he had first refused to believe, by perfecting his 'dynamo', as he called the generator for continuous current.

Spectacular as the advent of electric lighting was, it represented only one aspect of the use of electricity, which was rapidly gaining in popularity among industrial engineers. For a century, the reciprocating steam-engine had been the only important man-made source of mechanical energy. But its power was limited to the place where it operated; there was no way of transmitting that power to some other place where it might have been required. For the first time, there was now an efficient means of distributing energy for lighting up homes and factories, and for supplying engines with power.

Ritchie's electric motor

The engine which could convert electric energy into mechanical power was already in existence. As early as 1822, nearly a decade before he found the principle of the electric generator, Faraday outlined the way in which an electric motor could work: by placing a coil, or armature, between the poles of an electro-magnet; when a current is made to flow through the coil the electro-magnetic force causes it to rotate—the reverse principle, in fact, of the generator.

A Scotsman, William Ritchie, a Londoner, Francis Watkins, an American, the blacksmith Thomas Davenport from Vermont, a Russo-German physicist, de Jacobi, and the Belgian Z. T. Gramme, whom we have already mentioned: these were some of the men who built electric motors during the middle decades of the nineteenth century. Jacobi even succeeded in running a small, battery-powered electric boat on the Neva river in St Petersburg. All of them, however, came to the conclusion that the electric motor was a rather uneconomical machine so long as galvanic batteries were the only source of electricity. It did not occur to them that motors and generators could be made interchangeable; only in 1863 did the Italian, Pacinotti, build a machine which could be used for both purposes, either to convert mechanical power into electric energy, or electric energy into mechanical power.

In 1888, Professor Galileo Ferraris in Turin and Nikola Tesla —the Croat-born pioneer of high-frequency engineering—in America invented, independently and without knowing of each

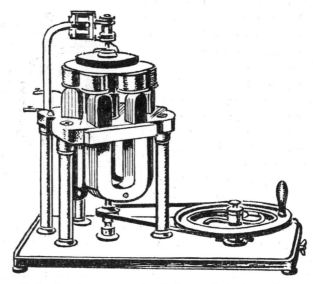

Early electric generator by Stöhrer, a Leipzig mechanic

other's work, the induction motor. This machine, a most important but little recognized technical achievement, provides no less than two-thirds of all the motive power for the factories of the world, and much of modern industry could not do without it. Known under the name of 'squirrel-cage motor'—because it resembles the wire cage in which tame squirrels used to be kept in nineteenth-century nurseries and made to operate little toy treadmills—it has two robust circular rings made of copper or aluminium joined by a few dozen parallel bars of the same material, thus forming a cylindrical cage. It is built into an iron cylinder which is mounted on the shaft, and forms the rotor, the rotating part of the machine. It is exposed to a rotating magnetic field set up by the stator, the fixed part of the machine, consisting of many interconnected electrical conductors called the winding. The relative motion between the magnetic field and the rotor induces voltages and currents which exert the driving force, turning the 'cage' round.

Although the induction motor has been improved a great deal and its power increased many times over since its invention, there has never been any change of the underlying principle. One of its drawbacks was that its speed was constant and unchangeable. Only in 1959 did a research team at the University of Bristol succeed in developing a squirrel-cage motor with two speeds— the most far-reaching innovation since the invention of the induction motor. The speed-change is achieved by modulating the pole-amplitude of the machine.

From the day when Edison's lamps began to glow in New York, all the world asked for electricity. Already a year earlier, Werner von Siemens had succeeded in coupling a steam-engine directly to a dynamo. But the engineers had their eyes on another, cheaper source of mechanical power than the reciprocating steam-engine: that of falling water. We do not know which of them suggested the idea of a hydro-electric power station for the first time; it was probably very much 'in the air'. Back in 1827, Benoît Fourneyron, a young Frenchman, had won the first prize in a competition for the most effective water turbine in which the water would act on the wheel inside a casing instead of from outside. It was one of the prototypes of the modern water turbine. In the 1880's, an American engineer, Pelton, designed a turbine wheel with enormous bucket-shaped blades along the rim, and a few American towns with waterfalls installed Pelton turbines coupled to Edison generators. This type proved especially efficient where the fall of water was steep but its quantity limited; for a low fall of water the Kaplan turbine—so called after its inventor, Viktor Kaplan—with only four large blades, proved better suited. However, the type which appeals most to the engineers is now the Francis turbine for falls of water from 100 to 1,000 feet, with a great number of curved blades. The power station which convincingly showed the enormous possibilities of hydro-generated electricity was the one at Niagara Falls, begun in 1891, and put into operation a few years later with an output of 5,000 h.p.—it is 8 million h.p. today.

The early power stations generated direct current at low voltage, but they could distribute it only within a radius of a few hundred yards. The Niagara station was one of the first to use alternating current (although the sceptics prophesied that this would never work), generated at high voltage; this was transmitted by overhead cables to the communities where it was to be

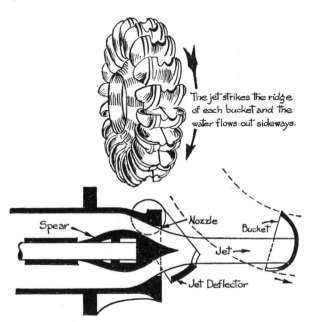

The jet strikes the ridge of each bucket and the water flows out sideways.

Spear  Nozzle  Bucket  Jet  Jet Deflector

The Pelton wheel and the needle and deflector to control
the jet of water

used, and here 'stepped down' into lower voltages (110 or 220) for domestic and industrial use by means of transformers. High-voltage transmission is much more economical than low-voltage; all other circumstances being equal, if the transmission voltage is increased tenfold the losses in electric energy during transmission are reduced to one-hundredth. This means that alternating current at tens or even hundreds of thousands of volts, as it is transmitted today, can be sent over long distances without much loss.

These ideas must have had something frightening to the people at the end of the last century, when electricity was still a mysterious and alarming novelty. The engineers who built London's first power station, with a 10,000-volt generator, at Deptford in 1889, and their German colleagues who set up a 16,000-volt dynamo driven by a waterfall in the River Neckar, to supply

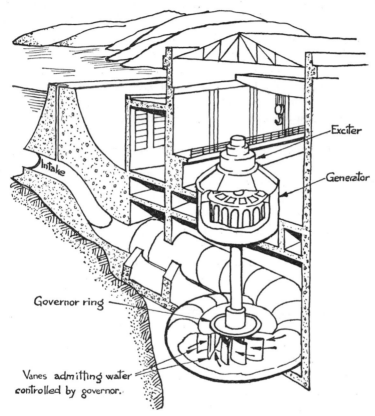

Exciter

Generator

Intake

Governor ring

Vanes admitting water controlled by governor.

A Francis turbine and generator (simplified)

Frankfurt, 100 miles away, with electricity in 1891—these men must have felt like true pioneers, derided, despised, and abused by the diehards. There were, of course, also some powerful commercial interests involved, for the gas industry feared for its monopoly in the realm of lighting—and with a good deal of justification, as it turned out.

Perhaps we might in this connection give a brief sketch of the

c

development of illumination. From his earliest times, Man has had an intense dislike of the dark—after all, it gave the beasts of prey and his human enemies a good chance to creep up and attack him. Besides, as soon as he had learnt how to use his brain the long winter nights with their enforced idleness must have bored him. Lightning, the fire from heaven, gave him the first 'lamp' in the shape of a burning tree or bush. He prolonged the burning-time of firewood by dipping it into animal fat, resin, or pitch: thus the torch was invented. It was in use until well into the nineteenth century; many old town houses in England still have torch-holders outside their front doors, where the footmen put their torches as their masters and mistresses stepped out of the carriages and sedans.

Rough earthenware oil lamps, with some plant fibre as a wick, were in use in the earliest civilizations; these lamps, though much refined, were still quite common a hundred years ago. The Romans are usually credited with the invention of the candle, originally a length of twisted flax dipped in hot tallow or beeswax which later hardened as it cooled off. Candles were at first expensive, and only the rich and the Church could afford them. As late as the 1820's, stearin candles—cheap and mass manu-factured—came into use, and still later they began to be made of paraffin wax.

By that time, however, a new kind of illumination had been introduced all over the civilized countries: gaslight. In the 1690's an English scientist, Dr John Clayton, observed that the gases which developed in coal-pits and endangered the lives of the miners were combustible. He experimented with pieces of coal, which he 'roasted' over a fire without allowing them to burn up, and found that the resulting gas gave a pleasant, bright flame. German and French chemists repeated his experiments, but a hundred years passed after his discovery before gas became a practical form of illumination.

William Murdock, a Scotsman who started his career as a mechanic with Boulton & Watt and was later made area manager for Cornwall for the sale of their steam-engines, took up Clayton's idea. He built an iron cauldron in his cottage garden in Redruth, and heated coal in it. This 'incomplete combustion' produced a mixture of highly imflammable carbon monoxide and nitrogen. He piped the gas into his house and fixed taps in every room. Many a night the people of Redruth stood in silent awe around Murdock's cottage, gazing at the wonderful new lamps which shed a bright light throughout the house.

After two years of experimenting, he persuaded his employers, Boulton & Watt, to let him illuminate their Soho factory by gaslight. The installation was completed just in time to celebrate the peace treaty of Amiens and the end of the Anglo-French war in 1802 with the first public exhibition of gaslighting in and around the factory.

A year later, gaslight came to London. Outside the Lyceum in the Strand the people of the capital saw for the first time a street bathed in light at night. But it was not Murdock who brought the new wonder to them. An energetic German, Friedrich Albert Winzer, who had probably read reports on Murdock's invention, forestalled him. Anglicizing his name to 'Winsor', he made great efforts to convince the public, the authorities, and the scientists that gaslighting was a good thing. Even after its début in the Strand he found it extremely difficult to rally public opinion behind him. 'London is now to be lit during the winter months with the same coal-smoke that turns our winter days into nights', complained Sir Walter Scott, and even such an eminent man as Sir Humphry Davy exclaimed that he would never acquiesce in a plan to turn St Paul's into a gasometer.

But the progress of gaslighting could not be stopped; the main argument for it was that it would increase public safety in the streets—it took much longer to persuade the people that there was no danger to their homes if they had gas tubes laid into them. In 1812, Winsor obtained a royal charter to found the Gas Light and Coke Company, which existed until 1948 when the gas industry was brought into public ownership. The introduction of gaslight in the factories had an especially far-reaching effect—it made the general adoption of night shifts possible. The first industry to do this was the Lancashire textile industry, for the workers at their looms were now able to watch the threads at any time of the day or night.

Samuel Clegg, Murdock's assistant, was responsible for many improvements; among other things he invented the gas meter, and put up gas lamps on Westminster Bridge in 1813. Three years later, most of London's West End was already gaslit, and by 1820 nearly all Paris. New York followed in 1823. In Germany there were many objections to be overcome until the advantages of gas-light were recognized; the leading Cologne newspaper attacked the new invention in 1819 'because it intervenes in the divine order of things, which has made the night a darkness only to be relieved by the moon ... because it banishes from people's minds the fear of darkness, which keeps the weak from indulging in sin ... because it makes the horse timid and the thief bold'. Why it should have this effect the paper did not say.

William Murdock lived long enough to witness the beginning of another development whose importance few people recognized at the time: gas cooking. In 1839 the first gas-oven was installed at a Leamington Spa hotel, and a dinner cooked for a hundred guests. For a long time, however, this idea did not catch on. But when towards the end of the century the electric light began to take over from the gas lamp, the industry was forced to make a new effort so as not to be squeezed out of existence. In 1885 the Austrian physicist Carl Auer von Welsbach introduced his incandescent gas-mantle, which quickly superseded the open (and dangerous) gas flames which had until then been in use. He used the same principle as Edison in his electric lamp; his gas-mantle was a little hood of tulle impregnated with thorium or cerium oxide. For a while, incandescent gaslight gained ground, and many people who had already installed electric cables had them torn up again. But in the end electricity won because it was more effective and more economical.

Only then did gas cooking emerge as a new aid to the world's housewives. It has still its place in the kitchen; gas-operated refrigerators, gas stoves, and central-heating systems are more recent developments. Gas has by no means outstayed its welcome in our civilization.

Auer himself was responsible for one of the decisive improvements in the electric bulb, the great rival of his gas lamp. Using his experience with rare earths he developed a more efficient filament than Edison's carbonized thread-osmium. It was superseded in its turn by the tungsten (wolfram) filament, invented by two Viennese scientists in the early 1900's. Since about 1918, electric bulbs have been filled with gas; today, a mixture of argon and nitrogen is in general use.

Is the incandescent electric lamp now also on its way out? In innumerable offices, factories, public buildings and vehicles, and a good many homes (especially in the kitchens) the fluorescent lamp has taken over from it. This is based on two scientific phenomena that have long been known : that certain materials can be excited to fluorescence by ultra-violet radiation, and that an electric discharge through mercury under low pressure produces a great deal of invisible ultra-violet radiation. Professor Becquerel, grandfather of the scientist whose work on uranium rays preceded the discovery of radium, attempted to construct a fluorescent lamp as long ago as 1859 by using a Geissler discharge tube. American, German, and other French physicists worked on the same lines, and eventually the new type of lamp found its first applications for advertising (neon light). The difficulty was the production of a daylight-type of light with sufficient blue in its spectrum. In the 1920's three German engineers patented such a lamp, and in the 1930's an American, Dr Arthur H. Compton of the General Electric, developed a model for general use.

The modern fluorescent lamp consists of a long, gas-filled glass tube, coated inside with some fluorescent powder; this lights up when excited by the invisible ultra-violet rays of an arc passing from the electrode at one end to that at the other. Strip lighting is extremely efficient and needs little current because it works 'cold' —i.e. very little electrical energy is turned into waste heat as in incandescent lamps. It is roughly fifty times more effective than Edison's first carbon-filament lamps.

The mercury or sodium vapour lamps which are now used on the roads are 'discharge' lamps, invented in the early 1930's. They have a 'conductor' in the form of a gas or metallic vapour at low pressure; this is raised to incandescence by the electric current, and emits light of one characteristic colour, greenish-blue (mercury vapour) or yellow (sodium vapour). They are 'monochrome' lamps, that is, they emit light of only one colour, which makes it easier for the motorist to distinguish objects on the roads; it is also less scattered by mist or fog. True, that light makes people look like ogres—but it makes our streets definitely safer by night.

It is most important to remember that electricity is only a means of *distributing* energy, of carrying it from the place where it is produced to the places where it is used. *It is not a 'prime mover'* like the steam-engine or even the water mill. A generator

is no use at all unless it is rotated by a prime mover. During the
first few years of electric power there was no other way of moving
the generators than either by the force of falling water or by
ordinary steam-engines.

Soon, however, there came a new and very efficient prime
mover, the steam-turbine. We have seen that it is, in fact, quite an
old idea; Giovanni Branca's seventeenth-century engine was the
prototype. The success of the reciprocating steam-engine, however, overshadowed the concept of the turbine, although some
inventors in the eighteenth and early nineteenth centuries built a
few models. Among them was Richard Trevithick, the pioneer of
the steam carriage; he made what he called a 'whirling engine' in
1815, with a wheel 15 feet in diameter revolving at 300 revolutions per minute. It failed because it could not produce enough
power. What most of these inventors did not realize was the fact
that such a turbine would have to rotate at enormous speed to be
efficient. Only James Watt had some idea of this; when Boulton
remarked that a steam-turbine might put his reciprocating engines
out of business, he replied: 'Without God making it possible for
things to move 1,000 feet per second, it cannot do much harm.'

Yet some engineers were convinced that if it could be built, the
steam-turbine would be a much more efficient and powerful
prime mover than the reciprocating engine because it would
short-cut the complicated process of converting steam energy
into rotary motion via reciprocating motion. But the problems
involved in building such a machine seemed formidable, especially
that of high-precision engineering. It was only towards the end of
the nineteenth century that engineering methods were developed
highly enough for a successful attempt.

Two men undertook it almost simultaneously. The Swedish
engineer, Gustaf Patrik de Laval, built his first model in 1883. He
made the steam from the boiler emerge from four stationary
nozzles arranged around the rim of a wheel with a great number
of small blades; reacting to a steam pressure of 3,000 lb. per
square inch, de Laval's turbine wheel rotated at up to 40,000
revolutions per minute. He supported the wheel on a flexible
shaft so that it would adjust itself to fluctuations of pressure—
which, at such speeds, would have broken a rigid shaft in no
time.

De Laval geared an electric generator to his turbine after he had succeeded in reducing the speed of rotation to 3,000 r.p.m. His turbo-generator worked, but its capacity was limited, and it was found unsuitable for large-scale power stations. Although the simplest form of a machine has often proved the most efficient one in the history of technology, this was not the case with the steam-turbine. Another inventor, and another system, proved much more successful.

Charles Algernon Parsons, one of the six sons of the scientifically minded Lord Rosse, grew up in the family's rambling old castle in Ireland and in their splendid London residence near Hyde Park. In 1876, at the age of 22, he exchanged the carefree university life at Dublin and Cambridge for an apprenticeship at an engineering works in Newcastle upon Tyne, and it was here that he began to work on the idea of a steam-turbine, for which he foresaw a wide range of applications. The reciprocating steam-engine, which was unable to convert more than 12 per cent of the latent energy of coal into mechanical power, was not nearly efficient enough for the economical generation of electricity— energy leaked out right and left from the cylinder, the condenser, the sun-and-planet movement of the connecting-rod and wheel. Besides, there were limits to the size in which it could be built, and therefore to the output: and Parsons saw that the time had come to build giant electric power stations.

As he studied the problem he understood that the point where most would-be turbine inventors had been stumped was the excessive velocity of steam. Even steam at a comparatively low pressure escaping into the atmosphere may easily travel at speeds of more than twice the velocity of sound—and high-pressure steam may travel twice as fast again, at about 5,000 feet per second. Unless the wheel of a turbine could be made to rotate at least at half the speed of the steam acting upon its blades, there could be no efficient use of its energy. But the centrifugal force alone, to say nothing of the other forces which de Laval tried to counter with his flexible shaft, would have destroyed such an engine.

Parsons had the idea of reducing the steam pressure and speed, without reducing efficiency and economy, by causing the whole expansion of the steam to take place in stages so that only moderate velocities would have to be reached by the turbine wheels. This principle still forms the basis of all efficient steam-turbines today. Parsons put it into practice for the first time in his model of 1884, a little turbine combined with an electric generator, both coupled without reducing gear and revolving at 18,000 r.p.m. The turbine consisted of a cylindrical rotor enclosed in a casing, with many rings of small blades fixed alternately to the casing and to the rotor. The steam entered the casing at one end and flowed parallel with the rotor ('axial flow'); in doing so it had to pass between the rings of blades—each acting virtually as a nozzle in which partial steam expansion could take place, and

A modern 500,000-kW single-line turbo-generator

the jets thus formed gave up their energy in driving the rotor blades.

It was more a complicated solution of the problem than de Laval's, but it proved to be the right one. The speed of 18,000 r.p.m. used the energy of the steam very well, and the generator developed 75 amperes output at 100 volts. The little machine, built in 1884, is now at the Science Museum in South Kensington.

Parsons expected, and experienced, a good deal of opposition —after all, there were enormous vested interests in the manufacture of reciprocating steam-engines. He began to build some portable turbo-generators, but there were no buyers. Strangely enough, a charity event created the necessary publicity for the turbine. In the winter of 1885–6, a pond near Gateshead froze over, and a local hospital decided to raise funds by getting young people to skate on the ice and charging for admission. The Chief Constable of Gateshead had the idea of asking Mr Parsons to illuminate the pond with electric lamps, powered by one of his portable 4-kW turbo-generators.

The event was a great success, and the newspapers wrote about it. The next step was that the organizers of the Newcastle Exhibition of 1887 asked Parsons to supply the current for its display of electric lighting, and from that time he never looked back. He founded the Newcastle and District Lighting Co., set up a turbine factory, and built bigger and bigger machines. A London hotel and soon afterwards the Metropolitan Electric Supply Co. ordered turbo-generators; then came Cambridge and Scarborough, and eventually the biggest order of the 1890's: two 1,000-kW turbo-generators for the City Corporation of Elberfeld, in the industrial Rhineland. Parsons, who died in 1931 at the age of 76, lived long enough to see one of his turbines producing more than 200,000 kW. He also succeeded in introducing his steam-turbine as a new prime mover in ship propulsion—a dramatic story with which we shall deal in the next part of this book.

Until this day, the steam-turbine has held its place as the great prime mover for the generation of electricity where no water power is available. The steam which drives them in the power stations may be raised by coal, oil, natural gas, or atomic energy —but it is invariably the steam-turbine which drives the generators; Diesel-engines are the exceptions, and are only used where smaller or mobile stations are required and no fuel but heavy oil is available. Today's steam-turbines, large or small, run at much lower speeds than Parsons's first model, usually at 1,000–3,000 r.p.m.

When, a quarter of a century after Charles Algernon Parsons's death, the first nuclear power station in the world started up, his steam-turbines were there to convert the heat from the reactor into mechnical energy for the generators. The atomic age cannot do without them—not yet.

# 4

Atomic Energy

ALL the prime movers, natural and man-made, which humanity has harnessed to ease its burden of labour and raise its standard of living are, in fact, attempts at utilizing the energy of the sun: it sustains organic life on earth with its light and heat, it makes the water circulate between the heavens and the sea, it creates the wind, and it has filled for us a vast storehouse of coal and oil, the mineral deposits from bygone ages of vegetation. What our inventors did when they built power-producing engines was to change one form of energy—such as the heat of burning coal— into another, the mechanical energy of rotating wheels or the light of an electric lamp. They could not create energy from nothing; they could only release it by some chemical process. This means that although the molecules, or combinations of atoms, may break up and form new combinations, the atoms themselves remain intact and unchanged.

There is one source of energy, however, which owes nothing to the heat and light of the sun; nor can it be harnessed by a chemical process. It is the energy of the atomic nucleus.

The term 'atom', coined by the Greek philosopher Democritus 2,500 years ago, is rather misleading. It means 'the indivisible', and it is a relic from the times when people believed that all matter consisted of very small particles which were unchangeable and indivisible, and that each element had its own special kind of particles. Only the medieval alchemists hoped that they could, by some magic, change the particles of one element into those of another—lead, for instance, into gold.

Today we know that atoms are neither unchangeable nor

indivisible. The story of research into the nature of the atom has
been told many times, and as it is one of scientific discovery it does
not really belong in this book. It may be sufficient to recall that
Marie and Pierre Curie, by their discovery of radium in 1898,
made the whole theory of the indivisible atom crumble, because
here was an element which disintegrated and sent out rays,
consisting of particles much smaller than the atom.

Another discovery, made three years earlier, seemed to point
in the same direction: that of the X-rays by Professor Wilhelm
Konrad Röntgen at the University of Würzburg, Bavaria. Using
a cathode-ray tube, he found that the radiation emanating from
it was able to penetrate thin matter like wood and human flesh,
but was stopped by thicker objects such as pieces of metal and
bones. It was only later that the nature of these mysterious rays
was discovered: particles of negative electricity, called electrons,
turn into electro-magnetic waves, of the same kind as light but of
shorter wave-length and therefore invisible, when they strike a
material object such as a metal shield in the cathode-ray tube.

These and other phenomena and discoveries around the turn of
the century were deeply disturbing for the physicists, and they
saw that the whole traditional concept of the structure of matter
had to be completely revised. More than that: the borderline
between matter and energy seemed to disappear. When, as early
as 1905, Albert Einstein published his *Special Theory of Relativity*,
in which he declared that matter could be converted into energy—
very little matter into very great energy—there was a storm of
protest in the scientific world. But little by little the evidence that
he was right accumulated, and within a few years an entirely new
picture of the atom emerged from the studies and laboratories of
scientists in many countries—with the Cavendish Laboratory in
Cambridge leading the international team of pioneers in this field.
From that evidence Lord Rutherford, the New Zealand-born
scientist, and his young Danish assistant, Niels Bohr, developed
by 1911 their revolutionary theory of what the atom was really
like.

That picture of the atom has since been elaborated and filled in
with more details. It is not yet complete; but its essential features
are known to be correct—otherwise there would be no atomic
bombs, which few people would regret, or nuclear power stations.

Broadly speaking, the atom is a miniature solar system, with a 'sun', the nucleus, and a number of 'planets', the electrons, revolving around it. All the matter of the atom is concentrated in the nucleus: there are protons, particles with a positive electric charge, neutrons, particles without a charge, and some other particles whose role and nature is still being investigated. The electrons, which have next to no mass and weight, are negatively charged; in fact, they are the carriers of electricity in all our electric wires and appliances.

Normally there are as many positive protons in the nucleus as there are electrons revolving around it, so that their charges cancel each other out and the atom as a whole is electrically neutral. But if for some reason an atom loses a proton or an electron or two, its electrical balance is disturbed, it becomes negatively or positively charged and is called an ion.

The atoms of all the elements contain the same *kind* of particles; what distinguishes them from each other is merely the *number* of particles—of protons in the nucleus and of electrons revolving around it. Hydrogen, for instance, being the lightest and simplest element, has only one of each; uranium, the heaviest element occurring in Nature, has 92. So all you have to do to change one element into another is either to knock some protons and a corresponding number of electrons off each atom, or add them; in fact, this process is going on in Nature all the time. Theoretically, we could change lead into gold, as the alchemists dreamed of doing, by removing three protons and electrons from a few billion lead atoms, which have 82 of each; then we would get gold atoms with 79 protons and electrons each. However, the knocking-off process would be much more expensive than the gold we would get.

The neutrons, which are present in the atoms of many elements, are of particular importance in the utilization of atomic energy. Most elements are mixtures of ordinary atoms and so-called isotopes: the isotope atoms have more, or fewer, neutrons than the ordinary atoms. An isotope differs from the ordinary form of the element only in weight, but chemically it behaves in exactly the same way. Water, for instance, is a mixture of ordinary molecules of hydrogen and oxygen atoms and of 'heavy' ones; the heavy hydrogen atom has an extra neutron in its nucleus. Uranium, on the other hand, has an isotope whose nucleus contains fewer neutrons than the ordinary element. This isotope—

atomic weight: 235; atomic weight of ordinary uranium: 238—has a very special significance in nuclear physics because it is, like many other heavy-element isotopes, 'unstable'.

What does this mean? Nothing else but the phenomenon which the Curies discovered in radium. An unstable nucleus is one that is likely to break up into the nucleus of another element. Professor Otto Hahn found in Berlin in 1938 that when uranium atoms are bombarded with neutrons they split up in a process which he called 'fission' (a term used in biology for the way in which some cells divide to form new ones). The 92 protons of the uranium nucleus split up into barium, which has 56, and krypton, a gas with 26 protons. Frédéric Joliot-Curie, the son-in-law of Marie Curie, proved some months later that in this fission process some neutrons from the uranium nucleus were liberated; they flew off, and some struck other nuclei, which in turn broke up, liberating still more neutrons. Enrico Fermi, an Italian who had gone to America to escape life under Fascism, developed the theory of what would happen if a sufficiently large piece of unstable uranium broke up in this way—there would be a 'chain reaction': the free neutrons would be bombarding the nuclei with such intensity that in no time at all the whole lump of uranium would disintegrate.

But it would not just turn quietly into barium and krypton as in Professor Hahn's laboratory experiment. There were now two smaller nuclei, no longer held together as before but pushed apart by electric repulsion, and flying off at great speed, with neutrons shooting about in all directions. And such sudden display of energy—for movement is energy—would, according to Einstein's famous Mass = Energy equation, correspond to some loss of mass. If the two parts of a nucleus which has undergone fission could be put together again (which, in practice, is of course just as impossible as in the case of Humpty Dumpty), their combined mass would be *smaller* than that of the original nucleus. What has become of the missing bits? They have turned into pure energy —into movement, into heat.

This was the theory that led, within the short space of four years, to the first atom bombs. On Monday, 6 August 1945, while cheerful crowds in England enjoyed their first bank holiday after the end of the war in Europe, one such bomb was dropped on the town of Hiroshima in Japan. It killed or injured nearly 200,000 people. Three days later another bomb was dropped on Nagasaki,

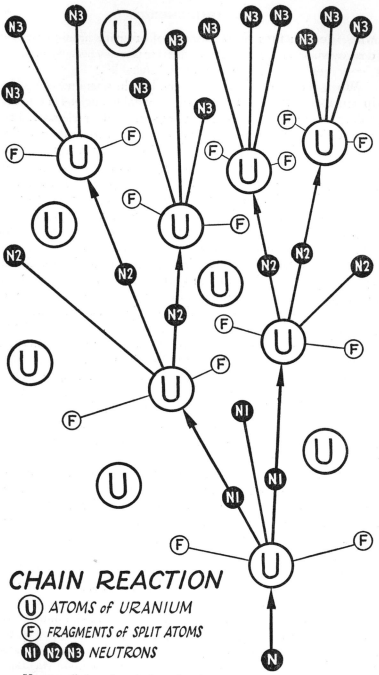

# CHAIN REACTION

Ⓤ ATOMS of URANIUM
Ⓕ FRAGMENTS of SPLIT ATOMS
Ⓝ¹ Ⓝ² Ⓝ³ NEUTRONS

Uncontrolled nuclear fission: the chain reaction in an atom bomb

with 65,000 victims. The centres of both cities were completely destroyed.

When the world had recovered from the shock of this unimaginable horror, people everywhere asked the scientists how soon they could apply the immense power of the fissioned nucleus to peaceful purposes. But this took much longer. It was considerably easier to use the nuclear chain reaction for destruction than for the production of usable energy for homes and factories—to control it and release it in small doses. Many problems had to be solved; the main one was that of 'braking' the released neutrons efficiently so that the chain reaction would not get out of hand.

The first atomic 'pile' or 'reactor', as the apparatus for the utilization of atomic energy is now called, had been set up by Enrico Fermi on the football ground of the University of Chicago in 1942. It was a somewhat crude assembly, whose main purpose was to get experimental proof for the theory of chain reaction. Fermi scattered rods of uranium through a stack of graphite blocks, which acted as a brake for the neutrons—a 'moderator', to use the technical term. We shall presently hear more about its function. Fermi used natural uranium, which is a mixture of the stable U-238 and the unstable U-235 in a proportion of 140 : 1. Thus there was only slight radio-activity, i.e. breaking-up of nuclei. In order to control it, Fermi inserted some cadmium rods into the pile; this metal absorbs neutrons very readily, and by pushing the rods completely into the pile he could stop the chain reaction altogether.

Fermi's assembly is still the basic blueprint of today's nuclear reactors. Their main parts are the fuel, the moderator, the control rods, and the cooling system. But the scientists and technicians have since developed a great many different types of reactors— some already in everyday use, others running experimentally in atomic research establishments or being built for special jobs and purposes of all kinds, from producing nuclear explosives for weapons to 'cooking' stable elements so that they become unstable isotopes for use in medicine, industry, agriculture, and research. Our main concern in this book, however, is with the reactor as a prime mover, as a producer of usable energy.

Why do we speak of the atomic age as a new chapter in the history of civilization, and why have the technologists made such great efforts to utilize the energy of the split nucleus? For a long time the shadow of a future without sufficient fuel loomed over mankind. Coal has been mined at a steadily increasing pace which set in with the Industrial Revolution, and some experts predicted that in Britain, for instance, an acute shortage of cheaply mined coal would set in after 1980. Oil is still to be found in plenty, but consumption has been increasing in leaps and bounds all over the world. In short, mankind has been burning up its fuel 'capital', which cannot be replenished.

Atomic energy is produced in a different way. It is not generated by the chemical process of combustion. It is released when nuclei undergo fission, and although here, too, matter is used up, the amounts are infinitesimally small compared with the energy produced. A few pounds of uranium 235 can be made to supply a medium-sized town with all the electricity it needs during a whole year. True, our reserves of uranium are limited. But there is one reactor type, called the 'breeder', which in fact produces more nuclear fuel than it uses! This type—the one at Dounreay in Scotland was the first of its kind to go into operation—has a 'blanket' of thorium, one of the most common elements on earth, which is turned into the artificial radio-active element plutonium when bombarded by neutrons. And there is good reason to hope that before long we shall be able to produce energy from ordinary sea-water by another nuclear reaction called fusion: we shall hear more about it later in this chapter.

So there is little doubt that mankind's energy problems will be solved in the near future, if they have not been solved already in principle. All we have to do is build nuclear reactors and supply them with atomic fuel. But how do we turn it into usable energy?

The 'classical' solution of this question, although it may soon be regarded as an old-fashioned one, is to conduct the heat generated by the fission process out of the reactor, make it boil water, and let the resulting steam drive turbines which, in their turn, drive electric generators. It is a roundabout way, but it works well, although it is still rather expensive.

Britain's first two nuclear power stations were Calder Hall (opened in 1956) and Chapelcross (1959), both of the same type. The reactor 'vessel', a giant steel cylinder, contains a pile of pure graphite, the material from which pencil leads are made. It has many hundreds of vertical or vertical and horizontal channels; in some of them the fuel—rods of uranium metal in magnesium alloy sheaths—are stacked, in the rest there are the control rods made of boron or cadmium; these can be pushed in and pulled out. A

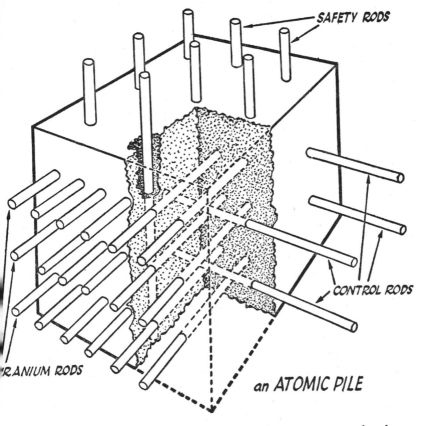

SAFETY RODS

CONTROL RODS

URANIUM RODS

an ATOMIC PILE

very thick concrete or steel wall around the reactor vessel—the 'biological shield'—prevents the escape of radio-activity.

As soon as the control rods are pulled out the chain reaction begins; uranium nuclei split up under neutron bombardment, and release more neutrons. These neutrons bounce off the graphite atoms so that they shoot to and fro through the reactor until they hit and split more uranium nuclei: the graphite acts as the moderator in this process, helping to keep the chain reaction going and preventing the 'capture' of fast neutrons by the nuclei through slowing them down. The uranium rods get hot (up to 400° C. in Calder Hall and Chapelcross), and this heat is removed by the 'coolant', carbon dioxide gas under pressure. It circulates through the reactor vessel in tubes, entering at the bottom at 140° C. and leaving it at the top at about 340° C.

The coolant gas, after leaving the 'core' of the reactor, is conducted to the heat exchangers. They are basically ordinary boilers in which water is turned into steam. The water is contained in steel pipes around which the hot coolant gas is blown; the resulting steam is directed into the turbines which rotate the electric generators. Calder Hall and Chapelcross have eight of them each, generating 180,000 and 140,000 kW respectively of electricity, which is fed into the national grid.

If the chain reaction gets too fast and the reactor becomes too hot, the control rods are lowered into the core automatically, thus slowing down the process; if pushed in completely they will stop it altogether.

Uranium as the fuel, graphite as the moderator, and carbon dioxide gas as the coolant are only one possible combination. Shippingport, America's first full-size power station on the Ohio River, uses ordinary water at a pressure of 2,000 lb. per square inch as the moderator as well as the coolant; the fuel elements are pellets of 'enriched' uranium, i.e. natural uranium with a specially high proportion of the radio-active uranium 235. Other power stations in Europe and America use liquid sodium or heavy water as coolants, while 'fast breeders'—so called because their neutrons are not slowed down before they hit the thorium blanket—need no moderator at all. Boiling water is also used as a coolant (most American nuclear submarines have this—see Part II); and in a West German research reactor the fuel has the form of potato-size thorium pellets, each with a small piece of U-235 embedded in its centre.

Some nuclear engineers believe that organic substances can be used as moderators and coolant fluids, others that the fuel should be given the form of a ceramic. A good deal of research work is done with various types of homogeneous reactors, in which fuel, moderator, and coolant circulate as a single, fluid mixture. British specialists, however, pin great hopes to their 'advanced gas-cooled reactor', basically of the same type as Calder Hall and

Chapelcross, but with much higher working temperatures, which will mean greater efficiency and economy.

This astonishing variety of reactor types shows that atomic energy is being groomed to do a great many jobs; a number of types are bound to fall by the wayside as soon as they have proved that they do not come up to expectations, but others will emerge. Nuclear power is still in roughly the same early phase as steam power was at the beginning of the nineteenth century, and it may not reach maturity until the end of our own century. By that time, however, we shall not only have fission but also fusion as a basic energy-producing nuclear process.

The theory of nuclear fusion was discovered in the early 1930's —years before that of fission—by John (now Sir John) Cockcroft and his assistant, Dr E. T. S. Walton, at the Cavendish Laboratory, Cambridge, where they worked under Lord Rutherford. Here they built a simple machine, which looked more like a couple of stove-pipes than an atom-smashing tool, for shooting electrically speeded-up protons at the nuclei of light elements, such as lithium. The result was that the lithium nuclei turned into nuclei of helium. This was strange; for helium is heavier than lithium. Somehow the helium atoms must have been formed not only by splitting but by subsequent accumulation of protons and neutrons. It was only later that it dawned on the physicists that some such process is responsible for the way in which the stars, including our own sun, produce their tremendous energy.

Today we know that in the sun light elements—mainly hydrogen—are turned into heavier ones, such as helium. This 'thermo-nuclear' process of fusion, as it is called, takes place at fantastically high temperatures (in the centre of the sun the temperature is believed to be about 15 million degrees centigrade). The heat fuses the nuclei, which would normally repel each other because they have the same (positive) electrical charge; heat means violent movement of particles, in other words: energy. Thus the hydrogen nuclei bump into each other and combine to form helium nuclei, with a simultaneous release of energy. As in nuclear fission, some mass is converted into energy in the fusion process, but the sun can keep up its rate of loss of mass—five million tons per second—for some thousands of million years.

This process is only possible where light elements are concerned; hydrogen, the lightest of them, has the smallest electrical charge, and therefore the repellent force of its nuclei can be more easily overcome than that of heavier elements. If there was any chance at all of producing nuclear energy from fusion—this was a point about which scientists agreed—it could only be done by using hydrogen: in short, by emulating on earth the process that makes the sun shine.

Again, as in the case of atomic fission, this was first achieved in the form of a weapon, the hydrogen bomb. After two years of intensive work in America, the first 'thermo-nuclear device' was tried out on an island in the Pacific in 1952, and less than a year later Russia exploded her own H-bomb in the Arctic. Ever since, the world has had to live under the shadow of this ultimate horror —a bomb a thousand times more powerful than the fission bomb of Hiroshima. Even the testing of these weapons has proved to be highly dangerous because it contaminates the atmosphere all over the world with radio-active 'fall-out', isotopes which can produce cancer of the bone and blood. No one doubts that a nuclear war fought with fission and fusion bombs would mean the suicide of mankind.

As these lines are being written many scientists in at least half a dozen countries are busy trying to find a system to tame the energy of the H-bomb for peaceful use, but no decisive 'breakthrough' has been achieved. It may, however, come at any moment. In August 1957 British physicists working with their thermo-nuclear device called 'Zeta' believed they had succeeded, but this turned out to be a mistake. Still, the scientists' efforts towards that goal are all based on the same basic principle, and some time somewhere another Zeta will achieve the 'breakthrough'.

In these experiments the heavy hydrogen isotope deuterium— which has an extra neutron in its nucleus—plays the decisive part. At very high temperatures the protons are detached from the electrons revolving around them, and the neutrons fly off at great speed, thus providing extra energy, i.e. heat, as the protons melt together to form new nuclei. There are many difficult problems to overcome before the thermo-nuclear power station based on this process can become a reality, but that of fuel supply is the least of them: the oceans of the earth are a practically inexhaustible source of deuterium, and its extraction from sea water is neither complicated nor expensive. One gallon of sea water may be sufficient to yield as much energy as 100 gallons of petrol, and a bucketful containing one-fifth of a gram of deuterium could keep a five-room house warm for a whole year.

The real trouble starts when we attempt to produce the very high temperatures required to achieve thermo-nuclear fusion. Up to 1950, the highest temperature ever produced in a laboratory was 30,000° centigrade. All the Zeta-type assemblies, therefore, are machines designed to reach temperatures of many millions of degrees for heating deuterium gas. This is done electrically. When an electric current is passed through a gas it sets up an electric discharge in it, with a corresponding rise in temperature. A hollow vessel—either ring-shaped or tube-shaped, and usually made of aluminium—is partly encircled by a huge electro-magnet which produces the field that heats up the deuterium inside. But if the hot gas touched the walls of the vessel they would melt, and the gas would cool down; therefore, it must be kept in the centre. This is done by another intense magnetic field around the gas, usually by winding an electrically charged cable around the vessel. In this way the gas, which tries to resist that 'pinch effect', is prevented from lashing about like an angry snake as soon as the current is switched on and the temperature rises.

Zeta, the British assembly which was originally built at the atomic research establishment in Harwell, had a ring-shaped (torus) form; the 'pyrotron', set up at the University of California, was designed as a linear tube with a special 'mirror' effect: the magnetic field was made much stronger at either end so that the 'plasma', as the gas in the machine is usually called, assumed the shape of a sausage—thick in the middle and pinched at the ends. This arrangement had the effect of a magnetic mirror; the particles racing around in the plasma were reflected back from both ends into the centre, which increased the temperature and also the probability of the particles bumping into each other to achieve fusion. Another American fusion research instrument did away with the magnetic coils, and used a layer of accelerated electrons instead for the production of the necessary magnetic field.

When one of the scientists' teams working with these machines achieves genuine fusion—a temperature of up to 500 million degrees centigrade may be needed to start a thermo-nuclear process which can maintain itself—the question of how a thermo-nuclear power station could work will become topical. As in a conventional power station, coal-fired or atomic, the heat could be used to produce steam for the turbo-generators. But by that time there may be a better and more direct way of turning heat or radio-activity into electricity.

There are several basic systems of doing this. One, called the 'thermionic converter', uses the principle of the cathode-ray tube in which electrons, particles of negative electricity, are given off by a hot strip of metal, the cathode, in a vacuum. The heat necessary to produce this effect could be that generated in a nuclear reactor; the greater the temperature difference between the cathode, or 'emitter', and the anode, or 'collector', the greater will be the yield of electrons and therefore of electric current. There is, at least theoretically, no reason why a nuclear power station should not be operating on this principle once the technological problems have been solved.

Atomic as well as conventional power stations may be made much more efficient by the gas-blast system of generating electricity. It is based on the fact that a blast of very hot gas (at least 2,000° centigrade), which could be produced by a fission or fusion reactor, becomes an electrical conductor and generates current when moving through the poles of a powerful magnet. American and British research laboratories are working on this scheme, but the principal problem is that of finding materials which can withstand such temperatures for any length of time.

Another system—which might be better suited for smaller, mobile electricity producing units—is based on a discovery recorded already by the Curies around 1900, but neglected by scientists for nearly half a century. That was the observation that radio-activity could produce electricity directly in certain materials. When, after the Second World War, cheap radio-active sources—isotopes—became available the idea was taken up at last. The first, somewhat crude 'atomic battery', as it was called, was produced in 1954 by a research team in the laboratories of the Radio Corporation of America: a little box containing a thin wafer of the isotope, strontium 90—one of the dangerous elements in radio-active 'fall-out' after H-bomb tests; it bombarded with its particles a semi-conductor crystal, an adaptation of the transistor (which we shall describe in Part III of this book). The current generated in the crystal by the radio-active emanation of the strontium isotope was strong enough to produce a buzzing noise in an earphone.

Five years later a more advanced model of the atomic battery was demonstrated by the scientists of the U.S. Atomic Energy Commission. 'Snap-III', as they had christened it, was able to generate 5 watts of electricity from a tiny pellet of the radio-active isotope, polonium 210 (but the research team explained that the cheaper isotope, cerium 144, might be even more suit-able). The pellet was placed in the centre of the battery, sur-rounded by twenty pairs of thermocouples arranged like the spokes of a wheel (a thermocouple, originally an electrical thermometer, has two wires of different metals joined at both ends; if there is a difference in temperature between the two ends, an electric current flows through the wires). The radiation from the isotope, generating heat, made an electric current flow through the thermocouples. The whole device was no bigger than $5\frac{1}{2}$ by $4\frac{1}{2}$ inches, and weighed only 5 lb., which made it suitable —among other purposes—for powering electric instruments in space vehicles, where long life and light weight are essential.[1]

Isotopes for direct generation of electricity will be available in growing quantities as the utilization of atomic energy spreads to more and more countries. One of the major problems connected with nuclear power stations is the safe disposal of radio-active waste; burying it, or dumping it into the sea, is not everywhere the best means of getting rid of it. But when devices such as atomic batteries are mass produced they will require great quantities of radio-active 'waste' products; they must, of course, be made absolutely safe for everyday use.

How can we tell if we are the target of radio-active emanation? It is invisible and inaudible, and we cannot feel it—unless and until we have received too much of it and become ill. But there is a vital tool in our nuclear age, the Geiger counter in its manifold forms, which measures radio-activity accurately. Invented by Hans Geiger, a German physicist and one of Lord Rutherford's close collaborators, in the 1920's, it is an ingenious instrument

[1] In June 1961 the United States fired three satellites into orbit with one rocket. Instruments and transmitters in one of these were powered for the first time by an atomic generator (not a reactor) using radiation from a tiny piece of Plutonium 238, the heat from which was converted directly into electricity.

which can make any type of radiation, whether in the form of particles or of electro-magnetic waves, visible and audible.

The Geiger counter consists of a metal cylinder filled with gas at low pressure; two electrodes—one being the cylinder itself, the other a fine wire stretched along its centre—are maintained at a large potential difference, usually about 1,000–1,500 volts, but no spark is allowed to pass between them. Only when some sub-atomic particle or unit of electro-magnetic radiation pierces the thin metal of the cylinder and produces ionization (i.e. when the gas atoms become electrically charged), there is a sudden discharge between the electrodes, and the potential drops for the fraction of a second. This can be made either visible on a dial, or audible in a pair of headphones. Frequently, simple counting devices such as telephone counters are attached to the tube to register the number of incoming particles.

Geiger counters are being made and adapted for all kinds of purposes—light ones for uranium prospecting; built-in types for atomic power stations and research establishments; counters with warning signals for factory workers who have to handle radio-active matter and whose hands and clothes have to be checked; counters which can test human breath for traces of radon gas, and so on.

The part which nuclear energy is likely to play in transport will be discussed in Part II of this book. There are still other things it can do. Unlike any other prime mover, it is also an explosive—unfortunately, we may add. But like any other explosive it can do tremendous services to mankind, and as it is infinitely more powerful than the most efficient chemical ones such as T.N.T. or dynamite, it can carry out much more ambitious tasks.

Among these are the excavation or deepening of harbours, canals, and rivers; the removal of shipping obstructions such as wrecks and rocks at a fraction of the time and cost of conventional methods; the facilitating of mining by blasting away the earth cover above mineral deposits, or by deep underground explosions; the recovery of oil from rock or shale, which would give many oil-short nations independent sources of fuel; the opening-up of new sources for underground rivers, by breaking the rock cover, for irrigation of desert areas; the production of vast quantities of radio-active isotopes for medicine, agriculture, industry, and research at very low cost by underground explosions.

Finally, a new source of energy could be created by 'depositing' the heat of a nuclear explosion deep underground and using it—just as volcanic heat is used in some parts of the world—for the production of power. It has been estimated that an atomic blast 3,000 feet underground in a suitable geological formation would produce about 8,000 million kilowatt hours of electrical energy at a cost of 0·04$d$. (less than ½ cent) per kilowatt. In short, the peaceful uses of atomic energy are vast and tempting—but we must stop squandering it on weapons of mass annihilation.

# 5

◇◇◇◇◇◇◇◇◇◇◇◇◇◇◇◇◇◇◇◇◇◇◇◇

# Direct Energy from the Sun

WE KNOW that all the energy mankind has ever used comes from the sun, with the exception of nuclear energy. If we took all the world's reserves of coal, oil, and natural gas and burnt them up at the same rate at which we receive the sun's energy, our whole supply would last less than three days. Yet we are only now beginning to use that vast and almost inexhaustible source of energy in the sky directly.

The most primitive device for catching and trapping the heat of the sun is the gardener's greenhouse. Its modern offspring is the solar water-heater, usually a coil of pipes placed in a shallow box on the roof of a house, embedded in black concrete (black accepts the sun rays more easily, white reflects them) and covered with a glass pane. The water circulating in the pipes is heated by the sun and then pumped into a hot-water tank from which the household takes its supply. In Florida alone, more than 50,000 homes get their hot water in this way, and in Israel it has become general practice to install solar water-heaters in new rural houses.

A more complicated but also more efficient device is the heat pump. It is, in fact, a refrigerator in reverse. It picks up as much heat as it can get either from the atmosphere, the soil, or from water (a river or a lake); this amount of heat, which is of course rather small in winter, is made to act on a liquid with a very low boiling-point so that it changes into a gas. The gas is then compressed by means of a pump and goes into a condenser coil, where it changes back to a liquid, thus setting its heat free; this can be made to heat the house or to provide hot water. Many heat pumps can be switched to reverse action so that they cool the air in summer.

Various types of 'solar houses' have been designed by engineers and architects, especially in America, where many thousands of them have been built. In these houses, some medium is used to store the heat of the sun and release it gradually as required. Water is a good medium for the purpose, but Glauber's salt (hydrated sodium sulphate) is even more efficient. It melts at a temperature of 90° F., taking in a large amount of heat which it releases again when it turns back into crystals. Twenty tons of the salt, in 'heat bins' in the cellar of the solar house, have been found to be sufficient to keep the rooms comfortably warm in winter—with heat collected in the summer!

Another interesting medium is gravel, incorporated in the walls of the house, which it keeps warm on sunless days; by means of a small ventilator, hot air from a heat collector on the roof is circulated through the gravel, which releases its accumulated heat at an even rate.

These efforts at utilizing the heat of the sun show that the engineers are well aware of the great possibilities of solar heating but also of its limitations. Many countries, especially in what we call the moderate zones (to say nothing of the cold regions), do not enjoy enough sunshine to make a solar house worth building, while the tropical zones have no use for extra heat. There, however, cooking by solar energy is becoming more and more important in everyday life.

India has a very limited supply of fuel—its main source for the home is dried cow dung, which of course would be much better employed in fertilizing the soil. But India has an abundance of sunshine. As early as the 1880's, an Englishman working in India, W. Adams, suggested the introduction of a cheap solar cooker, but until fairly recently no really efficient device suitable for mass production had been invented. The Indian National Physical Laboratory and one of the United Nations agencies eventually developed solar cookers, which are being used increasingly in Indian homes. One type uses a reflecting mirror and a pressure cooker, another has four flat mirrors and an insulated heat-collecting box filled with Glauber's salt crystals, which continue to release heat when the sun has already set.

In the Sudan and East Africa a simple type of solar cooker has become fairly popular. It consists of a concave aluminium reflector $4\frac{1}{2}$ feet across, mounted on an upright iron rod; the concentrated rays of the sun fall on the pot or pan placed on a wire-mesh holder which is attached to the reflector.

Another very important device is the solar 'still' for the distillation of fresh water from salt water, usually working on the principle of a salt-water container covered by a sloping glass roof; as the heat of the sun evaporates the water, the vapour condenses in droplets on the glass roof from where they trickle down into a fresh-water collector. The equally valuable salt is left behind in the salt-water container.

Solar furnaces are still very much in the experimental stage. French scientists are operating them in their research station in the Pyrenees; they are very large—one has a flat reflecting mirror made up of 516 panes and covering an area of 43 feet square and a 31-foot by 33-foot parabolic mirror at a distance of 80 feet. The heat produced by this arrangement is sufficient to melt 130 lb. of iron per hour. The Russians have built an enormous 'helio-boiler', consisting of an 80-foot tower surrounded by twenty-three concentric railway tracks; bogeys move around on these tracks, each carrying a 10-foot by 16-foot reflector to concentrate the sun's rays on to a boiler in the tower. It is claimed that this machine produces enough superheated steam for a turbo-generator with 1,000 kW output.

The most efficient way of generating electricity from sunlight, however, seems to be the 'solar battery'. The first of this type was demonstrated in 1954 by a team of scientists from the American Bell Laboratories. It operated with semi-conductor crystals similar to those used in transistors (see Part III), either of germanium or of silicon. When sunlight strikes such a crystal, an electric current is generated. A Bell battery of 400 silicon cells was able to produce a 12-volt current. Since its first demonstration, the solar battery has been extensively developed and has taken part in one of Man's greatest adventures—the sending of satellites and rocket vehicles into space. Solar batteries, as well as the already mentioned atomic batteries, are very suitable for powering the transmitters in space vehicles because of their long life.

Eventually, solar batteries may be developed to provide all the low-voltage current needed in a house. Their theoretical top efficiency is 22 per cent, corresponding to the generation of about 200 watts per square yard of the silicon surface.

French scientists have designed a solar lamp. It is about as big as a small suitcase; at the top it has a collector panel consisting of a few dozen photo-sensitive silicon cells, and the solar energy which they collect is stored in a small accumulator. The underside of the 'suitcase' consists of a fluorescent tube. During day-time the device is put out in the sun, and in the evening it is taken indoors and the lamp switched on. Depending on the time the collector has been exposed to the sun the lamp will then shine for a few hours.

Instead of semi-conductors the solar battery can also use thermocouples (as described in the foregoing chapter). Here, the problem is that of keeping one end of the thermocouple wires cool while the other is heated by the sun—otherwise there will be no current.

In the 1950's, the Solar Energy Committee of the British National Physical Laboratory made a suggestion which could help to provide tropical regions with perpetual energy: the planting of quick-growing forest wood such as eucalyptus, and its continuous combustion in medium-size power stations. A few square miles of eucalyptus forest would yield enough wood to fire the boilers of the power station for ever because the wood would grow as fast as it is used up.

Electricity from eucalyptus may not be the most efficient system of turning the energy of the sun into power, but it shows the ingenuity of our scientists in finding new ways and means to provide mankind with more and more energy; and that means: to raise its standard of living. In the old days, the stage of civilization reached by a nation used to be measured in pounds of soap per head and year; today it is the amount of horsepower or kilowatt-hours available to everybody which indicates the degree of civilization. The Western world has forty to eighty times as much energy at its disposal as the people in the undeveloped countries of Africa and Asia—and that means food, housing, clothing, health, transport, everything that goes into the daily lives of the population, and everything that is produced and consumed or exchanged for goods and services from abroad.

Now we have the technical means of generating enough energy to raise the standard of living to a decent level all over the world, and it is our noblest task for the rest of this century to see that no one anywhere is left with an empty stomach.

# II
# Transport

# I

❖◇❖◇❖◇❖◇❖◇❖◇❖◇❖◇❖◇❖◇❖◇❖◇

# Wheels, Roads, Bridges, and Canals

LET us imagine that by means of some time machine, or simply by magic, we are transported back to the age before mechanical civilization began. Deprived of the thousand and one things we are accustomed to in our daily lives we should feel completely helpless. How should we get food, clothes, shelter? All our requirements would present as many major problems. We should have nothing to rely on but our own hands and feet . . . and, of course, our brains. And we should begin to think how to tackle this or that task.

We should make some primitive weapons and go out into the woods and kill some large animal to last us for several dinners. Knowing nothing of mechanical means of transport we should rack our brains how to get the animal back to our residential cave. Dragging it through the forest would seem a back-breaking if not impossible job. But one of us might think of putting it on some branches or on a couple of long flat pieces of wood, a kind of simple sledge. This would make the task of pulling the load much easier; and we should have invented the first vehicle for transport on land.

If we had lived in that period, the mesolithic age—perhaps fifteen thousand or more years ago—we should not have known why a heavy load can be moved much more easily on a sledge than by dragging it directly over rough ground. We should have found out by experiment. Today we know that it is all a question of friction, the greatest of all natural obstacles to transport.

Friction is the resistance to movement that results from one thing rubbing against another; the rougher the surface, the greater the friction. Nothing, of course, is completely smooth;

D
95

Early transport: ancient Briton using a sledge

everything offers at least a little friction, but some things are much smoother than others. So when mesolithic Man fixed runners underneath the bumpy body of his prey, or on a large stone he needed for building, he reduced the friction between his load and the ground because the flat pieces of wood were much smoother than the load itself.

The first agricultural people made much use of the sledge; it was eventually built into one piece by connecting the two runners by cross-beams, tying the whole contraption together with strips of hide. In those regions where snow used to fall the sledge turned out a still better means of transport in winter because the snow offers an extremely smooth surface—and a frozen river or lake even more so.

That invention was, of course, made many times and among many tribes all over the world. Perhaps simultaneously, perhaps some hundreds or thousands of years later, Man made another great discovery. It may have happened like this: as he felled some tree trunks to use as fuel for his fire or for building, a heavy lump

Before the invention of the wheel: transport on rollers

of rock crashed across two of these trunks. And trying to push the rock away from his logs, he suddenly found that it rolled away with them. He must have been astonished and delighted to see that he could move the heavy stone quite easily on the tree trunks ... until it fell off.

There is no doubt that primitive Man made extensive use of rollers, as we call them. Rolling friction is still less than sliding friction because there is little 'rub' between the load, the rollers, and the ground. Roller transport was employed for a very long time; in fact, it is still being used in some parts of the world. It needs a group of people to operate it: some do the pushing or pulling, while others pick up the rollers from behind the load and place them in front. Thus it is a 'social' job which helped to create some kind of team spirit among the hordes of primitive men.

There are ancient monuments whose construction would have been impossible without roller transport: the Pyramids, for instance, or Britain's Stonehenge. Some of these enormous stones, arranged in the form of circles on Salisbury Plain in Wiltshire (they seem to have served some religious and astronomical purpose), were transported all the way from South Wales, where that kind of stone is found—a distance of almost 150 miles. The task could have been accomplished only with the use of rollers, even if they were brought part of the way by water.

Still, it was far from being an ideal system of moving heavy loads. The incessant shifting of the rollers from behind the load to the front was tiresome and slowed down the operation considerably. Again it must have been Man's intrinsic laziness which made him strive for improvement. He built a cart consisting of a platform for the load—made of logs tied together—and a single roller underneath, which was held in its place by four vertical pegs. The trouble with this vehicle was that there was a great amount of friction between the roller and the platform.

But it seems to have been from that roller cart that Man proceeded to make one of his most ingenious inventions—perhaps the greatest of all: the wheel.

How did it happen? Where? When? How often? We cannot say. We can only admire the brilliant brainwork of those uncouth, half-naked, ignorant ancestors of ours who thought of a device without which our entire civilization could not exist—no aeroplane could fly, no wristwatch tell the time, no factory work without wheels: they do indeed make our world go round.

Perhaps the sight of a roller worn down to a disc by friction gave a group of workers the idea; or a stick may have got stuck in a roller, thus forming a primitive axle; or it may have been the result of experiments carried out by some early technical genius: be that as it may, the wheel was there, and it had come to stay. For a long time it remained a rather clumsy affair, no more than a solid disc cut from a tree log, with a hole in the centre for the axle. But it could not have been made without tools—saws, drills, knives, planes; this points to the probability that its introduction

Stonehenge in Wiltshire, Britain's most famous prehistoric
monument

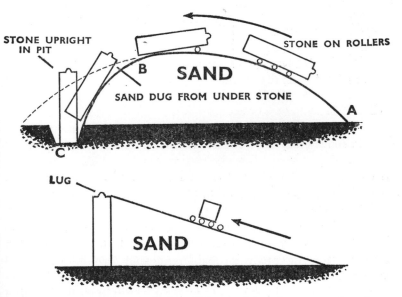

A possible method by which the trilithons of Stonehenge may have been
erected

became general only after the mining, smelting, and shaping of metal had been invented, for stone tools cannot had been efficient enough. Although some archaeologists believe that wheeled vehicles were in use among the lake-dwellers in the Swiss and German Alps as long as twenty thousand years ago, reliable evidence seems to show that the first carts with wheels came into

Primitive wheel cart, Formosa. The axle is fixed by wooden pins

use in Syria and Sumeria between 4000 and 3500 B.C. By 3000 B.C. they were fairly common in Mesopotamia, reaching the Indus by about 2500 B.C.

Strangely enough, the wheel was unknown in Egypt until several centuries later, but then it was greatly improved in that country. The Egyptians probably invented (around 1800 B.C.) the spoked wheel, a device much lighter and stronger than the disc wheel, which broke easily under a heavy load. By building the wheel from separate parts—hub, felloe, and spokes connecting the two—the stress could be more evenly distributed. The Egyptians also replaced the rough platform set above the axle by a proper box, or body. In this form, as a two-wheeled 'gig', the Greeks and early Romans took the cart over from the Egyptians, using it mainly as a war-chariot, for ritual purposes, and for racing. By that time the clumsy ox, the first animal to be trained as a beast of draught, had been largely replaced by the faster and more adaptable and elegant horse. The Romans eventually invented the four-wheeled carriage with sway-bar, making the front axle movable horizontally, and thus steering much easier. It was only with this improvement that the vehicle was able to become a universal means of transport.

Carriages by themselves, however, do not provide transport. They need roads—a truism to us, but few of the ancient nations recognized it until the Romans established their far-flung empire. The Greeks, who believed that trees, springs, groves, and gorges had 'souls' or were at least the abode of demi-gods, had hesitated to interfere with Nature, and the few highways they had built were more like temple avenues lined with tombs and religious monuments; on rocky ground, the Greek roads were not much more than two wheel ruts either carved out or worn down by carts, with no facilities for letting vehicles from the opposite direction pass. The Persians did better; they built highways from Susa to Asia Minor and India, effectively dotted with inns and

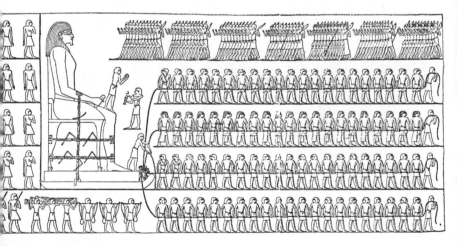

Before the Egyptians adopted the wheel they transported their giant statues on slave-drawn sledges under military guard

Transporting a column to the Temple of Diana at Ephesus in ancient Greece

Greek military chariot (painting on a vase)

relay stations. Their mail service was said to be excellent; but the main function of these roads—like that of Hitler's autobahnen three thousand years later—was that of facilitating military movements. The Chinese, too, had some very good roads, which were a strategic necessity for their rulers.

Early Roman two-wheeled cart for the transport of slaves and
prisoners

Roman four-wheeled baggage wagon

But whatever the achievements of these nations in the field of
highway construction were, they pale into insignificance when
compared with those of the Romans. They were the first people
to equip not only their own country with roads but almost the
entire known world, from the borders of Scotland to the Persian
Gulf and from the Caucasus to the Atlas Mountains; not, of
course, out of love for the inhabitants, but for military
reasons, and to make travelling easier and more comfortable for
their own merchants, officers, and officials.

As an organizational, technical, and administrative feat the
Roman highway system is outstanding. It extended over no less
than fifty thousand miles at the time of the emperors. Steppes,
mountains, rivers, or marshes were no obstacles to the Roman

engineers. They built roads to last, and to be used in safety and throughout the whole year by fast dispatch riders and foot-slogging legionaries, by light chariots and heavy covered wagons. Different methods of construction were used according to local materials and conditions. As a rule, a 'road bed' of large stone blocks was covered with a layer of smaller, broken stones, and this in turn by a layer of sand. The surface was made by using big basalt blocks or gravel set in lime mortar; in marshy regions,

Road in Pompeii, with kerbstones and flagstone surface

where there was little local stone material, wooden causeways on piles were built. Most roads had kerbstones; there were raised footwalks in the towns and villages. The width varied between 12 and over 20 feet, and in regions with heavy rainfalls the roads were given a good camber, or curvature, so that the water would drain away quickly.

The Roman highway system cost a great deal of money, but somehow it never became an intolerable burden for the treasury. Whenever the soldiers had no wars to fight they were detailed to roadmaking. Forced labour was also used extensively in the conquered countries. Wealthy Romans bequeathed their fortunes to the road fund, and the most efficient organizers were appointed road curators. Thus Julius Caesar was for some time curator of the Via Appia. The Emperor Augustus assigned a number of roads to his richest senators, and made them responsible for their maintenance; he himself took over the Via Flaminia. In the towns, maintenance and in many cases construction of the highways was the responsibility of the property owners.

Where passable roads were already in existence before the Romans came—for instance in England—they straightened and strengthened them, widened and paved them. Foss Way from Devon to Lincolnshire, Icknield Way from Stonehenge to East Anglia, Watling Street from Dover through London to Chester: these old English country roads were turned into splendid highways by the Romans.

As soon as the Romans had left the conquered countries their roads began to decay through disuse and lack of maintenance. With the Roman Empire the need for strategic long-distance highways disappeared. In many of those countries, as in Italy itself, there was no longer a strong central authority requiring an effective communication network; the small principalities which came into existence were not at all interested in maintaining good roads—these would have been too much of a help for invading forces from a neighbouring country. During the entire first half of the Middle Ages hardly a new road was made in the whole of what used to be the Roman Empire. Traffic had to move laboriously and at snail's pace along miserable tracks, the travellers being choked with dust in summer and getting stuck with their carriages in the mud in winter. When such a track had become completely unusable it was simply abandoned and another one started alongside it. Sometimes these tracks were so deep and narrow that in a wet season the water came rushing down, and the travellers had to swim for their lives.

England's roads were known as the worst in all Europe. In Germany, at least the 'King's Highways', the only routes for wheeled traffic, were kept in some modest state of repair, and in the thirteenth century things seem to have improved. The *Sachsenspiegel*, the oldest German code of law, contained a kind of Highway Code which said: 'The highways must be so wide that carriages can pass each other. The pedestrian must give way to the horseman, the horseman to the carriage, and the empty wagon to the loaded one.'

Just because England had such abominable roads this country produced the first modern road engineers. The most remarkable personality among them was John Metcalf, born in 1717. He was called 'Blind Jack of Knaresborough' because at the age of 6 he lost his sight after an attack of smallpox. Yet in spite of this handicap he became one of Britain's most efficient roadmakers. Within thirty years he built 180 miles of excellent highways, mainly in his own county, in Lancashire, and in Cheshire.

Metcalf used the same system as the Romans, giving his roads a good, solid foundation of stone blocks, and ramming in several layers of chips and broken tiles on top of them. The only difference was that Metcalf left them as the surface, without finishing his roads off with paving stones. He also used a slight camber for drainage.

The growing industrialization of the midlands and northern England had made the building of new roads an absolute necessity. That was Metcalf's chance, but it was no easy job to convince the authorities that he, a blind man, an itinerant fiddler (he actually played on the battlefields during the Rebellion of 1745), could build a highway. He was almost 50 when he was entrusted with the construction of a three-mile turnpike road. He did it faster, better, and cheaper than other engineers who had the use of their eyes. From that time he was asked to build one road after another.

Blind Jack had shown the way, but it was some time before others followed him. Thomas Telford, born forty years after him, left his native Scotland to become a bridge-builder farther south, but he returned to construct canals and roads, which were desperately needed to save the Highlanders from starvation. His main concern was that a road should be as level as possible, and that the centre strip should be strong enough for the heaviest loads. He used a two-layer foundation of stones, each about three inches wide, packed by hand, with smaller ones filling in the gaps. then came a seven-inch layer of broken whinstones, which was covered with gravel about one inch deep.

John Macadam, his fellow-countryman and contemporary, employed a different method. He used several layers of broken stone instead of large ones as a foundation; within a short while the small stones settled to form a hard, smooth surface. The system was quick and inexpensive, but Macadam's roads may not have lasted as long as those of Telford. He repaired existing roads by breaking them up and using the same material for the new ones.

There was little development in the technique of roadmaking until the motor-car made its appearance towards the end of the nineteenth century. By that time, however, the engineers had an excellent machine at their disposal—the road-roller. It was invented by a former farmer and agricultural mechanic from Kent, Thomas Aveling. He demonstrated that strange machine for the first time in 1865 : a veritable monster, driven by a steam-engine, which frightened the horses and country people. Wherever he

A steam road-roller around 1900

drove his machine it was met and followed by enraged villagers, the police banned it, and even court actions were brought against Aveling. The ice was broken only when, in 1867, the City of Liverpool ordered the first steam-roller. The Government authorities, however, began to take an interest in the new machine only after India and China had ordered it. Today, road-rollers are usually Diesel-powered; the heavy cylinders are filled with water to give them extra weight, but there are also 'open-cylinder' types which can be heated by suspended coke cauldrons from the inside for rolling roads with new asphalt surfaces.

In Britain a new epoch in modern road history began in 1878 with the Highways and Locomotive Act. It marked the end of the old turnpike system, under which road users were made to pay toll towards construction and maintenance; now, for the first time, the State recognized that it had to accept responsibility for the roads.

The roadmaker, too, has changed a great deal since the eighteenth century, when his various duties often included the handling of diseased meat and infected persons as well as other kinds of 'nuisance'; he had to see to the scouring of ditches—a most unsavoury and dangerous job in those sewerless days—and give 'publick notice every four months what defaults he finds', which was then read out in church on Sunday after sermon. It was a far cry from this to the establishment of the first Chair of Highway Engineering at London University in 1928.

In roadmaking today, different techniques are employed according to the job in hand, which may be a country lane or a motorway for fast-moving traffic. As a rule, however, foundations and surfaces are now recognized as two separate parts. Foundations are still being laid according to Telford's system (hand-pitched stones between subsoil and surface); by the pell-mell distribution of hardcore (large stones, old concrete, pieces of brickwork, etc.); or by the laying of large concrete slabs. Usually, a layer of clinker ashes to prevent water from 'creeping up' is put on top of the foundation, which is compressed by a ten-ton roller.

Most of the country roads are still made of waterbound macadam, which has the advantage that local slag, limestone, or flint can be used; this material is liberally sprayed with water while it is being consolidated by the road-roller. For heavy and high-speed motor traffic, however, a 'tar macadam' surface is now the rule: broken stone is coated with tar, a by-product from the distillation of bituminous coal in gasworks and coke-ovens. Tar macadam has gradually superseded the more expensive rock asphalt surface, which is laid hot with smoothing irons.

The most modern type of road, especially the motorway, requires concrete foundations, usually with a reinforcing steel structure embedded in it to resist the stress of very heavy traffic, as well as concrete surfacings. Concrete is an aggregate of hard stone (gravel), sharp sand, and cement, mixed with water. Concrete has the advantages that its required thickness can be calculated with great accuracy, and that its homogeneous mass distributes the load evenly. Concrete roads get an extra layer of waterproof paper, which is spread in great sheets over the foundation, to prevent 'water creep'. When the concrete has dried and hardened, a surface of asphalt or tar macadam can be applied, but the modern tendency is to leave the concrete as it is for a few years, and then surface it. However, fashions in road-making change, new materials, machines, and techniques are introduced every year, and a great deal of research is being carried out in Europe and America.

But even the best highway network would not be much good

Primitive footbridge

if the roads stopped every time they came to a river. Bridges are just as important as roads—and nearly as old.

The first bridges were no more than tall trees laid across streams, with their ends resting on the banks. Bridges made of boats, or pontoons, connected by timbers, were also used in early times; Xerxes crossed the Hellespont by this means in 450 B.C. Stone piers, probably put up at the time of Semiramis (c. 800 B.C.), seem to have served as supports for a beam bridge across the Euphrates at Babylon. In ancient China, suspension bridges—in which a long, narrow platform is hung from ropes or chains—were built over several rivers and gorges; they were also in use in the Inca Empire in Peru, with lengths up to 200 feet.

The Romans developed bridge-building along with road-making; many of their structures, including some impressive aqueducts, are still in use or at least in existence. Trajan's Column in Rome, erected around A.D. 100, shows the bridge he built across the Danube; it had timber arches and the piers are said to have been 150 feet high. The Romans favoured the semicircular arch in bridge-building as in their entire architecture.

For a thousand years after the dissolution of the Roman Empire, the construction of bridges ceased nearly completely in Europe; only very few important ones were built, such as that across the Danube at Ratisbon, across the Moldau in Prague, across the Elbe in Dresden, across the Rhône at Avignon, across the Main at Würzburg, and across the Arno at Florence—all of them in the twelfth century. The first London Bridge may have been built by the Romans, but nothing certain is known until the tenth century, when a wooden bridge existed. It was destroyed by a storm; another one was built but burnt down. Only in 1176 was the famous stone bridge begun by Peter de Colechurch, a chaplain; it was completed in 1209. Spanning 900 feet, with nineteen pointed arches, it had a drawbridge section so that ships could pass. Although frequently damaged, and heavily weighed down by houses built on the superstructure, it lasted for more than six centuries. Until 1750, when Westminster Bridge was completed, it was London's only bridge.

The great revival of the art of bridge-building began in Italy. Much as we admire the charm and beauty of the many hump-backed little bridges over the canals of Venice, they cannot be compared, as engineering achievements, with that over the Adda at Trezzo, which spanned the river in a single arch of nearly 240 feet length and 70 feet rise. Built at the end of the fourteenth century, it lasted for less than fifty years and fell victim to a siege of the castle of Trezzo. Another great Italian bridge built at the same time, the Ponte del Castello Vecchio in Verona, was deliberately destroyed by the Germans during their withdrawal from Italy in 1945, but rebuilt afterwards.

The scientific foundation of modern bridge-building, the knowledge of the composition of forces—statics—goes back to the fifteenth and sixteenth centuries, especially to the theoretical work of Leonardo da Vinci. But it was not until the late eighteenth century that iron was first used as a building material on a large scale. The first cast-iron arch bridge was built in England in the 1770's: that over the Severn at Coalbrookdale by Abraham

Darby, with a single 100-foot arch. Germany and France followed some decades later. The next phase was the construction of a number of suspension bridges held by cables or chains, especially in the United States; some of them, such as the 240-foot bridge over the Merrimac in Massachusetts, built in 1809, are still in existence.

Thomas Telford, the road engineer, was responsible for the famous Menai suspension bridge at Bangor, built in 1819–25, with a 580-foot span, and the Conway Castle bridge, built in 1820–6, with a 416-foot span. On the Continent, the first major cable suspension bridge was built at the same time in Geneva by a Swiss engineer, Henri Dufour, and his French colleague, Marc Séquin. Another French engineer, J. Chaley, put up what was then called 'the boldest structure ever built', the suspension bridge at Fribourg, Switzerland, with a span of nearly 900 feet. It was demolished in 1923 after ninety years of useful life.

Throughout the nineteenth and our own century, the suspension type of bridge has been very popular among engineers because the forces acting on it are easy to calculate and tests of material strength can be carried out with greater accuracy than with other types. It was, for instance, found during experiments in connection with the Geneva bridge that drawn wires are the most effective material for 'hanging' the platform, and most modern suspension bridges have steel cables consisting of thousands of wire strands. The main span of the Delaware bridge, built in 1926 to carry the Philadelphia–Camden highway, is 1,750 feet; two suspension cables, each 30 inches in diameter and consisting of 18,666 wire strands, are holding it. Older but no less imposing suspension bridges are the three over the East River at New York. The great Hudson Bridge between New York City and New Jersey, with a central span of 3,500 feet, is America's most striking structure of this kind; it was built by a team of engineers working under O. H. Ammann. The new suspension bridge across the Golden Gate, San Francisco, is even longer; it has a central span of no less than 4,200 feet and two side spans of 1,100 feet each.

Europe's largest bridge will span the Tagus at Lisbon in 1965. Suspended from two 750-foot towers it will be 260 feet above the river, and have a free span of 3,318 feet. The people of Lisbon, who have never had a bridge yet, say that it will command one of

the most beautiful views in the world. It will also open up the flat
hinterland south of the Tagus with its new steel plants.

In 1963 Britain will have its new Forth Road Bridge, a most
impressive suspension bridge with a centre span of 3,300 feet and
two side spans each about two-fifths as long, and with elegant
500-foot-high steel towers. There will be 30,000 miles of wire in
the two suspension cables, each of which is 2 feet thick and
contains 11,618 parallel wires of galvanized high-tension steel—
produced for the first time for this bridge. It will be only slightly
shorter than the Tagus bridge, a fitting partner for the cantilever
Firth-of-Forth railway bridge built by Benjamin Baker from 1882
to 1890, which has an overall length of over 8,200 feet.

Yet we cannot say that all the problems of building suspension
bridges have been solved. There is, for instance, that of possible
additional stresses caused by strong winds—the collapse of the
bridge over the Tacoma Narrows, U.S.A., in 1940 showed that
even in our century the engineers may occasionally make fatal
mistakes. The same fate was prophesied to Brunel's famous
Clifton Bridge near Bristol throughout the thirty-two years of its
construction (1832–64); but with its 702-feet span, towering 245
feet above high-tide level, it is still in its place.

We have mentioned the cantilever bridge over the Forth. With
this type, known in a crude form already to the ancient Chinese,
long cantilevers are run from both sides towards the middle,
where the projecting ends are connected by girders—a stable and
elegant-looking structure. The Forth railway bridge has two
spans of 1,710 feet each and three cantilevers connected by independent girder spans. The St Lawrence Bridge at Quebec has a
main span of 1,800 feet; the cantilevers are resting on points and
are anchored on the shore.

Where very long spans are not essential, the girder bridge is a
practical type. It owes its introduction in the early nineteenth
century to the development of wrought-iron techniques. The
Britannia Bridge over the Menai Straits, built by George Stephenson's son, Robert, from 1846 to 1850, demonstrated the great
possibilities of the new material to the engineering world. It has
tubular girders made from wrought-iron plates and angle irons,
with three masonry piers rising from the water, forming two 460-
foot spans; they are slightly longer than the spans of Brunel's
great bridge at Saltash, completed in 1859.

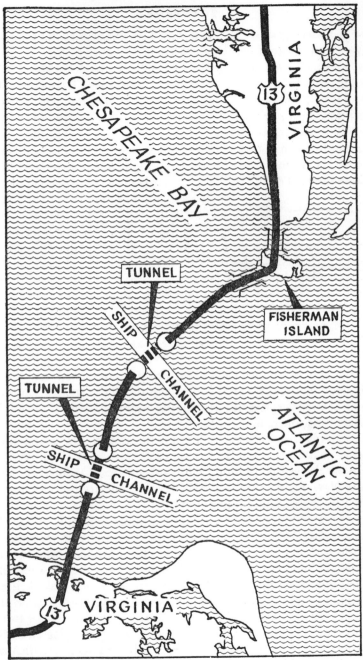

Route of the bridge and tunnel crossing of Chesapeake Bay, Virginia

Girder bridges are, as a rule, not very beautiful—they have a utility look about them which can mar the scenery. Arch bridges, on the other hand, may enhance the river view of a town very much, and have therefore been the engineers' favourite since antiquity. They cannot, of course, provide very long spans when built of stone or brick, but since the end of the eighteenth century iron, and later steel, has been used; and it was not until 1864 that a wrought-iron arch bridge of any major importance was built, that across the Rhine at Koblenz, with three openings of 315 feet length each. Today, the largest single-span arch bridge in the

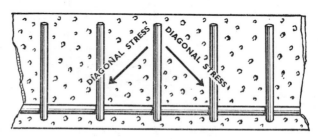

Reinforced concrete

world is the Sydney Harbour Bridge, completed by Ralph Freeman in 1932; its arch has a span of 1,650 feet. The highest bridge, however, is that between Norway and Sweden across the Svine Sund, opened in 1946.

A unique combination of bridge and tunnel, due to be completed in 1963, is being built across Chesapeake Bay, Virginia, to provide the last continuous road link on the 'Ocean Highway' from New York to Jacksonville, Florida, and to lop off some 70 miles from the motor route along the American east coast. Until the 17½-mile bridge tunnel is opened, motorists have to use the ferry across the bay. The new crossing consists of 12 miles of trestle 30 feet above low-water level. Four artificial islands, each 1,500 feet long, serve as cradles for two tunnels, each more than a mile long, under the main ship channels; two high-level bridges permit the passage of larger ships, and there is a 1½-mile causeway across a natural island.

In the Middle Ages bridge-building was regarded as an act of piety; today, it is not only a technical job but also an artistic one, as well as the fulfilment of a basic social need, and the engineer will have to take into account the requirements of the people who are going to use his bridge before he decides on design and material. But above all, there must be beauty—a requirement for which there are no fixed rules. The type and intensity of traffic it is meant to carry is just as important in planning as the span over which it has to be carried and the clearance required under it for

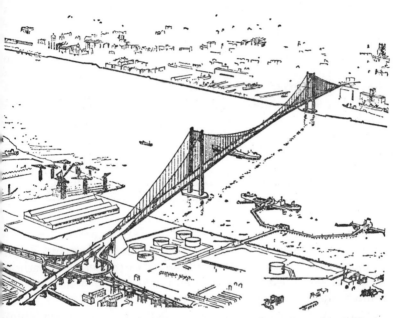

Artist's impression of the Mersey Bridge, seen from Birkenhead. The roadway is 280 feet above the river

ships, railways, or road traffic. The materials may be timber, stone, brick, steel, light alloy, or reinforced concrete; the last three are the main materials today, concrete being the favourite one. It is weak in tension and has therefore to be reinforced with steel bars embedded in it or, better still, 'prestressed': here the reinforcement takes the form of wires put into the wet concrete; they can be tightened by jacks when the concrete has set.

A good bridge must be efficient, economical, and graceful at the same time, and most of the famous bridges have been built according to aesthetic principles. There are, however, a few exceptions.

One of the best-known bridges in the world—not because of
its size or beauty, but because it has become one of the landmarks
of the town to which it belongs—is London's Tower Bridge. It is
an 'opening bridge', a type which is many centuries old, origin-
ating in the ancient drawbridge which used to guard the approach
to the medieval castles across the moat. Built by Sir Horace Jones
and Sir J. Wolfe Barry at the cost of £1½ million and opened in
1894, it has two sham-Gothic towers 200 feet apart and consists of
two outer suspension bridges; the two centre sections, which are
part of the roadway, can be raised within 1½ minutes to allow
ships to pass to and from the 'Pool of London'. Each of the
drawbridge 'leaves' is 100 feet long. Tower Bridge is not a work
of art, but no Londoner would miss it for any other bridge in the
world.

Road-making and bridge-building are very old crafts but
canal-digging is nearly as old. Surprisingly, a comparatively
recent achievement of engineering, the Suez Canal, is no more
than a modern completion of one of the earliest projects in the
history of transport.

Both Herodotus the historian and Strabo the geographer, who
lived four centuries after Herodotus, around the time of Christ's
birth, speak of a canal across the isthmus of Suez, linking the
Mediterranean with the Red Sea. It was begun in the seventh
century B.C. by Necho, King of Egypt, and Herodotus says that it
cost the lives of 120,000 slaves—probably a slight exaggeration.
Necho's successor completed it, but the desert sands blocked it
up again and again, and eventually the Egyptians gave up the
struggle. They also built many irrigation canals and waterways
connected with the Nile, traces of which can still be discerned.

Necho's great adversary, Nebuchadnezzar, King of Babylon,
was a great canal-builder himself. Travellers in the Euphrates
region can still follow the canal he built from Hit to the Persian
Gulf, 400 miles away. It seems to have served three purposes:
navigation, irrigation, and defence against the bellicose nomadic
tribes. The Grand Canal of China, from Tientsin to Hangchow, is
even longer—650 miles; it took six centuries to build, from the
seventh to the thirteenth, but is still in everyday use. The Chinese
tried to solve the problem which hampered canal development
in the Western world—that of overcoming different levels—by

Early Italian sluice

raising and lowering boats from one level to another with cradle-
and-wheel tackle, on rollers, or in movable tanks.

But only when that problem was really solved, by the invention
of the lock, canals became one of the principal means of cross-
country transport. The lock is a simple but ingenious means of
raising and lowering ships from one canal level to another: it is a
large 'chamber' made of wood, brickwork, etc., with gates at both
ends; there are sluices built into them near the bottom, to be
operated from the top of the lock. When a boat has entered the

chamber the gate behind it is closed and the sluices of the gate in front are opened so that the water can pour in or out, whichever the case may be. When the water level in the lock has reached that of the canal stretch ahead, the gate in front is opened and the boat continues its journey.

The Dutch claim that they invented the lock, but it is more likely that two brothers, Domenico, from Viterbo in Italy were the inventors around 1480. Some years later Leonardo da Vinci built six locks which linked the canals of Milan. However, the Dutch were among the first nations to make extensive use of the invention; Holland is still the canal country *par excellence*. The French, the Swedes, and the Russians all built canals with locks in the sixteenth and seventeenth centuries; England was one of the last countries to make use of canals, but then it soon surpassed many others. The man who was responsible for the first and best canals in Britain was James Brindley (1716–72), who started out as an apprentice to a wheelwright in Derbyshire and received very little education. But he was a genius of an engineer, and he used to say that his technical knowledge 'came natural-like' to him.

He had already made a name for himself as a machine-builder and machine-doctor when, in the early 1750's, the Duke of Bridgewater, who owned coal mines in Lancashire, entrusted him with the construction of a 40-mile canal from Worsley to Manchester for the cheap and speedy transport of coal. Completed in 1755, the 'Bridgewater Canal', which was later extended to the Mersey, was England's first industrial canal and in its time one of the greatest 'artificial curiosities' in the world, admired by engineers and laymen alike. Brindley had hardly finished it when he went to work on another canal from Manchester to Liverpool, some 30-odd miles in length, to provide transport for Lancashire's produce to the sea-going ships, and for raw materials from the port to the mills of Manchester.

The great success of Brindley's work encouraged others, and within three-quarters of a century—until the railways began to take over the job of transporting people and goods—Britain had the benefit of about 3,000 miles of excellent canals, among them the Caledonian, Forth-and-Clyde, Crinan, Grand Union, Trent Navigation, Gloucester and Berkeley Ship, Leeds and Liverpool, and Birmingham canals. During the first period of the Industrial

Revolution they were the main carriers of heavy freight, raw materials, and finished products; many also had passenger boats.

Today Britain still has more than 2,000 miles of canals in use, the most important and longest being the Grand Union system which links the midlands with the Port of London. And even those which no longer serve a practical purpose have endeared themselves to the people with their idyllic calm and old-worldly charm, reaching from our noisy and crowded cities into the lovely, peaceful countryside—waterways of yore worthy of exploration and rediscovery.

The young United States built its first canal in 1792, starting from South Hadley, Massachusetts. There followed a number of commercially and industrially most important waterways such as the Chesapeake and Ohio Canal, the 365-mile Erie Canal linking Lake Erie with the Hudson River, the Morris Canal from Phillipsburg to Jersey City, and—to mention a twentieth-century venture—the 790-mile State Barge Canal from New York City to Buffalo. America's waterways are maintained by the United States Army.

The most spectacular kind of canal is, of course, that which cuts through an isthmus, opening a new, short route where previously a whole continent or peninsula had to be rounded. The shortest of them is the Corinth Canal, only 4 miles in length, connecting the Gulf of Aegina with that of Corinth. In the early days of Greek shipping, boats were dragged by men and beasts across the isthmus. Caesar suggested the construction of a canal, and it was begun under Nero in A.D. 67—but completed only in 1893.

We have mentioned the earliest beginnings of the Suez Canal. It occupied the minds of many rulers throughout the centuries, from Haroun-al-Rashid to Napoleon, but it was the French diplomatist and engineer, Ferdinand de Lesseps, who worked out the project when he was consul at Cairo in the 1830's. He obtained permission to pierce the isthmus of Suez in 1854, after some complicated negotiations with the Turks, who were then the overlords of Egypt, the French Government, and financial circles in western Europe.

It took de Lesseps ten years to build the canal that was to save all ships sailing between Europe and the East the journey around the African continent. Financial troubles, epidemics, accidents, political intrigues, technical difficulties of every conceivable kind presented as many problems to the intrepid French engineer, but he solved them one by one. On 17 November 1869, half of Europe's royalty and all the world's diplomats and dignitaries attended the opening ceremony of the Suez Canal, as it was to be called. Verdi had been commissioned to create a new opera for the event: *Aida*, which was performed for the first time that night.

Ferdinand de Lesseps was the hero of the day, and he would have been allowed to spend the rest of his life in peace and comfort had he not embarked on an equally ambitious scheme, that of piercing the Central American isthmus, a few years later. The idea of connecting the Atlantic and the Pacific by a canal goes back to the days of the Spanish *conquistadores*, and already in the sixteenth century at least four possible routes were discussed. Rivalries between the Spanish, the French, and the British gave the engineers no chance to work out their plans; then, early in the eighteenth century, the Spanish colonial empire collapsed, and there were long periods of revolution and civil war in Central and South America. Eventually the magnificent example of the Suez Canal inspired the politicians and financiers to start the new venture, and de Lesseps was entrusted with its execution in 1879.

He chose the 44-mile route across Panama as the most suitable one, but it involved the construction of a number of locks, and the cost was considerable. Work began in 1881, but the Panama Canal Company went bankrupt in 1888 when less than a quarter of the work was done. There was an enormous financial scandal which rocked France; de Lesseps, then 84 years of age, and his son were accused of mismanagement, bribery, and corruption, and both were imprisoned. Although de Lesseps was eventually exonerated he died a man broken in health and spirit. The Americans took over the canal project from the French, and it was not until 1914 that the first ship went right through from ocean to ocean. The French attempt to build the canal cost the lives of perhaps 50,000 people, and the American one another 5,000 lives —tropical diseases and epidemics took that frightful toll.

Another important canal linking two seas is the Kiel Canal, which cuts through Holstein from the Baltic to the North Sea; Germany built this 61-mile waterway in the 1890's mainly as a naval canal, at a time when ambitious Wilhelm II ventured to challenge Britain's power at sea. Later, however, the Kiel Canal proved its worth as a most valuable waterway for merchant shipping, providing a useful short cut between the Atlantic and Channel ports on the one hand and Scandinavia and Russia on the other.

Holland, the most canal-minded country in the world, claims that it has the 'biggest' canal: the 'Nieuwe Waterweg' connecting Rotterdam to the sea. The claim is founded on the fact that this 13½-mile canal has a record depth and width—it is 41 feet deep, with a width of 246 feet at bottom and of 525 feet at water level.

Our own time has seen—and is going to see—some outstanding feats of canal engineering. The St Lawrence Seaway, opened in 1959, has doubled Canada's sea coast and provided the United States with a northern shore. Incorporating the famous Welland Ship Canal (opened in 1930) and other canals between Lake Erie and Lake Ontario, the new Seaway permits ocean-going ships to sail right through to Chicago. Seven new locks were constructed between Montreal and Lake Ontario, and a 22-foot deep waterway was dredged along a 300-mile stretch extending along the St Lawrence River and across the lakes. It is estimated that fifty million tons of cargo pass annually through the Seaway.

The St Lawrence system includes a number of great hydroelectric schemes, which is the modern way of water engineering. So does the gigantic Indus scheme, due to be completed in the 1970's, which will change the lives of dozens of millions of inhabitants of the Indian subcontinent. It extends from Karachi, on the Indian Ocean, to the foothills of the Hindu Kush, almost to the borders of Russia and China and across those of Afghanistan. It will provide irrigation for 100 million acres of land, half a million kilowatts of electrical power, and sorely needed transport by linking the Indus and half a dozen other rivers by canals. The World Bank, Britain, Canada, Australia, the United States, Western Germany, and New Zealand are financing the scheme.

Russia has emerged in our time as a first-class engineering nation, and considering the vast distances between the population centres, the immense expanses of farming country, and the rapidly growing need for power in the Soviet Union it was only logical for the engineers to make the fullest possible use of canals. Their primary purpose is usually irrigation, with transport and power-generation taking the second and third places. The Russians embarked on their canal schemes on a large scale only in the

1930's; the war interrupted most of them, but progress has been rapid since 1945.

The first great canal of the Soviet era was the Baltic–White Sea Canal, opened in 1933—a 140-mile waterway which is virtually a 'staircase' for ships, rising to 350 feet on its way from Leningrad to Murmansk. The White Sea is now linked not only with the Baltic but even with the Caspian Sea deep down in the south by way of the Volga–Baltic Canal. The Dnieper, which runs for 600 miles across the Ukraine, was tamed and made to work the enormous Dnieproges power station with a capacity of more than half a million kilowatts.

Moscow has been turned into Russia's most important inland port through the conversion of the Volga into a navigable water-way from Kalinin to the Caspian Sea, connected by canals to the Sea of Azov and the Black Sea. The vital link bringing Moscow into the system was the construction of the 80-mile canal from the River Moskva to the upper Volga in 1932–7.

As long ago as 1569 the Turks made an attempt at linking Russia's two great rivers, the Volga and the Don, by a canal, and from the days of Peter the Great the project occupied the minds of the engineers. It was finally carried out between 1947 and 1952, mostly—like other projects of the Stalin era—by forced labour. With an overall length of 63 miles, the Volga–Don Canal now links the Stalingrad region with the eastern bend of the Volga.

But this has by no means completed Russia's canal system. Projects have been started up and down the country, and they include the biggest hydro-electric stations in the world—one, at Kuibyshev, with 2·1 million kilowatts, and another, at Stalingrad, with 1·7 million kilowatts capacity. And beyond the Urals lies Russia's greatest challenge—Siberia, still waiting for the magic touch of modern engineering.

# 2

# Railways

WHEN we speak about the 'Iron Road' we think of railway tracks and trains as an entity. In fact, the railway is about 2,500 years older than the locomotive.

Very early in his technical career, Man discovered that it was much easier to move his sledges, and later his carts, on a parallel track made of smooth stone or wooden beams, or cut into the hard road surface. The ancient Greeks used the latter type of tracks—grooves of 5–6 inches depth and 2–3 inches width, 3 to 5 feet apart—to push their decorated floats along the temple roads at religious festivals; and they built a haulage-way with wooden rails for shifting ships across the isthmus of Corinth to save them the long journey around Cape Matapan. The Greeks discovered that a man or a horse can pull loads up to eight times greater along rails than along an average country road. The Romans, too, used groove rails on many of their military roads.

Like so many technical achievements of antiquity, the idea of the railway was lost during the Middle Ages, to re-emerge only in the fifteenth or sixteenth century. Railways seem to have been built first in German mines, which were then the best developed in Europe, for hauling coal and ore along the galleries and out of the pit. The miners pushed the little carts themselves or used horses for the job. Towards the end of the sixteenth century a number of German miners were called to England to modernize her pits; they brought the 'tramway' with them, as it was then called, thus introducing the rail into the country that was to be the cradle of the Iron Road.

These ancient tramways consisted of two wooden beams laid side by side, no more than an inch or so from each other. An iron

Early German mine rail with
gauge prong

prong fixed to the bottom of the truck or to the axle ran in this gap to keep the wheels from leaving the rails. Around 1630, a Northumbrian mine owner by the name of Beaumont had the idea of connecting the two beams by means of sleepers and increasing their distance considerably; when the wooden rails had been worn out by the heavy trucks he fixed strips of iron on top of them. But then it was the wooden wheels which wore rapidly—until they, too, were made of iron.

There was, however, the difficulty that the wheels would slip off the rails now that the guiding prong had been abandoned. To prevent this the rails were equipped with flanges along one side to keep the wheels on them. Towards the end of the eighteenth century an English engineer had the idea of fitting the flange to the wheel instead of the rail. This proved to be much more economical and so successful that ever since all rail vehicles have been fitted with flanged wheels.

The first iron rails were cast by a mining engineer, Reynolds, at Coalbrookdale in 1767, and another Englishman, Jessop, created the mushroom-formed cross-section of the rails, which is still generally used today. The scene was set for the appearance of the railway in the true sense of the word. Goods were waiting to

Wooden rail, used in a mine near Newcastle in the
seventeenth century

be carried safely and quickly across the country, people everywhere needed a speedy means of transport; there was the general
feeling that getting from place to place on land must no longer be
the privilege of those rich enough to have their own carriages, or
hardy enough to endure a long journey by stage-coach or on
horseback.

We are apt to think that throughout history the brainwaves of
individual inventors were enough to start off some new development. But it is easy to see that inventions in themselves, and the
men who made them, are bound to fail if there is no necessity, or
at least no demand, for that innovation, if there is no 'social basis'
for it. This is the reason why so many inventions have been made

Cugnot's steam-driven gun carriage

several times until eventually the time for their introduction was
ripe. On the other hand, the development of people's way of life,
of a new social order, of production and demand stimulate
inventors' brains to work along certain lines. It may, therefore,
not have been pure chance that the rail and the steam-engine
reached maturity both at about the same time, and that they were
brought together for the first time in England, the country where
social and economic developments were quicker than anywhere
else in the world.

'The locomotive is not the invention of one man', said Robert
Stephenson, 'but of a nation of mechanical engineers.' That
'nation' was a cosmopolitan one, for France and America produced steam-driven vehicles long before Britain, but in those
countries there did not seem to be much need for that invention
yet. In 1763 the French artillery officer, Nicolas Joseph Cugnot,
built his first model of a steam carriage with the help of the

National Arsenal. It was tried out on the roads, but after a few slow journeys it ran amuck and overturned. It was locked up in the Arsenal so that it could do no harm, and the development came to a standstill.

An American engineer, Oliver Evans, built a steam-carriage in the 1770's, but again there was little interest, and the roads were too rough for it. This was also the reason why William Symington's road locomotive failed in Edinburgh in 1786. William Murdock, the inventor of the gaslight, also experimented with such a vehicle, but his employers, Boulton & Watt, discouraged him from going on with it because James Watt himself had taken out a patent for a steam carriage.

Richard Trevithick, a young Cornish mining engineer and steam-engine enthusiast, made a few model locomotives in his workshop in the 1790's, as a first step to building a life-size carriage for road transport. In 1801 he had completed a giant iron coach with a chimney in the middle and seats for the passengers around it. He called it *Puffing Devil*. On Boxing Day he invited his friends for the first ride. The vehicle moved at a brisk pace for a few hundred yards, but then the engine broke down, and the carriage was pulled into the coach-house of an inn, where Trevithick and his friends had a good meal. Suddenly there was an acrid smell: he had forgotten to put out the fire, the boiler had become dry, and the hot engine had set the coach-house alight. That was the end of the *Puffing Devil*.

His second steam-carriage took to the road in 1803; he drove it all the way from Cornwall to London, but by then the engine had become worn out. Trevithick came to the conclusion that the locomotive was not an ideal vehicle for the open road. It was he who set it on rails for the first time. Looking for a customer for a rail-bound locomotive he found that the Pen-y-Darran iron-works in South Wales had a good tramway leading to Cardiff. Here Trevithick built his steam-engine on wheels, the first ever designed for rail transport: a clumsy little monster with a big fly-wheel and a cogwheel which connected the front and the rear axles—both, in fact, quite unnecessary gadgets. The locomotive, however, pulled ten tons of iron and seventy passengers in five wagons at a speed of 5 m.p.h. along the ten-mile railroad.

Trevithick was now convinced that he was on to a good thing. But how was it to be introduced to the country? He had the idea

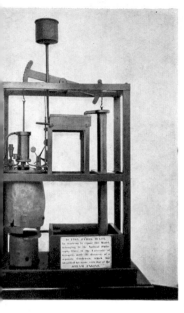

*Top:* James Watt at the age of 57.

*Left:* A model of the Newcomen engine which prompted James Watt to his invention of the separate condenser.

*Bottom:* A Boulton & Watt steam-engine of 1797.

*Top:* William Murdock's house at Redruth which he lit by gas in 1792. The coal gas was generated in an iron retort in the back yard.

*Bottom:* A Parsons turbo-generator set of 50,000 kW. capacity, installed at Chicago in 1923.

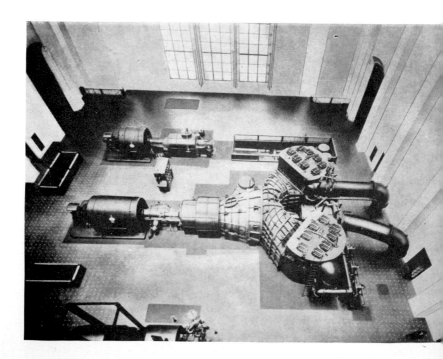

*Top left:* An early Siemens direct-current generator.

*Top right:* A Crookes's tube, the earliest form of the cathode-ray tube.

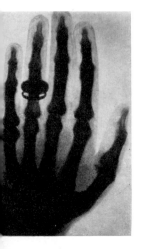

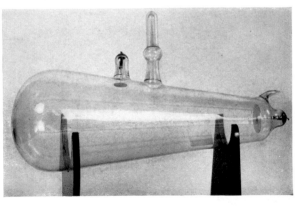

*Bottom left:* One of the first X-ray photographs, taken by Prof. Röntgen himself—his wife's hand.

*Bottom right:* An early pear-shaped X-ray tube.

*Below, top:* The room at the Cavendish Laboratory, Cambr
where Lord Rutherford worked from

*Below, bottom:* The nuclear power station of Hunter
Ayrshire, with a capacity of 320,000

*Opposite, top:* The 'Stellarator' at Princeton University, New Je
a research machine for the study of thermo-nuclear react

*Opposite, bottom:* Insertion of a radio-active isotope
into the pituitary gland of a cancer pa

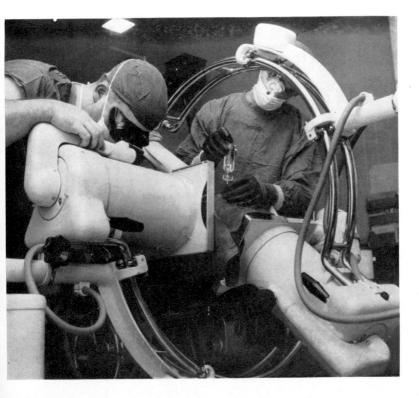

*Top:* Old London Bridge, *c.* 1750.
The roadway passes in a
tunnel through one of the houses.

*Bottom:* Sydney Harbour Bridge.
It is suspended from 128 cables,
each 2¾ in. in diameter.

*Top:* The Panama Canal.

*Bottom:* The Suez Canal.

# 1829.

## GRAND COMPETITION
### OF
## LOCOMOTIVES
#### ON THE
## LIVERPOOL & MANCHESTER
## RAILWAY.

### STIPULATIONS & CONDITIONS

ON WHICH THE DIRECTORS OF THE LIVERPOOL AND MANCHESTER RAILWAY OFFER A PREMIUM OF £500 FOR THE MOST IMPROVED LOCOMOTIVE ENGINE.

#### I.

The said Engine must "effectually consume its own smoke," according to the provisions of the Railway Act, 7th Geo. IV.

#### II.

The Engine, if it weighs Six Tons, must be capable of drawing after it, day by day, on a well-constructed Railway, on a level plane, a Train of Carriages of the gross weight of Twenty Tons, including the Tender and Water Tank, at the rate of Ten Miles per Hour with a pressure of steam in the boiler not exceeding Fifty Pounds on the square inch.

#### III.

There must be Two Safety Valves, one of which must be completely out of the reach or control of the Engine-man, and neither of which must be fastened down while the Engine is working.

#### IV.

The Engine and Boiler must be supported on Springs, and rest on Six Wheels; and the height from the ground to the top of the Chimney must not exceed Fifteen Feet.

#### V.

The weight of the Machine, WITH ITS COMPLEMENT OF WATER in the Boiler, must, at most, not exceed Six Tons, and a Machine of less weight will be preferred if it draw AFTER it a PROPORTIONATE weight; and if the weight of the Engine, &c. do not exceed Five Tons, then the gross weight to be drawn need not exceed Fifteen Tons; and in that proportion for Machines of still smaller weight—provided that the Engine, &c. shall still be on six wheels, unless the weight (as above) be reduced to Four Tons and a Half, or under, in which case the Boiler, &c., may be placed on four wheels. And the Company shall be at liberty to put the Boiler, Fire Tube, Cylinders, &c. to the test of a pressure of water not exceeding 150 Pounds per square inch, without being answerable for any damage the Machine may receive in consequence.

#### VI.

There must be a Mercurial Gauge affixed to the Machine, with Index Rod, showing the Steam Pressure above 45 Pounds per square inch; and constructed to blow out a Pressure of 60 Pounds per inch.

#### VII.

The Engine to be delivered complete for trial, at the Liverpool end of the Railway, not later than the 1st of October next.

#### VIII.

The price of the Engine which may be accepted, not to exceed £550, delivered on the Railway; and any Engine not approved to be taken back by the Owner.

N.B.—The Railway Company will provide the ENGINE TENDER with a supply of Water and Fuel for the experiment. The distance within the Rails is four feet eight inches and a half.

PRINTED BY RICHARDSON, 1829.

## THE LOCOMOTIVE STEAM ENGINES,
WHICH COMPETED FOR THE PRIZE OF £500 OFFERED BY THE DIRECTORS OF THE LIVERPOOL AND MANCHESTER RAILWAY COMPANY.
DRAWN TO A SCALE ¼ INCH TO A FOOT.

### THE "ROCKET" OF MR. ROBT. STEPHENSON OF NEWCASTLE.
( WHICH DRAWING A LOAD EQUIVALENT TO THREE TIMES ITS WEIGHT TRAVELLED AT THE RATE OF 12½ MILES AN HOUR, AND WITH A CARRIAGE & PASSENGERS AT THE RATE OF 24 MILES.
COST PER MILE FOR FUEL ABOUT THREE HALF PENCE.

### THE "NOVELTY" OF MESSRS. BRAITHWAITE & ERICSSON OF LONDON,
WHICH DRAWING A LOAD EQUIVALENT TO THREE TIMES ITS WEIGHT TRAVELLED AT THE RATE OF 20¾ MILES AN HOUR, AND WITH A CARRIAGE & PASSENGERS AT THE RATE OF 32 MILES.
COST PER MILE FOR FUEL ABOUT ONE HALFPENNY.

### THE "SANSPAREIL" OF MR. HACKWORTH OF DARLINGTON.
WHICH DRAWING A LOAD EQUIVALENT TO THREE TIMES ITS WEIGHT TRAVELLED AT THE RATE OF 13½ MILES AN HOUR. COST FOR FUEL PER MILE ABOUT TWO PENCE.

*Opposite:* Catalogue of the 'Grand Competition of Locomotives' at Rainhill, October 1829.

*Left:* George Stephenson.

THE OPENING OF THE LIVERPOOL & MANCHESTER RAILWAY SEPᵗ 15ᵀᴴ 1830,
WITH THE MOORISH ARCH AT EDGE HILL AS IT APPEARED ON THAT DAY.

RAILWAYS OF TOMORRC

*Top:* The first 'Alweg' monorail
on a test track at Cologne in 19

*Bottom:* The American lightwei
'Aerotrain', which weighs only 1
as much as conventional tra

A window in the Parish Church of Stoke Poges, Buckinghamshire, showing a man on a bicycle-like machine and bearing date 1642. The origin of the window is unknown.

*om:* English ladies on their 'Hobbyhorses' (1819).

*Left:* A 'Penny-farthin
bicycle of 18

*Opposite, top:* A Benz c
sent from Mannheim to
English motorist in 189

*Opposite, bottom:* Hen
Ford's Model 'T'—the famo
'Tin Lizzie' (190

*Right:* An early Diesel-engine.

*Bottom:* The original 'Brighton Rally' of 1896. The first two cars to arrive were a Levassor and a Panhard.

*Top:* The *Great Western*, built by I. K. Brunel
1837, on her first voyage to New York.

*Bottom:* A model of the stern of S.S. *Francis Smith*,
with its original two-turn screw propeller (1836).

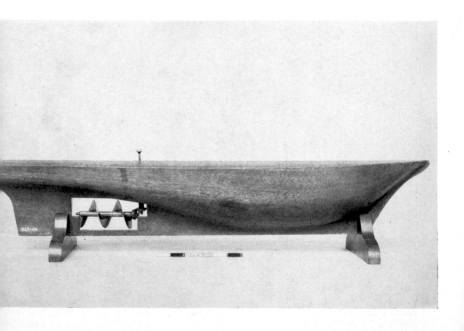

*Top:* Iron into steel—a Bessemer converter blowing. *Inset:* Sir Henry Besse

*Bottom:* The N.S. *Savannah*, the world's first nuclear-
powered merchant ship, launched in 1959.

of demonstrating his railway to the people of London. In 1808 he built his 'Steam Circus' in Euston Square: a small circular railway, the trip costing one shilling. Londoners crowded to this new merry-go-round, but before it had paid its way one of the engine wheels broke, the locomotive overturned, and the enterprise had to be abandoned.

From that day bad luck dogged Trevithick; he caught typhus, went bankrupt, and emigrated to Peru; when civil war broke out in that country he went on to Chile and then to Colombia, but had little success with various projects. He returned to Europe and died a poor man, at the age of 62, in 1833. He lived long enough to see another man succeed where he had failed—George Stephenson.


Born in Wylam near Newcastle in 1781, George Stephenson was the son of a stoker working on the pumping machine in the local colliery, and earning twelve shillings a week with which to feed and clothe his family of eight. None of the six children went to school, but had to work almost as soon as they could walk. George's first job, at the age of 8, was that of keeping the cows and geese of a neighbour from straying on to the horse-operated colliery railway. At 9, he went down the mine as a coal sorter, advanced to become an assistant fireman and later an engine-boy on the Newcomen pump which his father stoked. At 18 he could neither read nor write. He went to an evening school (at a fee of one penny per lesson), and it was one of his proudest days when he was at last able to sign his own name at the age of 19.

Engines fascinated him, and soon he knew more about them than many of the engineers who had studied mechanics and mathematics. At the Killingworth colliery where he worked for a number of years he was called the 'engine doctor'. Stephenson had the good luck to find in the owner of the mine, Lord Ravensworth, a man with an open mind and—if the cause appealed to him—an open hand. The young engineer succeeded in 'selling' him the idea of what he called a travelling machine for hauling coal along the tramway from the pithead to the canal.

After two years of intensive work, in 1814, the locomotive—it was called *Blücher* in honour of the Prussian general who had helped Wellington against Napoleon—was completed. It pulled

E

eight trucks loaded with 30 tons of coal up a slight gradient at
4 m.p.h. It was not a very good engine, and more costly to run
than a team of horses. But it proved to Stephenson that he was
right: that steam traction and rails belonged together 'like man
and wife'. He had no doubt that the overland transport of the
future would be worked by railways.

His next engine, built a year later, was much more efficient
because he had the idea of applying the exhaust steam to the
furnace, which improved the power of the engine very much. He
replaced the cast-iron wheels by wrought-iron ones, made a
direct connection between pistons and wheels, used ball joints
for the connecting-rods, and carried out several other improvements. He had learnt a great deal from *Blücher*'s shortcomings.

Other mine owners ordered locomotives from him, which he
built with the help of his 17-year-old son, Robert, whom he had
sent to good schools so that he would get a better education than
his father. But there was little public interest in these machines,
and for a long time George Stephenson stood alone with his conviction that 'if the country makes railroads, railroads will make
the country'.

Things took a decisive turn only after Parliament had passed
an Act authorizing the construction of a railway line between
Stockton and Darlington, in the Bishop Auckland valley, for the
haulage not only of goods but also of passengers. Stephenson, by
that time already the leading authority on locomotives, was commissioned to build the engine; he promised that it would do the
work of fifty-nine horses. It was built at the engine factory he had
established, with a Quaker business man, at Newcastle.

The ten-mile line was opened in autumn, 1825, with
Stephenson himself at the controls of his engine, the *Active*. It
pulled six wagons with coal and flour, a passenger coach with
the company directors and their wives and friends, twenty-one
wagons provisionally fitted with seats for less important passengers, and at the end another six coal trucks—altogether
thirty-three wagons. The passengers numbered 450 at the start
but about 600 at the end of the journey because many more people
had climbed into the wagons or were just hanging on to them.
The speed was by modern standards very modest, although it
seemed little short of fantastic to the journalist who wrote: 'Such
was the velocity that in some parts the speed was frequently

twelve miles an hour.' The ten miles were covered in 65 minutes; the return journey was made with music: the goods wagons were replaced by additional passenger coaches, one of which was occupied by a brass band.

For the first time, hundreds of people experienced the thrill of being transported by that new, mysterious power, steam; for the first time they felt the adventurous sensation of speed. Many of them must have gone through some anxious moments as they were carried along by that hissing and roaring engine, faster than the fastest mail-coach, with houses and trees rushing past them, country folk staring, horses shying, cows lowing. A new age had begun, the barriers of time and space which separated village from village and country from country were bound to crumble. 'You will live to see the day when railways will supersede almost all other methods of conveyance . . . when it will be cheaper for a working man to travel upon a railway than to walk on foot', Stephenson said to his friends at Stockton. 'I know there are great and almost unsurmountable difficulties to be encountered; but what I have said will come to pass as sure as you live.'

And difficulties there were indeed, although at first things seemed to move faster than even Stephenson had hoped. All England was talking about the little railway. It was a great commercial success; coal from the Darlington collieries found new markets, output rose, more employment was offered, and within ten years the new town of Middlesbrough, created near Stockton as a seaport for the shipment of coal, had 6,000 inhabitants. Other industrial regions in the interior of the country had already been clamouring for railways to connect them with the ports, especially east Lancashire. The obvious choice for the first 'long-distance' passenger and freight railway was the line from Manchester to Liverpool, and the obvious choice for the man to build it was George Stephenson.

As soon as the merchants in these two cities applied to Parliament for the appropriate Act the difficulties began. Liverpool and Manchester had been connected by the Duke of Bridgewater's canal seventy years earlier when it could easily handle the volume of goods traffic between the cotton towns and the seaport. Yet with the onset of the Industrial Revolution the canal proved inadequate; moreover, it was frequently frozen over in winter, and the Manchester factories had to close down because they could not get their raw cotton. But when the plan of a railway was put forward the then Earl of Bridgewater and his associates began a violent campaign of abuse against the new form of transport, calling upon the people to resist its introduction. The shareholders of the canal—and of all the other canals of Britain— saw their profits threatened by the works of that stoker from Northumberland. A parliamentary committee called Stephenson to London for a stiff cross-examination.

He went to Westminster, a figure then rarely seen in those precincts: a man of the people with a broad north country accent, powerfully built, with the huge hands of a manual worker, dressed without the refinements of the period. 'I was not long in it', he recalled about his appearance before the committee, 'before I began to look for a hole to creep out!' His ideas, claims, and calculations were ridiculed. The scheme was called 'the most absurd that ever entered the head of a man'. It was claimed that the terrible spectacle of a locomotive rushing by would affect people and animals—ladies would have miscarriages, cows cease to give milk, and hens lay no more eggs; the poisoned air from the engine would kill all livestock in the district and the birds in the trees; houses along the line would be set on fire by sparks from the locomotive; there would be no more work for the horses, which would die out as a result, and coachmen and inn-keepers along the deserted roads would become beggars while highwaymen would roam the countryside; the engine boilers would burst and scald the passengers to death—after they had gone mad because no human being could stand a speed of more than ten miles . . . and so on.

Trying to keep calm, Stephenson patiently refuted one of these absurdities after another. Shying horses? Well, some horses would shy at a wheelbarrow, he said. Cows had not ceased to give their milk, nor hens to lay, at Killingworth (the Stockton–Darlington line was not yet completed at that time). A committee member reminded him that once a locomotive boiler had burst because the drunken attendant had allowed the steam pressure to rise too much. 'You must blame the beer for that, not the steam', quipped Stephenson. He was even asked if he was a foreigner, because of his northern accent.

Other members, however, claimed that locomotives would be too heavy to move at all, and railways would eventually have to be worked by horses only. A speed of six or seven miles per hour was quite impossible. 'I will show he cannot go six', said a member, 'and I may be able to show that I can keep up with him by the canal.'

At this Stephenson could not resist the temptation to claim that he had achieved speeds up to twelve miles. He saw at once that he had blundered, for even his friends considered this as highly dangerous, and suggested that Parliament should impose a limit of 8 or 9 m.p.h. on all railways. One barrister, employed by the opponents of the Bill, said: 'So we are to gallop at the rate of twelve miles an hour, with the aid of the devil in the form of a locomotive, sitting as postilion on the fore horse, and an Honourable Member sitting behind him to stir up the fire!'

'And if a cow happened to stray upon the line and get in the way of the engine', said another, 'would that not be very awkward?'

'Very awkward indeed', replied Stephenson in his broadest Northumbrian, 'for the coo!'

There was nothing for the promoters of the Bill to do but to withdraw it in the face of all this furious and ignorant opposition. It was the greatest disappointment in Stephenson's life. However, the job of surveying the line had already been completed against very heavy odds, part of it by Stephenson himself. The canal owners had recruited a whole army of farmers who took pot-shots at the surveyors. The nights and the Sunday mornings, when everybody was in church listening to the parsons' sermons against the devilish railway, were the best times to get the work done. Once Stephenson surveyed a stretch on a moonlit night; but the forces of his opponents ambushed him and drove him away. He resorted to a trick: he had salvoes fired from shotguns from one stretch which had already been surveyed, and while the farmers rushed off in that direction he did his work elsewhere undisturbed. He took care to skirt the game preserves of his high and mighty opponents. The greatest natural obstacle, however, was Chat Moss, a bog of twelve square miles; but John Metcalf had already shown that a road could be made to 'float' on a swamp, and Stephenson intended to use a similar method.

Meanwhile, the good record of the Stockton–Darlington line proved that the prejudices and predictions voiced by the committee members were pure nonsense. A new Bill introduced in 1826 found at last the supporters of the railway in the majority, and it was passed in the Commons and the Lords. At once work began on the railway; Stephenson recalled his son, Robert, from America to assist him, especially with the tricky job of bridging Chat Moss. The workers were given boards which they fastened under their shoes so that they would not sink in. The edge of the bog was filled up and a broad embankment created. This bearing surface proved solid enough for the line to be built on it.

While the work on Chat Moss was still going on, Stephenson completed the locomotive with which he wanted to open the Liverpool–Manchester railway. However, British fairness demanded that other engine-builders, too, should be given a chance, and it was decided to assign the contract for the locomotives as the result of an open competition.

It is most interesting to compare the four locomotives which took part in the competition. It was held in the form of a 'race' near Rainhill, on the completed section of the line, in October 1829 (there were, in fact, five machines—but one of the competitors had to withdraw his engine when it was discovered that there was a horse inside it). The mere fact that there were other locomotive-builders besides Stephenson shows that this branch of engineering was already establishing itself in Britain, and that faith in the future of the railway was spreading fast among the engineers.

The conditions of entry were strict. The engines must consume their own smoke on the journey; they must not weigh more than six tons; they must pull a load of twenty tons at ten miles an hour or more; the steam pressure must not be more than 50 lb. per square inch; there must be two safety valves, one of them automatic; every locomotive must have six wheels, must be sprung, and must not cost more than £550. The winning machine would be bought for £500 by the company.

Two young engineers, John Braithwaite and the Swede, John Ericsson, turned up with their locomotive, *Novelty*, Timothy Hackworth with his *Sanspareil*, Burstall with his *Perseverance*, and Stephenson with his *Rocket*. To the thousands of spectators who had come to witness the great event, which looked very much like a horse race with machines instead of horses, these four engines must have had something mysterious. The competitors, however, eagerly examined each other's creations, noting every detail. One had a horizontal cylinder, another a vertical one, and the *Rocket* had it at an angle of 45 degrees; one carried its water supply at the top, another at the bottom or in a separate tender; the *Novelty* had an upright boiler, with the firehole on top and the fuel being carried in two small pails on the platform; three of

Stephenson's *Rocket*

the engines had no tubing at all in their boilers while Stephenson's engine carried five tubes: a layman, Henry Booth, the chairman of the railway company, suggested to Stephenson that he should put a number of thin tubes across the inside of the boiler and send the hot gases from the furnace through them on their way to the chimney so as to increase the surfaces of contact between the heat and the water—a principle which is still in use in all boilers and heat exchangers. The transmission of power from the pistons to the wheels was equally varied. The Rainhill race was to show which of these designs was the most efficient.

First at the start was the *Rocket*. It reached a speed of 13½ miles per hour. Then came the *Novelty*, which aroused tremendous excitement by going nearly twice as fast. On the second day, however, it came to grief: the bellows gave way, and it had to go into the repair shed. The *Sanspareil* was also unlucky; a defect was found in its boiler. The *Perseverance* crawled along the track at only 6 m.p.h.

Now the *Rocket* got into its stride. It covered the two-mile track twenty times with a load of 13 tons at an average speed of 15 miles an hour, eventually reaching the 'fantastic' speed of 29 m.p.h.! The repaired engines *Novelty* and *Sanspareil* broke down again. The *Rocket* was the winner. Stephenson's creation did a victory run without load at 35 miles an hour—an amazing spectacle for the crowd. Many onlookers believed that the engine-driver had been killed by the rushing air, and that the locomotive was running wild. But when Mr Dickson, the driver, stopped it right at the grandstand and stepped down smiling, there was boundless enthusiasm.

With this excellent machine and seven others, also made by Stephenson, the Manchester–Liverpool line was opened on 15 September 1830. Unfortunately, the great occasion was marred by the first railway accident: William Huskisson, the Liverpool Member of Parliament, an ardent supporter of the railway, was knocked down by the *Rocket* and severely injured. Stephenson sent him at once back to Liverpool on one of the engines, but Huskisson died a few hours later.

But even this accident did little to slow down the progress of the new means of transport, and Stephenson was the most popular man in England. It is interesting to note that right at the start of railway development the suggestion was made to form a State-owned company; but Parliament insisted on small private companies so as to avoid a monopoly. The necessity for central-ized control was not appreciated until over a century later.

Thus the first decades of the railway were marked by enormous speculation and irresponsible financial manœuvres. In 1845, for instance, there were no fewer than 620 railway projects in Britain; only a handful of them materialized, and thousands of people lost their money. In 1846, nineteen out of twenty-one railway companies in France went bankrupt. In Germany, where the first railway was opened near Nuremberg in 1835 (with a Stephenson engine and an English driver), the scandal of one of the big companies drove the man who had done most to promote the railways, Friedrich List, to suicide.

George Stephenson did what he could to check this boom-and-bust development, but he was unable to stop the 'railway mania'. He refused to be drawn into the mad race for profits from his creation, and advised speculators to get their money back as fast as they could or they might not get it back at all.

All over Europe his engines were used to open new railway lines, and for a long time after his death (in 1848) British locomotives enjoyed a virtual monopoly. For this reason, Stephenson's standard gauge—4 feet 8½ inches—was adopted in most countries.

In the development of the U.S.A. throughout the nineteenth century the railways played a decisive part. Up to 1830 there was little communication between the industrial and commercial East, the cotton-growing South, the agricultural Middle West, and the yet undeveloped West Coast. The first railway line started out from Baltimore towards Ohio in 1831, and in the 1840's Boston was linked with Albany and New York with Buffalo. The first locomotives were imported from Stephenson's works, and even the rails came from England. Only after the Civil War did the American railway industry begin to grow. In 1864 work on the first trans-American line started from either side, and in 1869 both sections met in Utah—a dramatic occasion which made a powerful impact on the nation.

The importance of the railways for America is shown by the innumerable inventions and innovations which originated in that country. In 1859 George Mortimer Pullman invented the sleeping-car; in 1869 George Westinghouse used compressed air for the first time to act on the brakes of a railway train—a most important invention because it allowed much higher speeds, which were too dangerous as long as there were only handbrakes operated by the train guards; in 1871 came the automatic coupler, in 1874 the block-signal system, in 1875 the first refrigerator freight wagon, which permitted the transport of perishable food-stuffs all over the country, and in 1900 the first all-steel cars for passengers and goods, which reduced the risks to life and freight in case of fire and accident. Today the United States have the greatest railway mileage of any country in the world, nearly a quarter of a million miles—more than ten times as much as Britain or France, and three times as much as the Soviet Union, which has an area nearly three times as large as the U.S.A.

A great deal of the rapid development of the world's railways

* E

in the second half of the last century was due to the new processes of making steel for rails and wagons cheaply and efficiently. We shall describe them in Chapter 4.

There are few natural obstacles which the railway has not yet conquered. We have told the story of the great bridges which enable the railways to continue on their way from one end of a continent to the other; enormous viaducts, such as the 20-mile-long structure across the Great Salt Lake, Utah, or the Long Key Viaduct in Florida, carry the trains across stretches of water where conventional bridge-building is impossible. The Trans-Siberian railway links European Russia with the Pacific Ocean across an expanse of land over a quarter of the earth's circumference long; the African jungle, the South American pampa, the Australian bush have all been conquered by the railway.

Perhaps the most ingenious feats of engineering in modern land transport are the tunnels. The Romans, masters in the art of hydraulic engineering, built a number of tunnels for water supply and drainage, among them the $3\frac{1}{2}$-mile tunnel through Monte Salviano, which provided a run-off for Lake Fucino; road tunnels were built near Naples—the 'Grotta' connecting the town with its suburb of Bagnoli—and on the Via Flaminia, to mention only two of them. Considering that there were no mechanical aids, to say nothing of explosives, these tunnels were astonishing achievements.

The modern age of tunnelling began in Switzerland in 1707 with the construction of the *Urner Loch*, the 'Hole of Urn', on the St Gotthard road; it was blasted (with gunpowder) and hewn out of the rock along a stretch of 200 feet. A hundred years later the French built a tunnel for the St Quentin Canal at Tronquoi through treacherous sand layers. Stephenson built the first railway tunnel—gaslit—at the Liverpool end of his line from Manchester. But the most spectacular tunnelling feat of the early nineteenth century was Sir Marc Isambard Brunel's Thames Tunnel between Rotherhithe and Wapping, begun in 1825 and completed against fearfully heavy odds in 1841—the first of all river tunnels; 1,500 feet long and 13 feet wide, it was one of the miracles of the age. Brunel had to devise himself most of the techniques he used. Eleven times the river broke in, twice from the roof; anyone but this intrepid technical pioneer would have given up.

After 1850 the Swiss embarked on some most ambitious tunnel schemes—without them they could not have benefited from the railways which then began to link up the countries of Europe. The first of them, cut through Mont Cenis, was begun in 1857 and took fourteen years to complete; it has a length of nearly 8 miles. For the first time, compressed air was used for rock drilling (it was a description of this technique in an American magazine which gave George Westinghouse the idea of his compressed-air brake). The Mont Cenis Tunnel connects Lyons and Turin.

A year after completion of the Mont Cenis Tunnel, that through the St Gotthard—for the railway line from Milan to Zürich—was begun. Now the engineers had the benefit of the newly invented dynamite, and the job was done in nine years although the tunnel is more than 9 miles long. Austria followed with its Arlberg Tunnel, built from 1880 to 1884, with a length of over 6 miles; it connects Innsbruck with Lake Constance.

Within seven years (1898–1905), the longest tunnel in the world was built through the Simplon range, on the Genoa–Geneva railway. It is more than 12 miles long, and the enormous mass of rock towering up to 6,400 feet above the tunnel exerts such a pressure that the temperature of the tunnel walls reaches 100° F. In 1963 a dream which had fired men's imagination ever since Hannibal crossed the Alps became a reality with the completion of the tunnel through Europe's highest mountain, Mont Blanc, a joint effort of French and Italian engineers. This road tunnel, more than seven miles long, is now being used by 300,000 vehicles per year, carrying up to one million passengers.

As usual in tunnelling, the Mont Blanc cut-through was made from both sides simultaneously. There was a tolerance of only two inches when the French and the Italian sections met at the middle, about 6,000 feet under the summit of the mountain. After the geometricians had worked out the angles—including the curves and the cambers—the blasting began, and the rock drills moved in. Those used at the Mont Blanc were electrically driven to avoid exhaust fumes: three-level 'jumbos', as these drill assemblies are called, each with fifteen hammer drills which attacked the entire cross-section of the tunnel simultaneously. Caterpillar-tracked mechanical scoops and grabs cleared the stone away from behind the drills. Work went on in three shifts for twenty-four hours a day; every month the tunnel was pushed forward by more than 800 feet. A few hundred yards behind the drills and scoops came an enormous concrete mixer which prepared the 2-foot concrete lining of the tunnel.

There are, in fact, two tunnels, one eight feet above the other; the upper one is the 23-foot-wide roadway, the lower one is reserved for ventilation, drainage, and for the light and signals cables. There are lay-bys every 300 yards on the roadway, with air-conditioned waiting-rooms and telephones so that motorists can summon help in case of a breakdown or accident.

However, even these Alpine tunnels will not be the world's longest for more than a few years once the old and ambitious scheme of the Channel Tunnel gets under way. It dates back to the days of Napoleon, who believed he could coax the English into co-operating and then invade them through the tunnel. But it could not have been dug with the technical aids then available. Work actually began from both sides late in the nineteenth century, but stopped in 1883 when a wave of panicky fear gripped England. In our age of airborne weapons the threat of an invasion through the Channel Tunnel (which could be destroyed within a second if necessary) seems somewhat out of date, while economic considerations would favour the construction of such a transport link between Britain and the Continent. The tunnel plans dating back to about 1930 have therefore been revived and revised. According to them the two entrances would be near Folkestone and north of Boulogne while the actual submarine section would run between Dover and Sangatte, with a slight south-easterly curve near the middle. Technically, the construction would present much less difficulty than that of cutting through solid Alpine rock; the Channel floor consists mostly of chalk.

The only real problem is that of ventilation along the 30-odd miles of tunnel below the sea. Earlier plans to build it as a roadway have been abandoned because the exhaust gases would be too difficult to extract. The Channel Tunnel will be a railway tunnel for electric trains, with special trucks for motor vehicles. But there are rival plans; one favours a giant rail and road bridge across the Channel, another a combination of tunnel and bridge—with two 'holiday islands' in the middle. There is now no valid reason why some such new link between the 55 million people of Great

Britain and the 200 million West Europeans should not be created, and why it should not become a commercial success.

Steam-locomotive development made enormous strides along with the extension of the rail network over most parts of the world. It is a far cry from Stephenson's little *Rocket* to the most powerful passenger steam locomotives ever built, the 2-8-8-2 Class Y6b of the Norfolk and Western Railroad, U.S.A., with an overall length of 66 feet 11 inches, weighing 442 tons, and with a tractive power of over 150,000 lb. An even more powerful machine, the *Virginian*, 71 feet long and weighing 450 tons, was built especially for goods transport by the American Locomotive Company between the two World Wars. The steam turbine, too (see Part I), has been used extensively in locomotive design, particularly in Britain and Germany; on long hauls it may save up to 50 per cent of fuel, but it requires more steam for starting and at slow speeds than the reciprocating engine. However, after more than a century of satisfactory service the steam-engine began to disappear from the entire field of transport, to be replaced by the electric motor. The year of birth of the electric railway was 1881, when Werner von Siemens, the German engineer and industrialist, opened his first electrically operated tramway in a Berlin suburb. One of the rails carried the current, the other the return current; but this was soon found to be too dangerous, and Siemens adopted the overhead contact wire.

From that modest beginning sprang the phenomenal development first of the tramway and later the trolleybus as means of transport within the towns, then of the underground and overhead railway, also for urban transport, and eventually of electric traction on long-distance routes. In the early 1900's the electric tramway—frequently replacing horse-drawn trams—seemed the answer to many transport problems in the towns; but when motor-traffic increased immensely after the First World War, these cumbersome tramcars, moving inflexibly in narrow city centres, became more and more a hindrance rather than a help in maintaining transport across the towns. Some of them introduced trolleybuses instead because they move without rails, taking their current from two overhead wires. The general trend, however, was that of scrapping the tramways and operating motor-buses instead.

Underground and overhead metropolitan railways, on the other hand, have proved a lasting boon, especially in London, which has the most efficient network in the world. As early as 1863 the first underground steam railway, running in a deep, roofed trench, was opened, followed in 1870 by the Tower Subway, the first 'tube' railway in the world, but still steam-operated. The 'tube' system—two steel cylinders running side by side, each with a railway track and two current rails—recommended itself especially for London because the underground railway had to be built 100 feet deep into the clay, while Berlin and Paris have harder soil so that their tunnels could be built only a few feet below street level. Power stations for the supply of current were available well before the turn of the century; the first electric tube was opened in 1890, and from that time dates the gradual extension of London's network of tube railways. Today it comprises 280 stations and 4,000 coaches. There is also a completely automatic, narrow-gauge tube which carries only mails between Liverpool Street and Paddington; it was built in the 1930's, before 'automation' became the predominant trend in technology.

New York's first 'subway' was opened in 1904. Its stations, which are closer set than the London ones, number 475. It has been undergoing a continuous process of modernization since the early 1950's—there was much scope for greater comfort and efficiency. The Paris *métro*, however, has hardly been modernized since its opening a decade or so before the First World War, but Parisians seem to like it in its quaint and time-honoured state. Berlin, Glasgow, Madrid, Tokyo, Buenos Aires, and many other big cities have had underground railways for a long time; one of the latest is the Moscow underground, which was begun in 1932 but completed in stages only in the 1950's. It is a very efficient and probably the fastest underground of all, and has many modern technical features, though the architectural style of the stations may seem rather Victorian to the visitors from Western Europe. Technically even more modern is the Leningrad underground, which operates to a large extent with automatic control.

Mainline electrification began, at first at a leisurely pace, in a few countries with an abundance of hydro-electric power, especially Switzerland, southern Germany, and the United States. Electric trains had been an engineers' dream for a long time, but some mid-nineteenth-century attempts at running battery-operated locomotives were, of course, doomed to failure: too much power was required for hauling a heavy load, and the storage capacity of batteries was—and still is—very limited. The advantages of electric traction, however, were so obvious that the great capital cost of electrification seemed justified.

The system of sending high-tension current from power stations by an overhead wire network above the rails into the electric motors of the locomotives has indeed many advantages compared with steam traction. Operating costs are reduced by concentrating the generation of power at a few large installations, instead of generating it again and again in thousands of locomotive boilers. Fuels and energy sources which are not suitable for steam locomotives can be used: sub-standard coal, water power, natural gas, nuclear energy. The electric locomotive is more economical than the steam locomotive because it does not have to carry its own fuel or water. It does not use up energy except when it is actually working, whereas steam has to be raised in advance and fuel is wasted at stops and after the steam locomotive has finished its journey. In an electric locomotive no stoking is necessary, and controls are much simpler and easier to handle; besides, automatic controls and safety devices can be incorporated in the electric equipment. A higher train mileage can be achieved with less rolling stock because there is no time lost in fuelling.

For the passenger the absence of smoke and soot is the main advantage; there is no damaging of buildings and installations through the acid components of the engine smoke, and no danger of fire through sparks from the funnel. In tunnels, electric trains are vastly superior to steam-driven ones because the absence of smoke makes ventilation easier; on lines with steep gradients electric traction is more efficient than steam traction. On lines with many stops it has also the advantage of better acceleration.

There are two main systems of electrification; one uses direct current (D.C.) at voltages from 500 to 3,000, the other single-phase alternating current (A.C.) at up to 25,000 volts, the only major exception being the North Italian railways with a three-phase, 3,600-volt system. The usual system for suburban lines is that operating with D.C. at 600–1,200 volts, each motor coach equipped with 2 to 4 electric motors of 150 to 300 h.p. each. Up to voltages of 1,200 the current can be supplied by contact rails, but above this the overhead-wire system, with a bow-shaped 'collector' attached to the roof of the locomotive, is better and safer.

The power stations supply A.C., because D.C. loses too much of its energy when conveyed over long distances; but the train motors usually work with D.C. At the turn of the century the only method of converting the A.C. from the power stations to D.C. for the traction engines was that of making the A.C. turn a D.C. generator. Later, the mercury-arc rectifier was introduced, but it required a glass case or a water-cooled sheet-iron tank in which to operate; it permitted the current to flow through it in one direction only. A more recent device is the contact rectifier, which opens and closes metal contacts at each cycle. The most efficient modern transformer, however, is the germanium rectifier, a relative of the transistor (see Part III). It can be applied to a wide range of voltages and kilowatts, and is a simple, small and robust piece of equipment which needs no extra cooling. An interesting exception is the Euston–Liverpool line, which works with 25,000-volt A.C. locomotives; the first of them started service operation between Manchester and Crewe in 1960. This 3,300-h.p. engine, with a cruising speed of 90 m.p.h., is the most powerful locomotive in Britain; the use of the A.C. system makes transformers unnecessary and cuts down the need for 'feeder' stations along the line.

At the time of writing the world rail speed record is held by two French electric locomotives which achieved 205·6 m.p.h. in 1955, hauling three carriages. The record runs took place on the 1,500-volt D.C. line from Bordeaux to Dax. The fastest steam locomotives have not been able to exceed 130 m.p.h.

On principle, the idea that the steam locomotive has had its day has been accepted for a long time; however, in countries such as Britain, which has very limited hydro-electric energy but much coal, electrification was not regarded as an urgent matter until the 1950's, after some expert and Government committees had come out unanimously in favour of electrification because of its economy, efficiency, and cleanliness. Only the appearance of nuclear power, with its long-term promise of cheaper and abundant electric energy, gave the green light for complete electrification of main lines in Britain, and no more steam locomotives were commissioned after about 1955.

We shall later deal with the Diesel engine, which also plays its part in the modernization of the railways. Here it may suffice to mention that 'pure' Diesel locomotives and coaches have been found most useful on short-distance hauls and for shunting, and Diesel-electric trains on lines where electrification would be too expensive or has not been carried out yet. The Diesel-electric locomotive has many of the advantages of the electric one supplied with current from an overhead cable, but it is very heavy because it carries three sets of engines—the Diesel internal-combustion engine, an electric generator which is driven by it, and the electric motors. In a more recent type of locomotive the transfer of power from the Diesel engine to the locomotive wheels is carried out by a hydraulic gear. Experiments are also going on with nuclear reactors and gas-turbines as prime movers, which would operate electric generators supplying current to the motors. But here again cost and weight are major considerations—as well as safety in the case of nuclear reactors. It seems that the best way of using atomic energy for the railways is that of building nuclear power stations and supplying an electrified railway network with the current they produce.

Apart from the shift from steam to electric traction, rail transport has basically remained the same since Stephenson's days. The only really new development is that of the monorailway. The idea dates back to the beginning of our century, when some imaginative technicians believed that a train could be kept upright and standing on a single rail by means of gyroscopes—fast-spinning wheels which can preserve the equilibrium of a body. This system was never carried out because it did not seem safe and cheap enough to warrant the transition from two-rail to one-rail transport.

After the Second World War, however, a Swedish industrialist, Axel L. Wenner-Gren, backed the development of a monorailway running on a single rail track on which the coaches are firmly kept by flanges and rollers. They are electrically or Diesel-driven, and can be operated by drivers or remote control. At the end of the track they can leave the monorail and continue their journey on the ground like buses. The 'Alweg' railway, which takes its name from the initials of its backer, may offer a solution to the problem of getting passengers quickly to and from the airports as it could deposit them, or pick them up, right on the runways; it may also provide fast long-distance transport in regions of the world where no railways exist. The cost of building an 'Alweg' track is said to be only half of that of a two-rail track. Another possible development may be the 'air-cushion' railway based on the 'Hovercraft' principle, which we shall describe in Chapter 4.

# 3

◇◇◇◇◇◇◇◇◇◇◇◇◇◇◇◇◇◇◇

# Machines on the Road

ONE DAY in 1813 a young man on a strange vehicle raced through the streets of the German town of Mannheim: a kind of car with two wheels, placed one behind the other in a single track, and mounted on a simple wooden frame in the middle of which was a little saddle. The man was sitting on it while he pushed himself forward alternately with the right and left foot, not unlike a skater, thus giving the vehicle a speed hardly less than that of a coach-and-four. His arms were resting on iron bars, and his hands held a wooden rod connected to the front wheel, with which he could turn it where he wanted to go.

The street arabs were running after him, and many passers-by were roaring with laughter. The young man did indeed cut a funny figure, jumping and skating along the cobbled streets with his contraption, clad in the green service frock of a forest controller, and wearing a top hat. Though he was only 28, Baron Karl Friedrich Christian Ludwig Drais von Sauerbronn was already something of an eccentric. Son of a senior official of the government of Baden, and a godson of the margrave himself, he had his career cut out for him: either that of an officer or that of a civil servant. He chose the latter as the lesser evil. What he pined to do was to invent things; he was a born technician if ever there was one, but upper-middle-class etiquette made it impossible for him to study mechanics. Frustration had made him bitter and obstinate.

His demonstration of the 'running machine', as he called it, cost him his pensionable position and brought him nothing but scorn and enmity. He rode from Karlsruhe to Strasbourg, a walking distance of sixteen hours, in only four. He even obtained a patent from the Government, valid, of course, only in the

145

country of Baden. No one took any serious interest; at least not
in his homeland. When he died, almost penniless, in 1851, his
name was known only as that of the inventor of the 'draisine', a
hand-operated truck for repair and inspection on railway lines.
But in England, France, and America his one-track vehicle had
already made great strides.

It was, in fact, based on the sound reasoning that a walking
man uses much energy in shifting his weight from one foot to

Baron Drais on his 'running machine' (1813)

the other. He asked himself whether it was possible to invent a
simple vehicle which would keep the human body constantly in
the same axis while moving forward. No one before him seemed
to have thought of constructing a one-track vehicle to achieve
this;[1] people believed that such a contraption could never keep
upright. He thought that they were wrong, and he proved that
it was surprisingly easy to keep one's balance on a single-track
running machine.

It must have been this unexpected phenomenon which caught

[1] French technical historians claim that the earliest single-track vehicle with
two wheels appeared in Paris in 1808, but there is no evidence for this. A window
in the parish church of Stoke Poges, Buckinghamshire, however, shows a man
riding a bicycle-like contraption while blowing a trumpet; it bears the date 1642,
but artist and origin are unknown.

the fancy first of the French and then of the English fashionable
world. On the Paris boulevards and in London's Hyde Park these
running machines—called 'Hobby Horses' and, soon, 'Dandy
Horses'—appeared in great numbers, ridden by young men of
leisure and eventually by the ladies. Even the Prince Regent had
a special Dandy Horse made for himself, and enjoyed riding it in
public. A new industry for the manufacture of these machines
sprang up almost overnight; special halls were built in England
and America for the new sport, which amounted to a craze, ridiculed by the humorous writers of the day and by cartoonists such
as George Cruikshank. But the idea that this might be developed
into a new means of transport for the common people was not
yet pursued.

Twenty years passed before a young blacksmith from Dum-
friesshire, Kirkpatrick MacMillan, took it up. He fixed two cranks
to the axle of the rear wheel and operated them by long levers,
which he pushed with his feet. MacMillan travelled on this
machine from Dumfries to Glasgow, a distance of 74 miles, in
1842; it took him two days. Still there was no commercial interest
in the vehicle. Another ten years later, a German mechanic from
Schweinfurt in Bavaria, Philipp Heinrich Fischer, who had used
Drais's running machine as a schoolboy, fitted pedals to the front
wheel so that the abrupt, pushing movement of the rider's legs
became a continuous, revolving one which made the vehicle
travel much more quietly. Neither MacMillan nor Fischer, however, knew exactly why their machines would not topple over so
long as they kept moving. In fact, the rotating wheels have a
gyroscopic effect, not unlike that of a spinning top, and the faster
the vehicle moves the steadier it is.

A Frenchman, Ernest Michaux, founded the first bicycle
factory, and produced a model on the lines of Fischer's design. In
England, too, some workshops began to turn out bicycles with
front-wheel cranks; the rear wheel was slightly smaller. This type,
which gained some popularity around 1870, was known as 'boneshaker', and rightly so because it had unsprung wooden wheels.
The sports fans now took a hand in the development of the
vehicle. Since its speed depended on the revolution of the front
wheel they increased its size enormously while reducing that of
the rear wheel. Because of this grotesque shape it was called the
'penny-farthing'. Getting on and off it required the skill of a

circus artiste, but the rider could obtain considerable speed, and bicycle races became popular in England. 'Bicyclists are aware that they run dangers', wrote *The Times* in 1878, 'and suffer a certain percentage of casualties; but they have counted the cost and found it worth while running the risk.'

An Englishman, Lawson, successfully solved the problem of how to make the bicycle smaller and faster at the same time. He was the first to put the crank and pedals in the centre between the front and rear wheels. Hans Renold, a Swiss inventor who had settled in the midlands, contributed the roller chain which made it possible to transmit the power of the rider's legs from the pedal-operated gear wheel in the centre to a smaller one on the rear axle. Other inventors added the wire-spoke wheel, the sprung saddle, ball-bearings, gears and gearshift, and the free-wheel device, so that the modern 'safety bicycle' was more or less ready in its present form when J. K. Starley, of Coventry, began to mass-produce it in the 1880's. But there was one thing missing: an efficient tyre.

The 10-year-old son of a Scottish veterinary surgeon who had settled in Belfast, John Boyd Dunlop, was the cause of this invention. He pleaded with his father to help him win a tricycle race among the boys of his school; the solid-rubber tyre with which most cycles were fitted at the time did little to soften the jolts from Belfast's cobblestones. Dr Dunlop cut two pieces from an old garden hose, glued them together into rings, pumped air into the tubes, and fastened them to the rear wheels of the tricycle. The boy won the race, and kept riding merrily through the streets.

Only about a year later, in 1888, did a racing cyclist happen to see him and his vehicle. He advised Dr Dunlop to take out a patent; the newspapers wrote about it, and an Irish industrialist went into business with John Boyd Dunlop and began to manufacture these pneumatic tyres.

It was this invention which made the bicycle a practical, popular means of transport. There were only 300,000 bicycles all over the world in 1888; today there are about 75 million. Britain alone has 12 million; in Holland and Denmark there is one machine to every two inhabitants, and they are used alike by queens and schoolboys, postmen and sportsmen. It is the only completely silent vehicle; it can carry up to a dozen times its own weight, at speeds up to six times greater than that of a running man. It can move on all kinds of road and can be parked anywhere. It is still the most important—and most democratic—means of transport in many countries. In fact, it is a modern technical miracle.

Dunlop's invention came just in time to help the development

The pneumatic tyre made the bicycle a popular means of transport

of another vehicle which could not have conquered the world without the pneumatic tyre: the motor-car.

We have seen that the steam-car was a failure as a road vehicle. The steam-engine proved too heavy and its control too difficult for this purpose. Yet the need for mechanical road transport grew more and more urgent during the second half of the nineteenth century; so did the need for a small, efficient prime mover in industry. The latter came into being in the form of the electric motor when the problems of generating and distributing the electric current had been solved (see Part I). Some inventors, however, groped their way forward in another direction—towards the gas-engine.

A French engineer, Étienne Lenoir, built such an engine, in which ordinary coal gas was exploded, in 1863, and even made a little car which he drove with it. A Viennese engineer, Siegfried Marcus, used petrol vapour for the first time to drive a car through the streets of the Austrian capital in 1875, but the police banned it because it was too noisy. An Englishman, Edward Butler, exhibited a petrol-driven tricycle, with a two-cylinder motor, a carburettor, and ignition through a spark produced by a dynamo, in London in 1884. It was very much ahead of its time, but England offered little scope for inventors of mechanical road vehicles: those were the days of the notorious 'Red Flag Law' prohibiting any horseless carriage to go faster than four m.p.h. on the open road, and two m.p.h. in built-up areas; and a man with a red flag had to walk in front of any such 'street locomotive' to warn everybody of its approach. This law, of course, was the death sentence for Butler's car. All the money he had sunk in it was lost.

Meanwhile, things developed at a steady pace in Germany, starting with the invention of a gas-engine by a Cologne engineer, August Nikolaus Otto, in 1872. Although it depended on the mains for its gas supply it was a great step forward in the right direction. Otto used the cylinder-and-piston system of the steam-engine, but in his machine—and in all internal-combustion engines thereafter—the fuel was burnt inside, not in a separate furnace. Thus much less fuel was wasted than steam was wasted in the boiler and on the way from the boiler to the cylinder. Otto divided the operation up into four 'strokes': (1) suction (the gas, mixed with air, is sucked into the cylinder by the downward-moving piston); (2) compression of the gas-air mixture by the upward-moving piston; (3) ignition and expansion of the mixture (the power stroke): the piston is forced down; and (4) expulsion of the burnt gas by the piston moving up again. The cylinder has inlet and exhaust valves which are opened and closed mechanically by the engine itself. The piston-rod turns a crank-shaft, thus converting the reciprocating movement of the piston into a rotating one.

Gottlieb Daimler, a baker's son from Württemberg and a qualified engineer with much experience in German and foreign works, joined Otto at the age of 38 at his factory near Cologne to help in the development of the gas-engine. In his opinion this was the ideal prime mover for a road vehicle while Otto believed it should remain a stationary engine. There were two major alterations which Daimler thought necessary: instead of on mains gas the engine should run on petrol vapour; and Otto's ignition system (a permanent little flame outside the cylinder which exploded the gas at the point of maximum compression when a valve opened) should be replaced by electrical ignition inside the cylinder.

Daimler moved to Cannstatt near Stuttgart and built his first internal-combustion-driven vehicle—a motor-cycle. He tried it out in the backyard of his house in the autumn of 1885. He did not

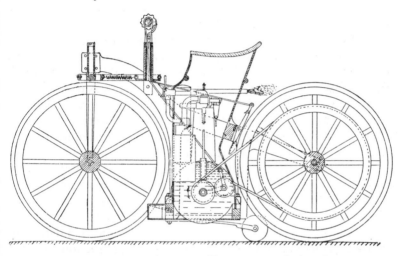

Daimler's own drawing of his motor-cycle (1885)

know at the time that no more than sixty miles from Cannstatt, in Mannheim, another inventor by the name of Karl Benz, ten years younger than Daimler, had already completed a little petrol-driven car a few months earlier.

Benz was a railwayman's son who had to work hard as a young man to keep his widowed mother and himself from starving. He achieved independence after a long struggle, and set up his own small workshop. The acquaintance with a 'boneshaker' bicycle prompted him to think of some way to mechanize road transport. Then he saw Lenoir's gas-engine, and his mind began to work on the same lines as Daimler's; he, too, came to the conclusion that some petroleum derivative might be suitable as fuel. It would be a comparatively cheap one; extensive oil reserves had been dis-covered in Pennsylvania in the 1850's.

The first Benz car was a tricycle with a four-stroke engine on the Otto principle, making 250–300 revolutions per minute as compared with the 120 revolutions of the stationary gas-engines. He invented his own electrical ignition system, and covered the engine with a 'mantle' containing cold water for cooling; the engine power was transmitted to the rear axle by means of two chains, with a primitive clutch in between. In order to surmount the difficulty of travelling around bends, when the outer wheel has to run faster than the inner one, he adopted an English invention: the differential gear, patented by James Starley in 1877. Steering was effected by a small wheel on top of a thin column in front of the bench which served as a seat for the driver and a passenger. The whole 'horseless carriage' with all its details was Karl Benz's own work, and it was the proudest day in his life when, one spring morning in 1885, his machine sprang to life in the courtyard outside his workshop and carried him around in a circle. In his excitement, however, he crashed against a wall, and that was the end of the first trial run.

At the 1887 Paris Exhibition, where Benz showed an improved model, no one took much notice; but a year later, when he drove it through the streets of Munich, it caused a sensation, and he was flooded with orders for motor-cars from many countries. He did not know—until he returned to Mannheim—that meanwhile his two sons, aged 15 and 13, had 'borrowed' another of his horseless carriages and driven their mother to Pforzheim and back, a distance of altogether 85 miles, even carrying out some repairs on the way. It was the longest journey a motor-car had ever undertaken until that time, and it proved that driving such a vehicle was, in the literal sense, child's play.

Gottlieb Daimler built his first four-wheeled car in 1886—a magnificent 'Motor State Coach' which looked like a carriage minus the horses, but it had only a $1\frac{1}{2}$-h.p. engine with one cylinder. However, it did 18 m.p.h. For some time he built his engines into motor-boats and even into a dirigible airship which started once but refused to rise a second time. From 1887 to 1889 Daimler, assisted by his chief designer, Wilhelm Maybach, worked on the perfection of the motor-car, and the model they were able to show at a Paris exhibition in 1889—a four-seater with a water-cooled engine and four gears—was no longer a carriage with the horses missing but a newly designed vehicle in its own right. A French firm of coach-builders acquired the licence to make Daimler cars, and from that time dated France's rise to become the leading motor-car country in the world. It was there that the first motor-car race took place in 1894 (Paris–Rouen–Paris); it was won by a Daimler car achieving an average speed of 20 m.p.h. Karl Benz, too, sold a great number of his cars to France. 'Germany was the father of the automobile, but France its mother', he used to say.

America had to wait a few years for its first motor-car. Only in 1893 did an American mechanic, Charles E. Duryea, succeed in getting the first petrol-driven vehicle on the road; he could travel about in it but he had no control over its speed. His next model was better, and he won many races against other imported and home-made automobiles in the years before 1900.

Detroit, destined to become the automobile metropolis of the United States, saw its first motor-car in 1896, driven by its maker, a young electrician by the name of Henry Ford. This home-made vehicle, with a two-cylinder, 4-h.p. engine, showed that the young man was an efficient mechanic with ambition and imagination. He believed that America, with its fast-growing wealth and its enormous distances, could use any number of automobiles. Yet there was still much stubborn opposition, especially by horse-dealers, breeders, blacksmiths, and fodder merchants, people who had much to lose in a country where (in the 1890's) 18 million horses and mules were doing most of the transport work which the railways could not carry out.

Ford was not so much an inventor as an improver and organizer. He saw where the main faults of the European cars lay: most of them were built for sportsmen and enthusiasts but not for the ordinary man who needed them for the strenuous tasks of everyday life. America required a foolproof, efficient, hardy vehicle, a truly popular means of transport, cheap to buy and economical to run. Henry Ford realized to an amazing degree his ambition to build such a utility automobile. It was his 'Model T'—nicknamed 'Tin Lizzie'—which made him one of the richest and most famous men in the world.

He built a new factory for its production, one-fifth of a mile long, specially designed for his 'assembly line', or conveyor-belt method of mass production, at a time when most European cars were still being hand made by craftsmen. To our eyes, the Tin

Lizzie of 1908—with her high body, her small engine hood, her open and doorless cabin—looks rather comical. But it was the car that put America on wheels. Fifteen million Tin Lizzies were sold between 1908 and 1927, when Ford at last decided that the time had come for more elegant models.

Britain had no part in the early development of the motor-car, thanks to the 'Red Flag Law'. But people like Frederick William Lanchester, the scientist and poet, who built a neat, tiller-steered vehicle in 1895, and the Member of Parliament, Evelyn Ellis,

An early Lanchester motor-car (1895)

rallied the motor enthusiasts and began a frontal attack on the out-dated law. Ellis bought a French car, and challenged the London police by driving it through the streets as fast as it would go, and without a man with a red flag marching in front of it. This defiant demonstration—no policeman dared to stop him—roused public feeling to such a point that in the autumn of 1896 Parliament abolished the 'Man with the Red Flag' after sixty inglorious years of rule.

This was the green light not only for Britain's motorists but also for its motor industry. It developed slowly, at first out-stripped by French and German factories, and later by American mass-production methods. After 1918, however, progress became more rapid, and the pace increased even more after the Second World War. In 1948 Britain took the lead as a car-exporting country, with a quarter of a million vehicles; ten years later this figure was twice as high; in the same period the car 'density' of the country rose from one to every twenty-four to one to every fourteen people. In the United States there was one car to every five people in 1948; ten years later the 'three-car family' was no longer an exception. Oil production has risen at approximately the same rate—up to 13 per cent in a single year; it is significant that refinery production of car petrol in Europe rose by no less than 450 per cent from 1937 to 1945.

All over the world the number of cars increases by about 15 per cent per year. Where will it all lead to? The motor-car has brought a cheap form of transportation to scores of millions of people within the short span of two generations, and it is still far from playing its part to the full in the so-called under-developed regions of the world. But in the big cities the phenomenal increase in the number of motor vehicles is causing an equally phenomenal headache to the town planners, the traffic engineers, the public transport authorities, the police, and the motorists themselves. When the first motor-buses appeared on the roads some years before the First World War, the speed of public transport in the cities increased by 50 to 100 per cent. Today it is back at the speed of the first horse-drawn buses of the 1830's. Congestion of urban roads is a world-wide problem which has to be solved soon if transport in the cities is not to come to a complete standstill; but this is a problem for the administrators rather than for the technicians, for the town planners rather than for the inventors.

There are, however, a few points where the two groups will have to meet if the traffic problem is to be solved. One is the design of new roads. Some towns, like Brussels and Paris, have shown the importance of underpass and fly-over roads and crossings in relieving congestion in the streets. English engineers have suggested that ring roads and motorways leading out of the big cities should be built over railway tracks so that no additional space is needed for them. American engineers have built 'speed-walks' and 'carveyors', short, closed-circuit underground rail-ways intended to make as many people as possible leave their cars and go short distances by public transport.

Another idea, which may make long-distance motorways safer, is that of the 'electronic road' with a built-in guide-rail, which beams electronic 'orders' to some receiving apparatus in the car, keeping it in its traffic lane at constant speed, and operating the steering gear and brakes if necessary to avoid a collision. As long as the driver is on such a road he can sit back, sleep, or read the newspaper, leaving the operation of the controls to electronics.

Such a car may have to be powered by a gas-turbine instead of a piston engine, because the former can be much more easily adapted to automatic control. The gas-turbine, an offspring of the aircraft jet-engine which we shall describe in detail in a later chapter, may be the automobile power unit of the future. Like the steam-turbine it has no reciprocating parts; the fuel—it can be cheaper oil such as paraffin or even coal-dust—is burnt in a combustion chamber, and the expanding gases act on the blades of a turbine. The machine needs much air; this is compressed by a compressor, which is driven by the turbine, and forced into the combustion chamber (or chambers) past the fuel atomizers. Combustion is not intermittent as in the piston engine, but continuous, and the gases are very hot when they strike the turbine blades. These features of the gas-turbine are common to the various varieties of the machine, whether it is used to drive the propellers of an aircraft, the screw of a ship, or the wheels of a motor-car; in the 'pure' jet-engine the turbine does no more than drive the compressor, while all the remaining energy of the exhaust gases is used to propel the aircraft.

The gas-turbine is basically a simple machine, easy to control, with a much better weight-energy ratio than the piston engine; it is also more robust, needs no gearing, and does not require high-grade fuel. Why, then, was the gas-turbine car not introduced long ago? There are snags. One is the very high temperature at which the machine works; alloys able to withstand the heat of the gases over long periods had to be developed. Then there is the problem of the hot exhaust gases which would endanger people and other vehicles on the roads. Fuel consumption is great, partly offsetting the advantage of cheaper fuel. The number of revolutions which the turbine has to make to be efficient is high, and this results in an unpleasant 'whine'.

Nevertheless, much progress has been made, and it is only a question of time before we shall see a substantial number of gas-turbine cars on the roads; many engineers believe that the turbine car will eventually supersede the piston-engine car altogether. In 1952 a British turbine car, made by Rover, reached a speed of over 150 m.p.h.; its engine weighed only 300 lb., compared with

1,000 lb. for a piston-engine of equal performance. Another
experimental British car, which has been tried out successfully,
had three turbines and eight compressors; it developed 160 h.p.
at 35,000 revolutions per minute.

The General Motors Company in America in 1958 tested its
experimental turbine car, *Firebird III*, in which the number of
revolutions had been reduced to 27,000 per minute and the gas
temperature to 870° centigrade. The weight of the engine, which
developed 225 h.p., was 600 lb. An arrangement by which a heat
exchanger returned up to 90 per cent of the exhaust heat to the

*Firebird III*, an American turbine car prototype

compression chamber increased the safety of the car considerably. However, the designers also incorporated a small 10-h.p.
piston-engine to supply the energy for a number of servo-
mechanisms, the electric generator, the air-conditioning system,
the pumps for the hydraulic suspension, and so on. The car, like
other experimental 'safety' models, had no steering-wheel and no
accelerator pedal; it had a small steering and control lever instead,
which the driver operated with one hand, and whose 'orders'
were translated into steering movements, acceleration, and
deceleration by an electronic system. This would also make the
adaptation of the car for driving along an electronic road
possible.

It will no doubt take a long time until a car of this type can be
mass produced cheaply enough to be in reach of the ordinary
citizen. By that time, however, something radical will have to be
done to make motoring much safer for all road-users than it is
now. Cars will be running not only on special motorways,
electronic or otherwise, without pedestrian traffic; they must also
be suitable for urban roads, where conditions are completely

different, and where safety is of supreme importance. The mounting toll of road accidents shows that a good deal of rethinking on the part of the designers will be necessary. So far, they have been concentrating on the speed, economy, and driver-safety of their models, not on the safety of all road users. In fact, the safer a car is for the driver, the more he will be tempted to drive too fast and with too little consideration for other people on the road.

Although turbo-engines for private cars will be coming, goods vans, buses, and the like may retain their special prime mover much longer. The turbine will have to offer substantial advantages if it wants to replace the Diesel, or heavy-oil engine.

This prime mover is nearly as old as the petrol-engine. Two English brothers by the name of Priestman patented a paraffin-oil engine—also an adaptation of the Otto gas-engine—in 1886. The oil was sprayed into a vaporizer, which was heated by a flame and the engine exhaust; the resulting gas was ignited in the cylinder by a spark plug. Another English inventor, Herbert Akroyd-Stuart, developed the idea of the heavy-oil engine further; he was the first to realize that the heat of the compression could bring about the ignition of the fuel in the cylinder, thus making the sparking-plug or some other separate ignition device unnecessary. Akroyd-Stuart submitted his patent specification in 1890, but he could not find sufficient support from manufacturers.

Meanwhile, a young German engineer, Rudolf Diesel, devoted all his energies to the perfection of a heavy-oil engine. His train of thought was set off by the lecture of a professor at the Munich Technical College, where he was a student, in 1878. The professor explained the conditions under which an 'ideal' heat engine might work, an engine infinitely more efficient than the steam-engine, which cannot convert more than 10 or 12 per cent of the latent fuel heat into energy. If, however, the temperature in the cylinder of an internal-combustion engine could be kept fairly constant during the change of state of the fuel, most of the heat created by that change would become energy. 'That idea kept following me', recalled Diesel; 'I used every moment I could spare to enlarge my knowledge of thermodynamics.'

Fourteen years after that lecture he knew the answer to the problem, and took out his first patent on an engine which had not yet been built; but he was sure it would work. Big German engineering firms, including Krupp's, enabled him to develop his invention, and he completed the first model in 1893. Although he had not quite succeeded in maintaining the cylinder at a constant temperature, he kept at least the pressure in it constant—in contrast with the ordinary petrol-engine in which the pressure changes very much during the combustion stroke. Diesel compressed the air in the cylinder so much that at the end of the compression stroke the temperature was high enough to ignite the liquid fuel, which was then injected at the top of the cylinder, without any spark plug or other ignition device. But the fuel was

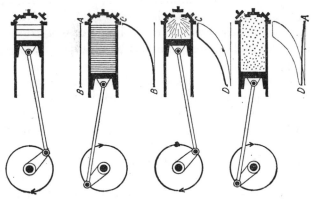

The action of the Diesel-engine (with diagram of forces A, B, C, D). *Left to right:* suction, compression, combustion (power stroke), exhaust

made to enter the cylinder gradually so that throughout the downward stroke of the piston the pressure was maintained and kept constant.

The advantages were obvious. The engine needed neither spark plugs nor ignition system or battery; it did not require a carburettor to change the liquid fuel into gas and mix it with air; and it could use cheap, heavy oil. The most efficient petrol-engine turns 28 per cent of the latent fuel heat into energy; the Diesel-engine, 35 per cent. There are, of course, some disadvantages, or the Diesel-engine would have superseded the petrol-engine long ago: the engine is about twice as heavy and more expensive; it is noisier, and the exhaust gases from the heavy oil are a great nuisance. It is more suitable for vans and buses than for private cars, although an increasing number of

F

taxis have been equipped with it in Britain and Germany because of its sturdiness and low fuel cost. It is most economical on long journeys and during long working-hours, and it can be built in bigger units than would be practical for petrol-engines. For this reason it was the Diesel-engine and not the petrol-engine that was adapted for ships and railways (see the previous chapter).

Rudolf Diesel lived to see no more than the beginning of the world-wide success of his engine. He embarked on all kinds of hazardous business transactions, including oil interests, and spent more money than he could afford. He disappeared from a Channel steamer in 1913, and only after his suicide did his private papers reveal that the financial position of the inventor whom everybody believed to be a millionaire had in fact been desperate.

It may seem that in our age of rapid technical development the inventors have paid too little attention to the possibility of basic improvements of the cylinder-and-piston internal-combustion engine, which has remained essentially the same since Otto established the four-stroke principle. The only revolutionary new design of practical value seems to be the 'rotary piston' engine invented by Felix Wankel, a motor engineer from Lindau, Bavaria; it was developed by the German NSU motor company in the late 1950's and subsequently, under licence, by the Curtis Wright Company in America.

Wankel's engine has a cylinder which is not cylindrical at all— it has an oval cross-section, and the 'piston' is a triangular rotating disc whose sides are slightly curved so that throughout its rotation there is always some space for the moving and expanding gases on at least two sides of the piston. The rotating piston also opens and closes the inlet and exhaust valves automatically. The four 'strokes' of the conventional internal-combustion engine— suction, compression, ignition (by plug) and power stroke, and exhaust—are completed as the piston rotates; but during each rotation the piston disc is pushed round by *three* power 'strokes'! In fact, the engine does the work of a three-cylinder machine with only one piston, rotating at the rate of 1,500 to 17,000 revolutions per minute. In this way a unit corresponding to a conventional engine of only 125 cubic centimetres develops almost 30 h.p.

In contrast to the conventional engine, the rotary-piston engine has only two moving parts, the piston—the inventor calls it the

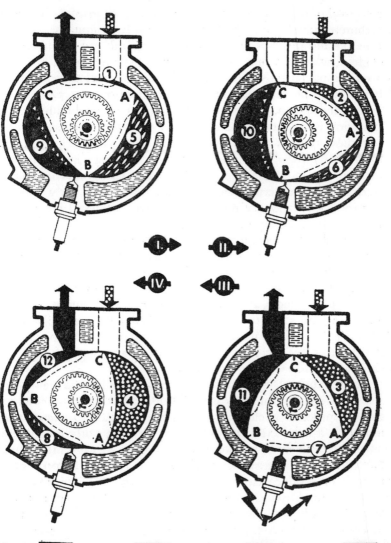

Wankel's rotary-piston engine

rotor—and the output shaft to which it is geared. It needs carburettor and sparking-plug, but it can burn low-quality fuel. Like the turbine, it is much more economical than reciprocating engines, which waste a lot of energy in their movements, and it needs no piston rods, crankshaft, and complicated valve control. It is, therefore, much cheaper to build, and only 25 per cent as heavy; the 30-h.p. unit weighs less than 25 lb., and its fuel consumption is the same as that of a conventional 125-c.c. engine. For these reasons the Wankel engine seems especially suitable for aircraft propulsion; there are still some snags in adapting it for motor-cars, but a prototype had its first successful road test at Neckarsulm, southern Germany, where it was built, early in 1960. A very large stationary model, of 32 litres, achieved 800 h.p. at 1,500 r.p.m. in America.

Few fields of technical activity have seen so many revolutionary changes in such short periods as that of transport, and we may ask when atomic energy will bring another series of important new developments. It is unlikely, however, that it will affect road transport, at least not in the foreseeable future, because nuclear reactors are too heavy and costly, and the problem of shielding drivers and passengers from dangerous radiations is too difficult to solve where the available space and carrying capacity are limited.

But the fuel cell may gain some importance in road transport, and in other technical fields as well. For more than a century and a half the process of electrolysis has been known to science and industry: if an electric current is sent through water it splits up into its constituents, hydrogen and oxygen. Already in the first half of the last century, scientists tried to reverse the process— that is, to produce current and water from the interaction of hydrogen and oxygen. They did not succeed in generating appreciable amounts of electricity, but the idea kept coming up in connection with the problem of inventing a light-weight, efficient device for storing electrical energy. Some research workers realized that it would be easier to store that energy not in the form of electricity proper, but perhaps as gas.

A young English chemist from Cambridge, Francis T. Bacon, began to experiment on these lines in 1932. Twenty-seven years later he was at last able to demonstrate his system of electrolysis-in-reverse. The fuel cell, under which name the device is known, consists in fact of a whole battery of cells in which electric current is generated; two electrodes, porous flat plates made from nickel powder, are suspended in a 40 per cent solution of potassium hydroxide and fed separately with hydrogen and oxygen gases at a pressure of several hundred pounds per square inch. When the

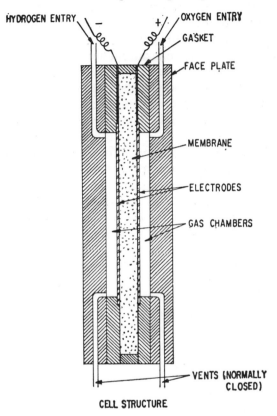

CELL STRUCTURE

The fuel cell

cells are working they run at a temperature of 200° centigrade, and the water formed out of the gases emerges as steam.

Mr Bacon's first model produced 5 kW of power at 24 volts, sufficient to drive a fork-lift truck or operate a circular saw or a welding apparatus. He believed that the efficiency of the fuel cell could be raised to 80 per cent, i.e. one pound of mixed gas would produce more than a kilowatt-hour of electricity.

In America a number of research teams advanced on similar lines, producing fuel cells with an efficiency of 250–300 watt hours per pound of weight (a standard car battery is rated at 8–10 watt hours per pound). An experimental tractor with an 'engine' consisting of 1,008 fuel cells and a 20 h.p. electric motor was tried out in the fields. Operated by propane and oxygen, the fuel cells produced 15 kW of electricity, which proved sufficient for pulling a plough. The Chrysler Corporation built a fuel-cell car with four electric motors, one attached to each wheel so that gearbox, transmission, differential, drive shaft, and rear axle were not needed. The Russians, too, are developing vehicles powered by fuel cells. The advantages of silence, economy, and, last but not least, the absence of harmful exhaust fumes are obvious.

The first application of the fuel cell was in an artificial earth satellite, where it generated current for the radio transmitters. But it may well revolutionize transport, even to the extent of eventually superseding the Diesel-engine in buses and lorries. Still later it may be used to drive trains and small ships. Private cars will probably be at the end of the list of vehicles which could make efficient use of the fuel cell, but there is no doubt that it has a great future.

# 4

## Ships

LONG before Man invented the wheel, even before he began to till the soil and domesticate animals, he began to build ships. How did the idea enter his mind? First, he must have ventured to go into the water himself, and found that he could swim; he watched and emulated other land animals crossing rivers and lakes. Then he probably played around floating logs, clinging to them when his strength failed. Eventually he may have sat on a log, paddling with his hands, and later with a flat piece of wood. And then he discovered that he could keep his log from rolling over by hollowing it out so that he could squat in it, and that he could travel faster if he cut the front of the log into a pointed end . . . and there was the first ship, a dug-out canoe.

We can still see this and many of the subsequent stages of shipbuilding development in everyday use somewhere in the world: the canoe in Africa and South America, the kayak of the Eskimoes in Canada, rafts made of logs in timber-producing countries, coracles (hide-covered, tarred skiffs) in Wales, catamarans (made of three logs lashed together) in Madras. Not so long ago, the Indians in Brazil were using what must have been the most primitive form of a sailing-ship—a canoe with a man holding up a leafy branch to catch the wind; and North American Indians sailed by means of spread-out hides or blankets held by one or two men in a boat while another was steering with a paddle.

It is easy to see why water transport began such a long time before transport on land. Water is comparatively level and free from obstacles, and there are no forests, hills, or swamps to cross. And there is the great advantage that friction is negligible, and

Ancient Briton in a coracle

consequently much less work has to be done to overcome it. On land the harnessing of the wind does not help much; at sea, a piece of cloth on a pole can drive a ship, as our forbears eventually found out. This discovery, which ranks with the first use of fire, marks the beginning of Man's utilization of the forces of Nature.

A slow but steady development of shipbuilding seems to have begun in the fourth millennium B.C. in the Middle East. Sails and masts, usually combined with oars (and slaves to work them), were fairly common from 3500 B.C. onwards; steering was done by an extra oar held by a man in the stern of the ship; in the larger and later ships it was lashed to the stern and operated by a lever, or a leather strap, to give it more power. Still, it was not a very effective steering mechanism because it was too easily deflected by the waves. This limited the size of the ships—and accordingly their range—on the one hand, and was a good reason for maintaining slavery on the other: galley slaves had to be employed in propelling the ship in the desired direction.

Shipping in the earliest period must have been restricted to the great rivers such as the Euphrates, the Tigris, and the Nile; the Egyptians were the first people to venture on the open sea. But their building material, reeds and acacias, was poor; so they coasted close to the shore up to the Lebanon to get cedars. With these they built ships large enough to undertake long journeys, still, of course, hugging the coast, for even moderate winds were dangerous for these slightly built ships which had only primitive mechanisms for reducing the active sail space; most Egyptian ships had a fixed yard, and the reefing was done by dipping the whole mast, which was mounted on hinges.

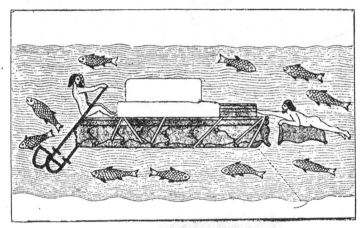

Assyrian raft made of inflated animal skins

We know very little about the vessels with which the Phoenicians undertook their amazing travels. Herodotus tells us that they sailed right around Africa. Be that as it may, it is certain that they were the first Mediterranean nation to trade with Britain, that they went as far as the mouth of the Rhine, and established sea routes to India, probably around 600 B.C. There is no doubt that with the Phoenicians shipbuilding and sea-trading must have been what we would call national industries. The bodies of their ships probably consisted of hardwood ribs, well joined, and their rigging permitted a certain amount of manœuvring. They could not, however, sail very close to the wind; sea journeys were a fine-weather occupation, and at the first sign of a storm the sailors had to shelter in a bay or port. This called for a great number of not too distant harbours, and the Phoenicians were responsible for building them—and populating them with their people—all around the

* F

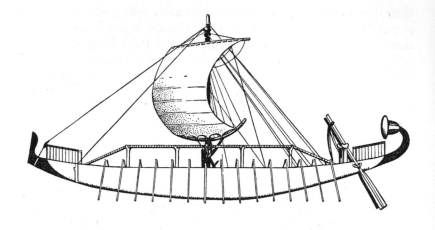

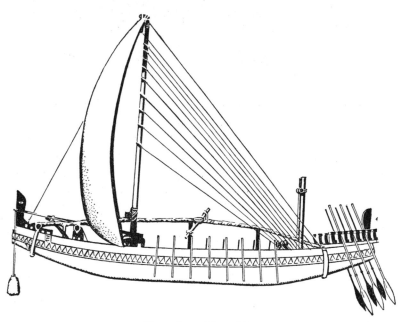

Egyptian sailing-ships

Mediterranean; most of the present-day harbours in that area were already in existence in ancient times.

The Greeks, who took over from the Phoenicians as a sea-faring nation, were also great harbour-builders and navigators, but their main interest lay in the military field. Their galleys were usually 130 to 165 feet long and 16 to 17 feet wide, manned by up to a few hundred galley slaves in two, three, and often many more tiers. A naval battle, such as that at Salamis against the Persians, must have amounted to sheer mass murder of the slaves, who went down chained to their burning ships.

Early Phoenician boats: from a relief excavated at the palace of Sargon II, King of Assyria (eighth century B.C.)

The rivalry between Rome and Carthage caused the quickest development in ancient shipbuilding. The Attic trireme, carrying a crew of 200–230 men, 170 of whom were rowers, in three tiers, was the standard man-of-war; the slaves sat in the open, but the soldiers were under cover in fore and aft decks. As a rule, there was only one large square sail. Besides their warships, the Romans built large freighters and also fast ships for carrying passengers and dispatches to the distant shores of their empire; Rome's merchant ships were fairly large: 500 to 1,000 tons, and occasionally as much as 3,000 tons. One of the latter was used to transport an Egyptian obelisk to the city of Rome (where it can still be seen at the basilica of St Peter), and then filled with sand and sunk to form part of the foundation of the breakwater for the harbour of Ostia, at the mouth of the Tiber. In 1959 three such scuttled ships, each 130 feet long, were excavated in good condition during the digging for the new Rome airport near Ostia. The Roman emperors had splendid houseboats and state galleys; in 1928 the Italians drained Lake Nemi to recover Caligula's two state barges—enormous ships, one of them being more than 230 feet long and nearly 80 feet wide, with anchors 13 feet long. Unfortunately the barges were destroyed during the Second World War.

Like so many other ancient crafts, that of shipbuilding declined during the early Middle Ages. But independently of the Mediterranean tradition the Norsemen or vikings in Norway developed a sturdy type of small ship with which they set out into the world when their numbers had increased so much that they were unable to feed themselves by hunting. They raided the coasts of western Europe from Iceland to Italy, established kingdoms in many countries, visited Greenland, and from there travelled as far as the North American continent—at about the same time when the Norman duke, William I, conquered England.

We should not know much about the ships with which the

How a viking ship was steered

vikings carried out their ventures if one of them had not been found in a Schleswig peat bog in 1863 and another excavated at Gokstad, in the Oslo Fjord, in 1880. Both ships were well preserved, and can now be seen at the Kiel and Oslo museums. They are about 80 feet long and 14 to 17 feet in maximum beam, each with a pine mast 40 feet high and with 16 oars a side; each oar was worked by two men, so that the crew of oarsmen was 64 per ship. The oars were very long, from 25 to 40 feet, and projected through portholes in the sides. There was a row of shields along the bulwarks for the protection of the oarsmen. The sails were simple, square pieces of canvas, and the steering was done by a paddle on the starboard side of the stern. The famous Bayeux Tapestry, a contemporary picture record of the Norman Conquest, shows a number of William's ships as pure sailing vessels without any portholes for the oars.

When the Crusaders embarked on their long journeys they found that pure, large sailing-ships were quicker and more efficient than galleys. The fleet of Richard Cœur de Lion, for instance, included among its 160 ships only 38 galleys. In that period—around 1200—the steering oar on the side of the ship began to disappear and make way for the more efficient rudder on the stern as we know it today.

But the real conquest of the high seas by seafaring man began only with the introduction of an instrument which, though it has altered greatly during these six or seven centuries, is still the heart of all navigation: the mariner's compass. Its early history is uncertain, although Chinese sources say that it was invented in 2634 B.C. However, some instrument of this kind seems to have been in general use in East Asia at the end of the third century A.D., and for some time it was believed that Marco Polo brought it back from his travels a thousand years later. But historians are rather inclined to credit a fourteenth-century Italian, Flavio Gioja, an armourer from Positano, with the invention of the first practical mariner's compass—though the fact of the earth's magnetism and the phenomenon that a magnetized iron needle will always point north had been known for a very long time. What Gioja did was to suspend the needle so that it could swing on a pivot, and enclosed it in a wooden box with a glass lid. Later, a circular card marked with the 32 points of the compass and swinging with the needle, was added. In this form, the mariner's compass was in use until the late nineteenth century. In the 1870's, however, Lord Kelvin (Sir William Thomson) turned it into a modern, reliable instrument which keeps steady while the ship is rolling, and is not subject to magnetic influences from the iron parts of the ship. Instead of one heavy needle there are eight thin steel strips, fastened to the ring of the circular card with silk thread. The compass bowl is filled with castor oil to prevent rocking, and bars of permanently magnetized steel under the centre of the card correct the heeling error due to the ship's own vertical magnetism.

What we now call naval architecture, shipbuilding as a technical craft and theoretical science, began only after the invention of the mariner's compass in the fourteenth century. Italy was at first leading in this field, but Henry V commissioned a number of large ships which put England in the forefront of Europe's naval nations, with Portugal and Spain as her greatest rivals. Yet the most glorious of all voyages of discovery, that of Columbus, was made with three incredibly small ships—of 100, 50, and 40 tons. Few modern vessels of such diminutive size would even today dare to cross the Atlantic!

But a hundred years later the sailing-ship had not yet quite supplanted the galley. Its end came with that of the Armada, when the faster English men-of-war outmanœuvred the clumsy Spanish galleys, which had to carry enormous crews of oarsmen. Even before the Spaniards reached the British coast many of these lumbering hulks were shattered by storms. It was clear to anybody with half a sense for the essentials of seafaring that oar-propelled ships would be of little use now that the tempting, distant shores of America and East Asia were to be explored.

Still, it was found necessary to strengthen the hulls of the traders considerably to make ocean sailing less risky. Another problem was that the usual nautical instruments—compass, astrolabe, quadrant, cross staff—were not much use in determining the longitude at sea, although they gave the latitude with reasonable accuracy. As soon as the mariner was out of sight of the coast with its familiar features, its harbours and lighthouses, cruising became somewhat hazardous. The only solution was the invention of a really accurate chronometer—but this proved the most difficult instrument of all to create. In 1675 Charles II founded the Greenwich Observatory, with its noon time ball, to give English seamen a focal point for determining the time, but forty years later the British Government had to offer a series of high rewards to any inventors of reliable timekeepers for ships at sea. Another fifty years elapsed until John Harrison, a carpenter's son, succeeded in making what became the most famous chronometer in the world. It was tested on a journey to Jamaica in 1761, and was found to lose no more than five seconds during its six weeks at sea.

Throughout the seventeenth and eighteenth centuries, sailing-ships had grown bigger, faster, and more elaborate. From the one-mast cutter to the four-masted barque or schooner there had developed a large number of distinct types for many different purposes in war and peace, and Britain was leading in the building of all of them. There were bulky East Indiamen, frigates made for speed, corvettes for warding off pirates, and finally that last and perhaps most wonderful type of sailing-ship—the fast, graceful, long and narrow clipper, specially built for the rapid transport of tea from the Far East to England, or for the wool trade. The clippers survived the coming of the steamship by three-quarters of a century because they achieved average speeds of up to 20 knots. Fast ships were also needed by Britain to carry immigrants to Australia; in this field there was keen American competition. One of the last clippers, the *Cutty Sark*, built in 1868 of wood and iron, is now preserved in a dry-berth at Greenwich. The Germans built clipper-type sailing-ships even as late as in the first decade of our century.

Attempts to use steam power for ship propulsion began many hundreds of years ago. One Blasco de Garay is said to have built such a vessel at Barcelona in 1583, and we have already mentioned that Denis Papin planned to equip the paddle-wheel boat with which he left Marburg for England in 1707 with a reciprocating steam-engine (see Part I). In 1736 an English mechanic by the name of Jonathan Hulls took out a patent for a tugboat engine, but it was never built. An American, William Henry, who had seen James Watt's engine, experimented with steam-driven model boats at Lancaster, Pennsylvania, in 1770; among those who watched these rather unsuccessful trials was a young man, John Fitch, who took up the idea and succeeded, sixteen years later, in building a steamboat driven by an endless chain of floating boards, rather like a caterpillar track; in another model he supplanted them by paddles, and reached a speed of 7 m.p.h. Fitch also suggested concentrating the force of the steam in a jet and driving a boat in this way; such a vessel was actually constructed by James Ramsey in 1793. It travelled at 4 m.p.h. on the Potomac. But to most other inventors it was obvious that the paddle-wheel was a more practical device if steam propulsion was to be achieved.

Fitch's *Perseverance*, with screw propeller at the stern

There is no doubt that William Symington, a Scottish mechanic, was the first to build a steamboat of reasonable efficiency. He began his experiments in company with Patrick Miller, a retired banker, and James Taylor, a teacher; they produced a steamboat in 1788, and tried it out on Lake Dalswinton, Scotland. It attained a speed of 5 m.p.h., which seemed to disappoint Symington's associates. At any rate, he carried on alone against heavy odds, and fourteen years later he was able to demonstrate his first practical steamboat, the *Charlotte Dundas*. He tried her out on the Forth and Clyde Canal in 1802; she was able to tow two 70-ton barges for six hours against a headwind so strong that no other ship on the canal dared to travel.

The first result of Symington's success, however, was that the use of steamboats as tugs on British canals was at once banned because it was feared that the banks would be damaged by the backwash. Symington lost all hope. His conviction that one day steamships might even cross the Atlantic was met with derision. Meanwhile, however, an American had taken up the development of the idea.

Robert Fulton, born in Pennsylvania in 1765, was a gifted artist, but mechanical things interested him no less than painting. He went to England to study art—and secured a contract to build

Symington's *Charlotte Dundas*

a cast-iron viaduct over the River Dee, a job which he carried out with efficiency although he had only read books about engineering. It was then that he watched the *Charlotte Dundas*, and the idea of the steamboat fascinated him. Called to Paris to execute a colossal painting for the first panorama show, he suggested to the French Directory the construction of a submarine, which he called the *Nautilus*, to attack the English Navy under water. The plan was received with enthusiasm, but nothing came of it as the invasion of England was called off. He was no more successful with another invention, the 'torpedo', a self-propelled underwater missile launched by special torpedo boats.

In Paris, Fulton made friends with the American ambassador, Robert Livingston, and discussed with him the idea of the steamboat. Livingston offered his backing. They bought an old Watt

engine, and built a small ship around it. They tried it out on the
Seine in 1803, but it broke in two. Another one was built, and
Fulton sought an audience with Napoleon. The great man,
biased by an unfavourable report by some Academicians, asked
Fulton: 'So you want to drive a ship with cigar smoke?'

Nevertheless, Fulton and Livingston went ahead with their
trials, which were reasonably successful but showed that a much

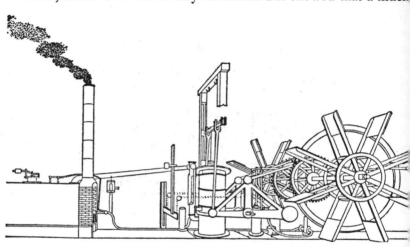

Engine and paddle-wheels of Robert Fulton's *Clermont*

better engine was required. Livingston secured a grant of 15,000
dollars from the American Government; a 20-h.p. engine was
bought from Boulton & Watt, and the first true steamship was
built to Fulton's design in New York. Christened *Clermont*, she
was a 180-ton ship, 130 feet long, with a 30-foot funnel and large
paddle wheels in the middle on either side. The New Yorkers who
crowded Hudson Quay when she started on her first journey in
August 1807 called her 'Fulton's Folly'.

The *Clermont* steamed up the Hudson to Albany, a distance of
150 miles, in 32 hours, and back in 30, without a hitch. 'Notwith-
standing that wind and tide were adverse to its approach', wrote
a newspaperman, describing the impressions of the Hudson
sailors who met the ship, 'they saw with astonishment that it was
rapidly coming towards them; and when it came so near that the
noise of the machinery and paddles was heard, the crews, in some
instances, shrank beneath their decks from the terrific sight, or

eft their vessels to go ashore; whilst others prostrated themselves
and besought Providence to protect them from the approach of
the horrible monster which was marching on the waves and
ighting its path by vomiting fire.'

The *Clermont* continued to serve on the New York–Albany
run for many years. Fulton built two more for service on the
Hudson, and some others for various purposes, including the
first steam-driven warship, the *Demologos*. He did not live to
witness her commissioning in 1815. At that time steam navigation
was already firmly established on the east coast of the U.S.A.,
yet on the European Continent there was still an absurd bias
against it. When Fulton offered, in 1812, to open a service on the
Danube between Vienna and Ulm, the Bavarian Government
asked a senior mining engineer for his opinion, and this man, who
later made amends by suggesting the construction of the first
German railway line, wrote: 'An engine of no less than 240 h.p.
would be necessary to propel a ship up the Danube. . . . Nearly all
its space would be taken up by the fuel required to drive it for a
single day. . . . The journey from Vienna to Ulm would take 40
days.'

The Scots were less sceptical. Henry Bell's *Comet*, built on the
Clyde in 1812, was the first steamship to take up regular service
in the British Isles; it ran between Glasgow and Greenock. This
was the beginning of the rapid development of Scotland's steamship industry; the *Marjory*, the first steamer to sail on the Thames
(1814), was also a Scottish-built ship, and so was the first steamboat to cross the Irish Channel in 1818. Another British ship, the
*Defiance*, introduced steam navigation on the Rhine in 1816, and
in the same year the *Lady of the Lake* began her regular run on the
River Elbe between Hamburg and Cuxhaven.

It was an American boat, however, which dared to cross the
Atlantic for the first time with steam power. In May 1819 the
*Savannah*, a sailing-ship with an auxiliary steam-engine, left
Georgia, and arrived in Liverpool twenty-five days later—a
record crossing, for ordinary sailing-ships needed thirty-two to
forty days for the journey. Eight more years passed before the
first steam-only crossing was made by the Dutch vessel *Curaçao*,
a wooden paddler built at Dover. She took a month to get from
Rotterdam to the West Indies.

Still, there was a long way to go from these beginnings to

anything like a reasonably priced passenger service between Europe
and America. Paddle-steamers consumed a great deal of fuel and
were expensive to run, and their speed was limited as the engines
could not be made too heavy; the wooden hulls would have
broken up. Wood has to be almost as heavy as the weight it
carries to have sufficient strength; iron can carry twice its own
weight, and steel even more. But there was a great deal of
prejudice against iron ships, and even experts believed they would
sink to the bottom of the sea like leaden ducks. Also, some of the
wooden paddle steamers became famous for their trans-Atlantic

Early paddle steamer

crossings, such as the *Great Western*, built by Isambard Kingdom
Brunel, the creator of the Great Western Railway and son of the
equally famous engineer, Sir Marc Isambard Brunel, in the 1830's.
Brunel's idea was the 'extension' of the London to Bristol
railway right to New York by means of a regular steamboat
service. The *Great Western*, a smart ship of 1,340 tons with a
440-h.p. engine, made her first crossing in fifteen days in 1838, in
a race against a small, decrepit harbour tug, the *Sirius*, chartered
by an American; this boat took three days longer. The double
event created a sensation on both sides of the Atlantic.

However, the days of the wooden paddle-steamer were
numbered. The iron age of shipbuilding began at about the same
time as that of the screw-propeller. It was first suggested by a
Swiss scientist, Daniel Bernouilli, to the French Academy in
1752; but as there were no suitable engines to turn the screws it
remained on paper. John Fitch had also experimented with the

crew-propeller, but his design was inefficient. In 1824 a Frenchman, Captain Delisle, suggested this new form of propulsion to
the Government, but the plan was laid aside.

Eventually, in 1828, an Austrian forest official, Joseph Ressel,
persuaded the owner of a Trieste shipyard to build an experimental boat with a 6-h.p. steam-engine and a screw of a turn and
a half between the sternpost and the rudder. The *Civetta*, as it was
called, cruised at $7\frac{1}{2}$ knots, but then a boiler tube burst, and the
harbour police refused permission for another try-out. Ressel
never succeeded in getting another chance.

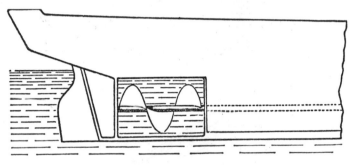

The $1\frac{1}{2}$-turn screw of Ressel's *Civetta*

Yet even the short life of the *Civetta* had shown that the principle of the screw-propeller was sound. It is a strange device,
going back to the Archimedean screw, which was used widely
and for many centuries as a machine for water-raising: a spiral
made of metal or wood, fixed around a rotating shaft, and enclosed in a tight-fitting container; when the spindle is sunk into
water and turned, the water rises in the container. If we imagine
the spindle fixed horizontally to the stern of a boat the revolving
screw will displace some water, thus moving the boat. In practice,
however, the effect of a screw is not quite so simple; it 'slips' in
the water, which is an elastic matter, and this reduces its efficiency.
The slip can be kept to a minimum by making the screw rather
large and rotating it at great speed. For this reason, it was first
necessary to develop powerful steam-engines with a high rate of
revolutions before the screw-propeller could be introduced as a
new means of ship propulsion.

Six years after Ressel, Francis Pettit Smith, an English farmer
with a bent for mechanical things, began to experiment with a

wooden screw-propeller. He drew the attention of the Admiralty
to his work, and was given an opportunity to build a 237-ton
ship, which he called *Archimedes*. In the belief that Ressel had not
been thorough enough by giving his screw a turn and a half, he
gave his two turns. The *Archimedes* was completed in 1838.

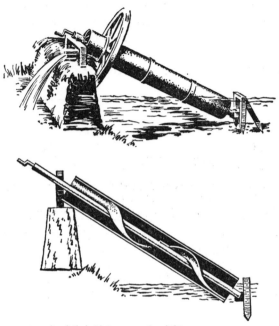

Archimedes' screw for lifting water

Her first trial was an astonishing success. The Admiralty had
required a speed of 4 to 5 knots; this was reached soon after the
start. After about half an hour there was a sudden knock at the
stern as though some hard object had hit the ship. Smith stopped
the engine at once to see what had happened. To his dismay he
found that a broken bottle had collided with the screw, and
knocked off one of its turns.

He decided to take the ship back to port, if possible under her
own steam, and started the engine again, expecting the speed to
be reduced to a snail's pace. The broken screw began to turn. But
to Smith's utter amazement the ship moved faster and faster—
knots, 6, 8, 10! It was almost unbelievable that half a screw could
propel the ship twice as fast as the complete one; but there it was

The *Archimedes* became one of the most famous ships of her time. She achieved up to 13 knots, and sailed from Portsmouth to Oporto in barely 70 hours, averaging nearly 11 knots. Smith took her on a triumphal tour around the British Isles. France and America hastened to build their own screw-propeller ships; within a few years the new means of propulsion was firmly established. The chance collision with the broken bottle had shown Smith that the single-turn screw was the most efficient design; later it was found that its performance could be even bettered if the single turn was not given the form of a solid piece but divided up into several—two to five—blades, and this is the design which is still used—on sea as well as in the air, wherever propellers are required.

Brunel decided to equip his *Great Britain*, which was to be the largest steamer of its time, with a screw-propeller. This ship, 322 feet long and with a displacement of 3,000 tons, was remarkable also because it was built of iron, and Brunel wanted to show that it would float after all, despite the experts' warnings. The *Great Britain* indeed made marine history by crossing from Liverpool to New York in 14½ days, the fastest until then, in 1845. But a year later she was wrecked on the Irish coast. Brunel had her refloated, and she had a long and successful life on the Australian run.

Then, however, Brunel overreached himself by building his ill-fated *Great Eastern*. With her 27,500 tons and 700-foot length she was half a century ahead of the technical developments of her time. Brunel gave her a 24-foot propeller as well as two 58-foot paddle-wheels, two sets of engines with five funnels, and six masts carrying 6,500 square yards of sail—just in case. The vicissitudes during her construction, with accidents and delays on end, wrecked Brunel's health. At last, in September 1859, she left her Thames berth on the way to Holyhead; but she did not get further than Hastings when there was an explosion which killed five men on board. A few days later Brunel died. The ship would have been a failure as a liner for the reason that no port in those days had facilities to handle a vessel of that size. She was eventually used as a cable-layer before being broken up in 1889.

The trend towards larger and faster ocean liners was not merely due to the engineers' and shipowners' desire to outdo one another in naval architecture; it was also due to social and

economic developments and requirements. Great masses c
people were waiting to be carried across the oceans, especiall
emigrants. For the poor between-deck passengers on board th
sailing-ships a crossing brought indescribable miseries. They ha
to take their own food for the long journey, and if storms delaye
the arrival many of them starved or even died of hunger. The
were allowed just enough space to stretch themselves on the bar
boards, or on their pitiful bedding, with their most valuabl
belongings serving as pillows. There are some figures from th
middle of the nineteenth century which give an idea of thes
conditions; between 9 September and 21 October 1853, sixtee
sailing-ships reached New York from various European ports
They had taken on board altogether 6,418 passengers; 334 c
them died during the crossing either from starvation or from th
hardships of the journey.

Iron had hardly superseded wood as the main shipbuildin
material when it was itself superseded by steel. The first steel shi
was launched in 1863, and ten years later steel had already re
placed iron almost completely. The reason was that a new, cheap
and efficient way of making steel had been invented by a
Englishman, Henry Bessemer. He was an all-round inventor, an
successful in most of his efforts, from a stamp-cancelling die t
bronze powder. After demonstrating to French officers durin
the Crimean War a rotating projectile which he had perfected, h
had the idea of attempting to produce steel by a more economic;
method. Steel was at that time still a luxury, costing £50 a ton c
more; it was used only for some tools, table-knives, and razor:
while engines, ships, and bridges were made of wrought iror
Steel was still made by the so-called 'blister' process fror
wrought iron, imported from Sweden at £15 a ton: the iron ba:
were packed in stone boxes filled with charcoal, and heated fc
several days to transfer some of the carbon from the coal to th
iron. This produced the gas, carbonic oxide, which puffed up th
molten metal into blisters. Finally, the bars were broken up int
small pieces and melted in crucibles holding up to 60 lb. each.

Bessemer's idea was to convert crude, cheap pig-iron int
malleable iron while it was still in a fluid state, and to keep th
metal in that state long enough for it to be cast into mould
without using any fuel. Instead, he planned to force fine jets c

air through the metal, causing the oxidization of its impurities such as carbon, phosphorus, silicon, sulphur, and so on. The intense heat created by this would raise the temperature of the metal above the melting point of steel (1500° centigrade). For this process he designed a very large retort lined with firebricks, and mounted on an axis so that it could be tipped—a 'Bessemer Converter', as it came to be called.

His first large-scale experiment was a complete success. 'I had now incontrovertible evidence', he wrote in his memoirs, 'that in the space of half an hour molten pig-iron could be raised to a temperature previously unknown without the employment of any combustible matter except that which it contained. At the same time it was deprived of its carbon and silicon, wholly without manipulation. What all this meant, what a perfect revolution it threatened in every iron-making district in the world, was obvious as I gazed on that first glowing ingot.'

Bessemer was right. First-class steel made from pig-iron at £3 a ton, within half an hour instead of six days, and without additional fuel—this was a revolution indeed. From that day in 1856 when he produced the first ingot, steel began to be used in more and more fields of engineering, for railway tracks, ships, bridges, engines, manufacturing machines, vehicles, and a thousand more things—from pocket-knives to skyscrapers. Indeed, the skyline of our modern cities would look very different without steel as a building material; New York's famous waterfront could not have come into existence without it. Steel production in Britain alone rose from less than fifty thousand tons a year to more than twenty million tons within a century, while the price fell by 80 per cent.

Bessemer's system is still widely used, although the open-hearth process invented by Sir William Siemens many years later has gained just as much importance; with this process, cold pig-iron and scrap steel are charged into the furnace hearth and melted down by means of pre-heating (the waste gases emerging from one end of the furnace are made to give up their heat to loosely stacked brickwork, and the direction of the gas flow is reversed at regular intervals). In this way, temperatures of 1,750° centigrade are obtained in the hearth. The impurities are thus made to leave the metal, which they cover in the form of a slag. Where steel is still being made by the converter method, today oxygen is blown into the pig-iron instead of air, which contains a large proportion of nitrogen so that the steel becomes too brittle for some purposes; several converter types have been developed for use with oxygen.

The fact that steel became available as an everyday material in the latter part of the last century had an especially marked effect on the development of transport. Neither the internal-combustion engine nor the steam turbine could have been made into efficient prime movers without it; iron cannot offer the same strength, elasticity, and long working life; nor can it be machined to the same accuracy as steel. Both prime movers began to play an important part in ship propulsion at the beginning of our century.

Charles Parsons's steam turbine, whose development we have already described (see Part I), made a rather dramatic appearance at Spithead during the naval review in honour of Queen Victoria's Diamond Jubilee in 1897. With a small launch, the *Turbinia*, Parsons threaded his way through the formidable array of battleships, cruisers, and destroyers, nearly running down a picket-boat sent out by the commander-in-chief to catch the insolent intruder. The *Turbinia*, 100 feet long, with a displacement of 44 tons, shot ahead with a speed of 35 knots; the fastest destroyers could do no more than 27.

Parsons's pranks at the naval review got him an order from the Admiralty to equip two destroyers with steam turbines, which were obviously superior to even the most efficient reciprocating steam-engines of the day. Both destroyers met with bad luck; one foundered in a fog, the other broke in two in a heavy sea, with much loss of life. Parsons's enemies—he had as many as any inventor of a new machine—blamed the turbine for these accidents; but the general introduction of steam-turbine propulsion in all classes of warships was only a matter of time, and from 1905 no more reciprocating engines were commissioned by the Admiralty.

Meanwhile, the first turbine-driven passenger ship, the small excursion boat *King Edward*, had been launched on the Clyde in 1902; she served for exactly fifty years—a record for any ship. In 1903 the first turbine ship, the small yacht *Emerald*, crossed the Atlantic, and in 1906 the first giant Cunard liners, the *Lusitania* and the *Mauretania*, each with four turbines totalling 70,000 h.p., were launched. A few years later Parsons developed the reduction-gearing so that slow cargo boats, too, could be fitted with turbines.

Oil-fuelled turbine liners have been the standard type of passenger ships since the time before the First World War, and are likely to be replaced by another form of marine propulsion only when nuclear power becomes the rule in sea transport. For smaller ships, the Diesel-engine, which we have described in the foregoing chapter, is more suitable for trawlers, tugs, barges, passenger vessels, and similar craft which do not require more than a few thousand h.p. By comparison, the *Queen Elizabeth*, still the world's biggest liner with a gross tonnage of nearly 84,000 tons, develops 200,000 h.p. with her steam turbines, giving her a speed of about 30 knots.

The gas turbine (see next chapter), which, like the Diesel-engine, can make use of cheaper fuel oils, has been somewhat of a disappointment in marine propulsion; its fuel consumption and operating temperature are the main problems. Since 1953, however, the so-called free-piston engine, in which medium-pressure, medium-temperature gas is expanded in a reversible turbine, has been successfully tried out in a number of ocean-going cargo boats, trawlers, coasters, and small naval craft. Another development is the gas-turbine-electric form of propulsion, working on the lines of the Diesel-electric engine (see the chapter on Railways). In 1952 a British tanker used this type of engine, a 1,200-h.p. gas turbo-alternator, for the first time on a journey from Plymouth to Curaçao; the first merchant ship to use a 'pure' gas turbine was an American freighter, the *John Sergeant*, in 1956.

Probably the greatest revolution in marine transport since the introduction of the steam-engine will be the change-over to nuclear power. After a hesitant start in the late 1950's, this development is now going ahead and offers exciting prospects.

Right from the day when a horrified world heard of the first atom bombs, nuclear energy has been regarded as the coming source of power for marine propulsion. But it took ten years to harness the energy of the split atomic nucleus for that purpose, and even then it was not a liner or a freighter but a military vessel that won the honour of being the first nuclear-powered ship: the United States submarine *Nautilus*. During its sea trials in 1955 it sailed 60,000 miles on a single charge of fuel, using up no more than 8 lb. of uranium. The *Nautilus* and its sister submarine, the *Skate*, accomplished a sensational feat by travelling from the Pacific to the Atlantic right under the Polar icecap at an average depth of 400 feet in 1958.

This unique journey was more than an isolated achievement. It demonstrated that the commercial route from Europe to the Far East could be cut almost by half if submarines instead of surface ships and nuclear power instead of conventional propulsion were used. The idea of the submarine as a tanker, as a cargo boat, and perhaps as a passenger liner began to be discussed.[1] A ship travelling on the surface has to negotiate resistance in two elements, water and atmosphere; winds, waves, and currents influence its progress, and the interaction of these forces makes accurate calculations impossible. Under the sea a vessel is safe from storms, waves, and surface drag; its motion is much smoother, and disturbances such as currents can be calculated in advance (although a good deal of research in this field has still to be done). Given the same engine power, a submarine can move more than twice as fast as a surface ship of the same size; or, to put it in a different way, an 80,000-ton surface liner would need an engine power of 1·1 million h.p. if it were required to travel at 40 knots while a submarine craft of the same displacement would need only 300,000 h.p.

These considerations have been in the engineers' minds for quite some time, but long underwater journeys with conventional engines are uneconomical and difficult because these engines need a lot of air. Atomic reactors, however, do not, and therefore the idea of commercial submarine transport became a practical proposition only with the advent of nuclear energy. But there was another problem which required solution—that of navigation under water. In order to derive the full benefit a submarine liner or cargo ship has to travel at much greater depths than a military submarine, and can therefore not use visual aids to navigation such as a periscope. Only the new system of 'inertial navigation', developed in the 1950's, enables a submarine to proceed at a depth of a few hundred feet. This system, first used for guided missiles and then tried out with astonishing success during the sub-Polar

[1] The first cargo submarine was built by Germany in 1916 to run the allied blockade by carrying raw materials for armaments across the Atlantic; it made several successful journeys before America's entry into the war.

journeys of the two American submarines, works with a combination of gyroscopes which measure the changing speed of the
ship in relation to two directions fixed before the start, and with
an electronic computer processing these data continually and
automatically. This ensures that the submarine keeps to its course
with great accuracy, while the latest radar and ultrasonic instruments help to avoid the danger of collisions with rocks or other
vessels.

Britain's (and possibly the world's) first nuclear-powered
cargo submarine, the 50,000-ton *Moby Dick*, will be ready for
service in the late 1960's. Six hundred feet long and powered by
an atomic reactor generating 75,000 h.p., she will be able to
operate for eighteen months without refuelling. Her job will be
to carry iron ore from Canada to Britain all the year round,
travelling right under the ice-locked Hudson Bay in winter.

By that time nuclear propulsion for surface ships may be fairly
common. The first of them to take to sea was the Soviet ice-
breaker *Lenin* in 1959. With its 50,000 h.p., this is the most
powerful ship of its kind; it operates throughout the cold season
without refuelling (an especially difficult problem with conventionally powered ice-breakers), keeping open the northern sea lanes for
shipping. The *Lenin*, with a displacement of 16,000 tons, is 440
feet long and has a top speed of 18 knots.

In 1961 America commissioned the first nuclear cargo and
passenger ship, the *Savannah*. She can accommodate sixty
passengers and carry 9,500 tons of freight at a speed of over 20
knots. Designed as an experimental ship, her running costs are
much higher than those of a steam-turbine vessel, but the
experience gained during her journeys serves as guidance for the
construction of other nuclear-powered vessels in a number of
countries.

One of the snags about nuclear power at sea is the size and
weight of the machinery, which makes it unsuitable for smaller
ships. The reactors must be housed in strong pressure vessels and
surrounded by heavy biological shields to prevent dangerous
radiation from escaping. The reactor heat is first conveyed to the
heat exchangers, where it raises steam, and this goes into the
turbines. Because of its weight the machinery has to be placed
amidships instead of aft as in most conventionally powered
modern vessels.

The future, however, may bring a development which seems sensible and logical to many shipbuilding engineers: the separation of the power unit from the ship, on the lines of the engine-and-carriages system on the railways. This would mean that the propulsion machinery is confined to a nuclear 'tug' which pulls the engineless passenger or cargo boat to its destination. There are several interesting advantages in this scheme: nuclear tugs could be in continuous operation (which would make the running of the reactor safer as well as more economical); they could pick up another ship for another journey as soon as they have reached their destination, without having to wait for the completion of unloading and loading. Refuelling of the tug reactors would be necessary only every nine or twelve months. The engineless liners or freighters could be built from much lighter materials, possibly from prefabricated units. There is good reason to believe that the nuclear-tug system would bring great economies, and thus price reductions, in marine transport.

Many strange means of transport have appeared in our century, the strangest of them being perhaps the 'hovercraft', developed since 1953 by an English engineer, C. S. Cockerell, and demonstrated for the first time in 1959; in Switzerland, a private inventor, Carl Weiland, had been working simultaneously on similar lines, some American motor-car companies were carrying out experiments, and a Canadian aircraft company was already building the prototype of a kind of 'hover jeep'. However, Mr Cockerell, assisted by a Government corporation which placed a contract for an experimental model with a leading engineering firm, won the race.

The hovercraft, or S.R.N. 1, according to its official name, is something in between a ship and an aircraft. As a shipbuilder, Mr Cockerell was trying to find a solution for the problem of the wave resistance which wastes a good deal of a surface ship's power and limits its speed. His answer was to lift the vessel out of the water by making it ride on a 'cushion' of air, which is somewhat similar to that in a car tyre. A pressure of about 15 lb. per square foot is created over the entire flat bottom of the craft, raising it by $1-1\frac{1}{2}$ feet from the water or ground; this is done by a great number of ring-shaped jets of air. The cushion is also strengthened by a phenomenon well known to pilots and aircraft engineers, the so-called ground effect—it tends to keep an air-craft a foot or so above the ground before it touches down, and it accounts for the fact that the amount of power needed to keep a helicopter just clear of the ground is only something like a quarter of that needed to hold it higher up in the air.

For these reasons the hovercraft is not a true aircraft because its action depends on the surface, water or ground, over which it rides. It cannot fly higher; it is not, for instance, a vertical-lift machine in which powerful engines are required to lift a com-paratively light craft. The prototype of this 'groundless vehicle' —another technical name for it—looked like a large oval saucer with a short funnel in the middle; this was the air-intake of the 450-h.p. engine which created the vertical air jets as well as propelling the vehicle at a speed of 25 to 30 knots by means of two larger horizontal jets at the back. It weighed about 4 tons and had a length of 30 feet, with a control cabin in front of the funnel and aircraft-type rudders.

The tests on the Solent in the summer of 1959, which included a harmless 'crash'—simulating an engine cut-out—caused a sensation, and when the S.R.N. 1 mounted the beach, climbed up the dunes, and 'sat down' on a road the large crowd of onlookers became convinced that they were watching the birth of an entirely new and unique means of transport (for the military observers it was, of course, just another troop-carrying vehicle). Later the hovercraft made its first Channel crossing, riding smoothly over the waves. In the early 1960's the first regular hovercraft services began to operate around the English coast—across the River Dee to North Wales, across the Bristol Channel, to the Isle of Wight —and on the Thames for pleasure trips with the new vehicle.

The implications and possibilities of the invention were obvious right from the start. As the Channel crossing proved, the waves of the open sea do not present any problem; if the craft is made big enough and moves fast enough there will not be any unpleasant vertical movement as in a rolling and pitching ship. One of the first applications could therefore be a fast and cheap passenger and car ferry across the Channel; the craft would start and arrive on dry land. Mr Cockerell did not indulge in pre-dictions, but his Swiss rival, Weiland, spoke of mammoth hover-liners of 350,000 tons weight, crossing the oceans at a height of about 8 feet at 100 m.p.h. or more.

British engineers are not yet prepared to go so far. They visualize the use of the new craft in countries with poor communications such as northern Canada, central Australia, Africa, and India, where large 'hover vans' of perhaps 40 to 100 tons could fly cargo and passengers over deserts and rivers. Tanganyika, for instance, sees in it an answer to the problem of her flooded roads.

American engineers, however, are thinking of air-cushion cars and trains. One suggestion is a hovering motor-bus, 27 feet long and weighing $4\frac{1}{2}$ tons, carrying 16 passengers or $1\frac{1}{2}$ tons of freight, over flat, roadless country. Another idea, worked out by a group of Ford engineers, is the hovering railway, which would travel above its rails, or over a single rail, on an air-cushion about one-thousandth of an inch thick; friction would hardly exist as metal would never touch metal, and speeds of 300 m.p.h. are believed possible. Several 'levapads', as the Ford engineers call the compressed-air cushions, keep the 'levacar' on the rail; propulsion is effected either by propeller or jet. The designers claim that their 'levacar' could become an efficient means of transport between town centres if elevated rails were built for it.

Plenty of ideas how to use the ground-effect vehicle have been put forward or have already been carried out: for instance, as a 'flying fruit-bowl' for carrying bananas from the plantations to the docks in tropical countries with bad roads; or as a 'hover-scooter' for two, delivered from the factory to the customer as a do-it-yourself kit. Sportsmen are promised a 'hoverabout' for six passengers for speeds of 100 knots or more over the water, and the British Royal Army Medical Corps had introduced a 'floating' stretcher, powered by two small petrol engines, which gives casualties a shock-free ride over rough ground.

Perhaps the importance of the new vehicle will lie less in offering additional transport to the people in Western countries, who have already all the facilities they require to get about and exchange their goods, but in opening up the under-developed countries where transport is literally a matter of life and death, and where a vehicle that needs neither roads nor harbours, neither rails nor airfields might be of tremendous value.

# 5

❖❖❖❖❖❖❖❖❖❖❖❖❖❖❖❖

# Flight

'Is THERE anything more foolish and ridiculous than wanting to fly, ride, and swim in the air?' asked a scientific writer at the beginning of the eighteenth century, and in 1782, one year before the Montgolfiers' first ascent in a balloon, the French astronomer, Joseph Lalande, a member of the Academy and celebrated savant, declared in a treatise that there was no means by which a human being could lift himself into the air and float above the earth. He was only repeating what the overwhelming majority of scientists believed to be the ultimate truth in this matter at the time.

Yet there was, visible to everybody, the puzzling evidence of bird flight. How did the birds do it? Why should Man be unable to emulate them? 'If God wanted us to fly He would have given us wings', said the pious. But somewhere deep down in Man's mind was the firm conviction that one day he would fly; in his dreams he soared like a bird, his legends and fairy-tales told him of human and superhuman beings who travelled through the air, and he had the feeling that if he could only discover the secret formula of flight some magic broomstick or carpet would be at his service for ever.

Scientific research in the field of aeronautics, as in many other fields, began in the Renaissance, and here Leonardo da Vinci is again the outstanding personality. Trying to answer the question why and how birds fly, he made many calculations, drew sketches, and built models of flying machines with movable and rigid wings. He invented, at least in theory, the helicopter and the parachute. But his famous notebooks, as we have heard, remained unknown, and were discovered only at the end of the eighteenth century. Da Vinci believed that Man could raise himself into the air with the help of ingenious machines—a principle which came to be known as 'heavier-than-air' flight. Gradually, however, another principle attracted the interest of a few scientific minds, that of 'lighter-than-air' flight.

Francesco de Lana, a Jesuit from Brescia, was one of the first to develop this idea. In a publication written in 1670 he said that

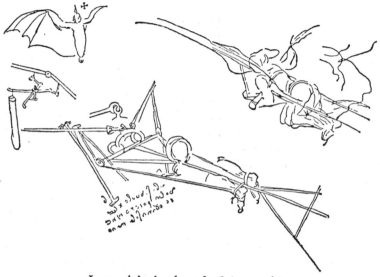

Leonardo's sketches of a flying-machine

four hollow metal spheres from which the air had completely been pumped out should be able to lift a ship and sustain it in the atmosphere because the spheres would be much lighter than the surrounding air. De Lana was, of course, wrong because a complete vacuum would have crumpled up his spheres like tissue-paper if they had consisted of thin metal, or they would have been too heavy if they had been thick. Yet there was something correct in his basic idea, that of making an airship lighter than the surrounding air.

There is good reason to believe that another Jesuit, the Portuguese Bartholomeu Lourenço de Gusmão, was the first flying man. Born at Santos in Brazil, the learned cleric attracted the attention of the court at Lisbon, and in 1709 petitioned the king to grant him a patent for his invention, an 'apparatus for travelling through the air', covering in one day what used to be a journey of 200 hours. It could be used, suggested the Jesuit, to convey news about conquered lands overseas, to send contracts and money from one merchant to another, to supply beleaguered cities and fly out people who want to leave them; even to 'discover the lands around the poles of the earth'.

Gusmão received not only his patent but also a chair at the University of Coimbra as a sinecure. Four months later, in August 1709, he demonstrated his airship at the court of Lisbon. If we are to believe contemporary accounts, it rose a few feet above the ground, but the wind drove it against a balcony; it was damaged, and sank to earth. Still, a man had flown for the first time, watched by thousands of spectators.

Several fanciful descriptions of the event have been given, including one claiming that the airman flew from Lisbon to Vienna via the moon. The accounts of what the airship actually looked like are no less imaginative, but it seems that it had fourteen small balloons of air-tight silk, supplied with hot air from retorts in the gondola. Gusmão must have

Leonardo's sketch of a parachute

known, therefore, that if air is heated it expands and grows thinner and lighter than the surrounding atmosphere.

It was his first and last flight. Powerful forces at the Portuguese court prevented him from building another airship; many people were afraid of any technical innovation, or imagined that they had something to fear from the invention, and there were no end of calumnies and intrigues against the Jesuit. He was even brought before the Inquisition and would have been charged with sorcery had he not managed to escape to Spain, where he died in 1724.

Three-quarters of a century passed after Gusmão's first flight before the hot-air balloon was re-invented—and, more or less by mistake, the hydrogen balloon as well. Joseph and Étienne Montgolfier, owners of a paper factory at Annonay, near Lyons, were obsessed by the idea of flying. They experimented with parachutes—Joseph actually jumped from the factory roof, holding a kind of giant umbrella—and with hydrogen, or 'combustible air', as it was first called by its discoverer, the English chemist Henry Cavendish (1766). The Montgolfiers realized that this gas, many times lighter than air, could be used to

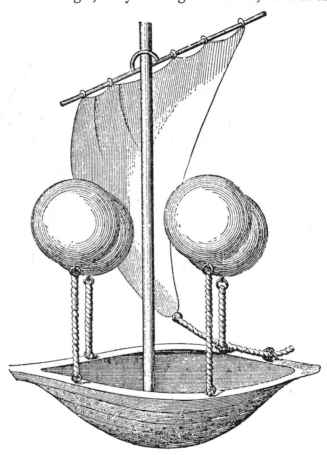

Francesco de Lana's airship

lift an airship; but it kept seeping out of the paper balloons which they used for their experiments, and it was difficult and dangerous to produce.

So they turned to hot-air balloons—under the strange misconception that they were experimenting with 'electric smoke'. Lighting a fire of straw and wool under spheres made of taffeta, open at the bottom, they watched them rise high into the air. In June 1783 they collected the citizens of Annonay and made a large, unmanned balloon rise almost 6,000 feet high; it came down a mile and a quarter away.

The local officials made a report on the event to the Paris government. They spoke of the mysterious 'Montgolfier air', which had the magical property of being able to carry a sack of taffeta up in the sky. What really made the sack fly was, of course,

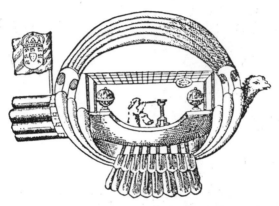

Contemporary 'artist's impression' of Gusmão's airship

that the air in it was heated so that it became lighter, bulk for bulk, than the surrounding atmosphere.

There was much shaking of heads and raising of eyebrows in Paris, and the report from Annonay was sent to the Academy of Science, which set up a committee to study it. But the newspapers and the public in general grew rather annoyed that a little provincial town should have witnessed such a stupendous event: if there were really balloons that could fly, they should fly in Paris. Lavoisier, the great chemist, recommended that the brothers Montgolfier should be consulted, and Professor Taujas de Saint-Fond collected within a few days 10,000 livres to pay for a balloon ascent from Paris. A letter was sent to Annonay inviting Étienne Montgolfier to come to Paris with his brother and demonstrate his balloon. However, the Parisians were too impatient to wait for the Montgolfiers' arrival, and Professor César Alexandre Charles, a popular scientist, offered to build quickly such a

Filling the first hydrogen balloon

balloon with the help of the brothers Robert, well-known makers of scientific instruments . . . though he could only guess what that 'Montgolfier air' was. He came to the conclusion that it could only be hydrogen.

The brothers Robert made a balloon of silk, with a diameter of 10 feet, and coated it with a rubber solution to make it air-tight. Meanwhile, Professor Charles set up a large barrel in the court-yard of their factory, and filled it with iron filings and water; then he poured sulphuric acid in small quantities into the barrel. A tube led from it to the balloon, filling it slowly with the resulting hydrogen gas.

This procedure took four days, and all those taking part in it must have been well aware that they were in constant danger of death. Owing to Professor Charles's precautions, however, no accident happened; at times he had a water hose playing on the balloon when it was getting too hot, to prevent an explosion. On 26 August 1783 the filling was completed; and now came the difficult task of removing the balloon to the Champ de Mars (now the site of the Eiffel Tower), where the ascent was to take place. This was done at night; torchbearers went ahead of the strange procession, which included a number of men holding down the buoyant balloon by means of a wooden frame. 'Some people in the streets were seen to be sinking to their knees, seized with superstitious fear', said a contemporary report.

On the afternoon of 27 August, after a cannon shot had rung out, Professor Charles gave the command to release the balloon from its ropes, and it shot up with great speed, cheered by 300,000 people—half the total population of Paris. At a height of about 3,000 feet it vanished in a storm cloud, emerging soon on the other side and floating on, out of sight. 'An indescribable feeling of amazement and enthusiasm filled the onlookers', said a report. 'The Parisians, always thirsting for sensations and excitement, enjoyed this unique and fantastic scene to the full.'

Against Professor Charles's wishes the balloon had been filled with too much hydrogen by the brothers Robert; as a result it burst as soon as the atmospheric pressure had become too low, and floated down after a journey of fifteen miles and a hundred minutes. The villagers of Gonesse, where it landed, had heard nothing of the great event at Paris, and when they found the strange, evil-smelling object lying in a field they believed it had come straight from hell, where, of course, everything stinks of sulphur. Two monks were summoned as experts and pronounced that Satan himself had sent the monster to Gonesse. The peasants armed themselves with pitchforks, flails, and stones, attacked the balloon, and tied it to the tail of a horse, which had to drag it across the countryside for an hour, until the balloon cover was no more than a torn rag. Some sceptics among the villagers, however, did not believe that the object had come from hell but that it was the moon which had fallen down, and which the people of Gonesse had now destroyed in their superstitious zeal.

No one knew that Étienne Montgolfier had come secretly to Paris and watched the ascent of the rival balloon. He went to the Academy and said that in his opinion hydrogen was too dangerous, and that hot-air balloons only should be permitted to ascend. Now all Paris knew that Professor Charles had, in fact, made his invention by mistake. The experts split into two camps, those who preferred Charles's system, the 'Charlière', and those who believed in the hot-air balloon, the 'Montgolfière'.

Within a fortnight Étienne Montgolfier built one for the first Paris ascent, nearly six times as large as Charles's balloon, using cotton lined with his favourite material, paper. The king expressed his wish to watch the event at Versailles on 19 September. As a step towards the ascent of human beings, Montgolfier decided to send up some animals—a system still in use in our age of space rockets. A sheep, a duck, and a cock were put in a basket suspended from the balloon. Strangely enough, Montgolfier still believed that only fire lit according to his 'secret formula', with straw and wool as fuel, would make the balloon rise.

The royal performance was not a complete success; the 'Montgolfière' stayed in the air only for eight minutes, and got entangled in a tree top. The rope holding the basket snapped, but the three animals were found to be alive. The cock, however, had an injured wing. There were lengthy learned discussions as to the reason for this accident: perhaps air travel was in some mysterious way dangerous to living creatures? Eventually Étienne Montgolfier's simple explanation was accepted—the frightened sheep had stepped on the cock in the confusion when the rope of the basket broke.

Meanwhile, Joseph Montgolfier had joined his brother in Paris, and they began to build the first man-carrying balloon. The brothers were half determined to go up themselves, but an adventurous young nobleman, Pilâtre de Rozier, who had already shown his courage by repeating Franklin's dangerous electric experiments with the kite and key, begged the authorities hard to let him be the first man to fly in a 'Montgolfière'. Permission was granted, and trial ascents in the new balloon, held by ropes, began on 15 October. It had a diameter of 54 feet and a capacity of 55,000 cubic feet; a ring-shaped gallery for the passengers had been built around the bottom of the balloon, and for the first time it was allowed to carry its source of heat up in the air: a wire cage containing the fuel, with some devices for stoking or damping the fire from the gallery.

De Rozier was joined by his friend, the Count d'Arlandes, during the tests, which went well. But the Montgolfiers were worried; if something happened to the aviators on their first free flight the whole idea of air travel would be nipped in the bud. The king himself suggested that two criminals under sentence of death should fly rather than the young noblemen, but de Rozier was furious that a couple of common rogues should deprive him of the glory of being the first man in the sky. He and d'Arlandes beseeched the king to give his consent, which was eventually granted.

The great event took place on 21 November 1783, in the Bois de Boulogne, watched by an enormous crowd. The balloon rose quickly despite a strong wind. In his description of the flight, d'Arlandes recalled how the fascination of seeing the earth from above kept distracting the two men from the job of attending to the fire. After a while they noticed that the fire had begun to eat holes in the envelope, and that the gallery was not too well connected with the balloon itself. 'We must go down', said d'Arlandes. 'But we are still over Paris', replied de Rozier. 'We must try to get beyond the town', said d'Arlandes.

They landed successfully in the open country, five miles from where they had started. People ran up to them and seized de Rozier's jacket, which he had taken off because of the heat from the fire cage, and tore it to pieces—everybody wanted to snatch a souvenir. The flyers and the Montgolfiers were acclaimed as national heroes. But Professor Charles had not been idle; nine days later his new hydrogen balloon was ready for its first manned flight.

From the technical point of view this was even more important than the ascent of the two noblemen, for Charles had improved his vehicle greatly. He had thrown a cord net over the balloon from which the 'car', or gondola, was suspended so that its weight was evenly distributed; he invented a gas escape valve operated by a rip-cord to make the balloon descend; he had the idea of taking up sandbags as ballast, and equipped the 'Charlière' with an anchor for landing, thermometers, and barometers for

* G

measuring the altitude: in short, he created the prototype of the
gas balloon which was to be in use for over a century.

The balloon, 27 feet in diameter and with a lifting capacity of
1,000 lb., was to start on 1 December 1783; tickets had been sold
at exorbitant prices, and again a vast crowd had assembled. But at
the last minute a police officer appeared and declared that the king
had prohibited the ascent because of the dangerous nature of
hydrogen. Professor Charles sent him back with the message that
he would shoot himself there and then if permission were refused,
taking the secret of his invention into the grave. An hour later
the officer returned with the permission, and the ropes of the
'Charlière' were cast off.

This flight turned out to be of the greatest importance in the
history of aviation. Charles had taken with him a passenger.
After drifting at a medium height for two hours, the professor
made a perfect landing—but only to let his passenger get out.
Rising again, the balloon set out on the first high-altitude flight.
Fascinated by the thrill of flying, of escape from gravity, Charles
made the balloon rise higher and higher, to no less than ten
thousand feet. Then he noticed that his ears began to ache, and
decided at last to come down.

A wave of enthusiasm spread through Europe; everybody
talked about ballooning. The 'Charlière' had won the day; soon
the hot-air balloon was eclipsed. Ascents were made in many
countries; aviation developed into a profession, and aeronautics
into a branch of science. Poets sang the praises of this vehicle that
freed Man from the earth, and philosophers indulged in fore-
casting how air travel would revolutionize society. Goethe witnessed an ascent at Cassel, and wrote enviously: 'Air balloons
have been invented. How near I was to this discovery! Somewhat
chagrined at not having made it myself.'

A new landmark in air travel was reached when, in January
1785, a mechanic from Calais, Jean Pierre Blanchard, and an
English scientist, Dr Jeffries, flew across the Channel. They
started from Dover, and at first everything seemed to be going
fine; but half-way across the balloon began to lose height, and
the airmen decided to cut away the car. Clinging to the network
of the balloon, they shed every piece of clothing they could spare,
including their trousers. Landing shivering but safely in France
they were greeted with much amusement by the villagers.

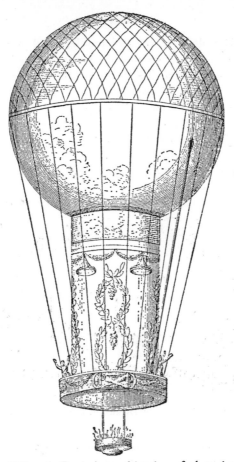

Pilâtre de Rozier's combination of a hot-air
and hydrogen balloon

Accidents began to happen. Balloons crashed, caught fire,
collapsed. Pilâtre de Rozier, the pioneer of human flight, became
its first victim; he built a combined 'Charlière' and 'Montgolfière', and ascended in spite of many warnings. The envelope
split in mid air and de Rozier and his companion were killed.

Like most inventions in modern times, the balloon was eagerly
studied by the military with a view to adding a new dimension to
warfare. As early as 1794 the French Army used a captive balloon
for observation, but the first aerial bombardment did not take
place until 1849, when the French sent 100 pilotless hot-air
balloons with bombs over Venice, then in Austrian hands. For

some time, Napoleon seems to have dreamed of a combined sea
and air invasion of England, but the engineless, rudderless
balloon was too much at the mercy of the winds to be of any use
in this matter. Still, balloons have been employed for military
purposes until recent times. They made their appearance in the
American Civil War, and during the siege of Paris in 1870–1 the
French used sixty-six of them to fly people and carrier-pigeons
out of the city—the pigeons returned later, with micro-photo-
graphed letters for the Parisians. Among those who left the

Barrage balloons over Britain in the Second World War

beleaguered capital by air was Gambetta, who hoped to organize
a new army in the south of France.

In the First World War captive balloons were widely used for
artillery observation and aerial photography; but few observers
survived, as it was child's play to shoot these large, stationary,
inflammable targets down. They were revived in the Second
World War to serve as a balloon barrage against low-flying
enemy aircraft. As a means of transport, however, they still were
much too dangerous and unreliable; once they were up in the air
there was no telling where they might land. Throughout the
nineteenth century they remained showpieces for stunts and
celebrations; in our time ballooning has survived only as a hobby
for intrepid sportsmen, while small balloons are used as radio
sondes in meteorology (see Part III).

Right from the start of the conquest of the air, the idea of the dirigible airship was foremost in the minds of aviators and inventors. Strange and impracticable suggestions were made: balloons should be fitted with sails and oars or hand-propelled screws; or trained birds should be made to pull them through the air, controlled by means of reins from the gondola. Someone even proposed to design the balloon in the shape of a rotating screw. Perhaps the sanest voice in this babel of technical nonsense was that of Jean Baptiste Meusnier, a French officer, who submitted only six months after the first ascent of the 'Montgolfière' a

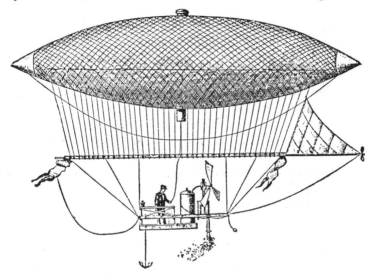

Giffard's steam-driven dirigible airship

treatise on the 'Balance of Aerial Machines' to the Paris Academy. He quite rightly pointed out that a dirigible airship must have an elongated form and several screw-propellers, but that it would need great power to drive it.

This last requirement proved to be the stumbling-block for all airship inventors during the next hundred years. There was only one prime mover, the steam-engine, which was again and again found to be too heavy in relation to its performance. The Frenchman, Henri Giffard, built a comparatively light, fast-rotating steam-engine into his experimental cigar-shaped airship, and made a successful ascent with it in 1852, but he came to the conclusion that only a very large airship, perhaps 250 feet long, would be of any practical use. Before he could persuade his backers to finance such a project he lost his sight, and later committed suicide.

Another steam-driven dirigible was flown by an American, Professor C. E. Ritchell, in Connecticut in 1878, but without much success. Electrical propulsion, by means of batteries, was tried out by two teams of French inventors, the brothers Tissandier in 1883 and the Captains Renard and Krebs two years later; a German technician, Paul Haenlein, used two gas-engines built by Lenoir (see Chapter 3), but they turned out to be unsuitable.

Only the advent of the petrol-engine, with its favourable ratio of weight and performance, made the development of the dirigible airship possible. But the story is not a happy one, and there is no other modern means of transport which cost so many lives during its short life-span—exactly forty years.

Gottlieb Daimler (see Chapter 3) and his chief assistant, Wilhelm Maybach, were asked to build a number of high-powered petrol-engines for airships in the 1890's. One of their first customers was the German engineer Dr Wölfert, who used a 10-h.p. engine in his small airship, which made a number of short flights at the time of the Berlin industrial exhibition of 1896. A year later he started again from the Tempelhof parade ground near Berlin, but the airship exploded in mid air, and Wölfert and his mechanic were killed.

Meanwhile, a timber merchant from Zagreb, David Schwarz, had succeeded in constructing an airship with an aluminium frame with the help of a metallurgist from Westphalia. He had developed his invention against heavy odds—including some unpleasant adventures in Tsarist Russia, where he was accused of being an Austrian spy. When he at last received a telegram that his ship was ready for its first ascent at Tempelhof, the excitement killed him. His widow carried on, and the airship, powered by a 16-h.p. Daimler engine, rose at Tempelhof in November 1897, piloted by a former locksmith. After a few minutes' flight the transmission belts of the propellers slid off, the strong wind seized the airship, and it crashed. The pilot escaped injury.

One of the officers who watched the ascent was a Württemberg Lieutenant-General, Count Ferdinand Zeppelin, who was determined to build a serviceable airship even if the project ruined him.

He sank a considerable sum of his own money in it, but his ideas were so ambitious that much more had to be raised among the population to carry them out. He, too, held that an airship could only fly successfully if it was big enough. His first design, of 1895, was a kind of 'Pullman of the Air', a powered dirigible towing several trailers like a string of sausages. Later he returned to the single-airship concept. He ascended over Lake Constance in July 1900 aboard his first 420-foot-long 'Zeppelin' with the help of a hundred soldiers who held the ropes, and before a crowd of twenty thousand people. This airship broke not only all speed records but also the prejudice of Germany's authorities and military circles against the dirigible airship. The giant 'cigar in the sky' roused boundless enthusiasm among the people wherever it appeared on its journeys.

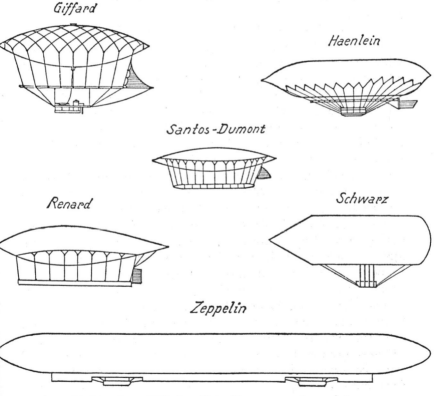

*Giffard*

*Haenlein*

*Santos-Dumont*

*Renard*

*Schwarz*

*Zeppelin*

Airships from Giffard to Zeppelin: a comparison of sizes

Those who doubted the practical value of the airship proved, however, right. Zeppelin built many more airships, one bigger than the other. But already in 1908 his fifth ship suffered a terrible disaster; it caught fire and crashed, with heavy loss of life. Collections and lotteries were started all over Germany to pay for more Zeppelins: they had now grown to be a symbol of national prestige. If airships had been a practical means of transport at all —and there were many experts who believed this—then Count Zeppelin's design was the one to adopt for the purpose. He built his ships with light but solid aluminium frames, hundreds of feet long, and divided the interior up into a number of gas compartments so that any damage and resulting leakage would not affect the whole vessel. His engines, most of them built by Maybach, were placed in several special gondolas outside the large passenger 'car' which, in his later models, formed part of the metal structure.

Before the First World War, in which the Zeppelins were to play their part, a number of other inventors flew their airships with various degrees of success. One of the earliest was an adventurous sportsman, Alberto Santos-Dumont, son of a Brazilian coffee magnate, who built his first airship—an 80-foot-long silk bag filled with hydrogen—in Paris in 1898. It crashed; so did most of the other thirteen airships which he built during the following eleven years, but somehow the intrepid airman survived each time. He became the talk of Europe with his landings, voluntary and involuntary, in the streets of Paris, in hotel courtyards, in the Mediterranean, or on tree tops. Although his small, limp type of airship, which had no metal frame, was dangerous and unreliable, he was the first airman to prove that flight, powered by petrol-engines, was not only possible but a logical development. In 1901 he won the prize offered by the French industrialist Deutsch de la Meurthe to the first man to fly round the Eiffel Tower in an airship.

The Frenchman, Henri Albert Julliot, engineer in a sugar factory, and its owners, the brothers Paul and Pierre Lebaudy, were the creators of the semi-rigid airship, whose gas-bag was stiffened by a metal framework on which it rested. Their first airship, the *Lebaudy I*, made several successful flights in 1902 and 1903, but eventually a high wind destroyed it. The constructors were later commissioned to build the first military airship, *La*

*Patrie*, 200 feet long, with a 70-h.p. engine. After a successful 150-mile journey it was torn from its anchorage by a storm, and disappeared somewhere in the Atlantic.

England had little luck with its airships. The engineer Cody built a non-rigid one, the *Nulli Secundus*, whose envelope was made from an especially light material, goldbeater's skin. On its commissioning journey from Aldershot to London it made an emergency landing in the grounds of the Crystal Palace and was unable to rise again. Its successors, the *Nulli Secundus II*, *Beta*, and *Gamma*, were not much luckier, and the first rigid airship built in Britain, Vickers's R 1—popularly known as the 'Mayfly' —was wrecked in 1911 before it ever flew.

Count Zeppelin, the pioneer of the rigid airship, had a formid-able rival in Germany, Professor August von Parseval, who perfected the non-rigid type, mainly for military purposes and as a sports vehicle. It incorporated two ballonets, or air sacks, counteracting the increased atmospheric pressure at altitude and assisting the rudders in controlling ascent and descent. Parseval's airships, too, suffered many crashes.

By 1910 Zeppelin had developed something like an aerial transport vehicle, although the small number of passengers it could convey was out of all proportion to the enormous size of the whole ship. As soon as the First World War began the Zeppelin works were placed under military command, and all the existing airships converted into bomb carriers. Already during the first year of the war England experienced its first air-raids. But German losses in this form of warfare were enormous. During the four war years, dozens of Zeppelins burst or went up in flames under gunfire; in a mass sortie in 1917, for instance, only four out of eleven Zeppelins returned to their bases. For the people who got their first taste of an air-raid, the droning monsters, slowly gliding in and out of the clouds and searchlights, with shrapnel bursting all around them, were like a vision of apocalyptic horror; but the 480 German airmen who died in their Zeppelins must have gone through terrible sufferings, knowing that there was little chance of survival. It was one of the most inefficient as well as costly and inhuman instruments of war ever employed.

By a stroke of fortune, one Zeppelin was brought down nearly intact over England; it served as a model for the design of some British airships, including the R 34. It was this ship which made the first Atlantic crossing. With a crew of thirty, commanded by Major G. H. Scott, it left East Fortune, Scotland, in July 1919, and landed 108 hours later on Long Island. A week later, this airship with its five engines, developing 1,250 h.p., completed its return trip to Pulham, Norfolk.

Count Zeppelin died in 1917, but his disciple and successor, Dr Hugo Eckener, continued to build larger and larger airships. Altogether 116 Zeppelins were completed between 1900 and 1926. Dr Eckener piloted the last of these giants of the air across the oceans, into the Arctic, and around the world. It seemed that at last Count Zeppelin's wish was coming true: that his airships should become a symbol of peaceful technical progress, of understanding and friendship among the nations.

But exactly twenty years after his death the most impressive of all Zeppelins, the 800-foot-long *Hindenburg*, which could travel at up to 180 m.p.h., suffered a disaster which meant, to all intents and purposes, also the end of the airship as a means of transport. Despite Dr Eckener's warnings the ship, with its gas capacity of 6·7 million cubic feet, had been filled with the highly inflammable hydrogen instead of the safe helium, because Hitler's Germany needed its meagre reserves of foreign currency to buy raw materials for its rearmament, and was too stingy to pay dollars for helium gas. In May 1937 the airship caught fire as it was landing at Lakehurst, and thirty-three people lost their lives.

America, too, had serious losses; her *Shenandoah*, a former Zeppelin handed over by Germany under the Versailles Treaty, and the United States Navy airship *Akron* both crashed, with great loss of life. Britain's worst airship disaster was that of the R 101 in 1930; it had started on an official flight to India but came down in France and was destroyed by fire. Forty-eight people were burnt to death, including the Secretary of State for India, an air marshal, and the designer. In this case, too, hydrogen had been used instead of helium.

These terrible accidents marked the end of the airship. But, meanwhile, another means of aerial transport had developed so well that lighter-than-air vehicles, slow and dangerous as they were, did no longer justify their existence. The heavier-than-air machine, the aeroplane, had come to stay.

From the very earliest times Man has watched the birds and

tried to imitate them. Their swooping and soaring, taking off and alighting puzzled him. How do they do it? Their bodies are solid, heavy objects, just like our own. Most insects, too, can fly; in fact, more than half of the nearly 500,000 species of creatures on our planet have wings. In the old myths and legends, gods and angels are described as superhuman beings endowed with the gift of flight; or at least they use celestial vehicles on their aerial travels —chariots drawn by winged horses or dragons, clouds, magic carpets. Occasionally humans are allowed to share this great adventure: Etana, a Babylonian queen, travels on the back of an eagle; Alexander the Great makes a flock of hungry birds convey him through the air by holding a horse's liver on a spear in front of their beaks (like a carrot in front of a donkey's nose); Sindbad the Sailor, in the *Arabian Nights*, travels by means of the giant bird roc. In Germanic mythology, Wieland the Smith makes a gown of feathers and flies with it to spite his enemies, and the most famous of all ancient sagas of flight tells of the Greek inventor, Daedalus, who made for himself and his son, Icarus, pairs of wings with which they flew from Crete. Daedalus reached the mainland, but Icarus flew too near the sun, the wax with which his wings were fastened melted, and he fell into the sea.

Strangely enough, while indulging in his dreams and fantasies Man never realized that he was holding the key to the problem of mechanical flight in his hands: the kite. Traditionally, the invention of this plaything is ascribed to one Archytas of Tarentum in the fourth century B.C., but the Chinese, the Koreans, and other Far Eastern nations have known it for much longer. The origin of kite-flying may have been religious, and it still plays a ritual part among the Maoris. Even when scientists such as Benjamin Franklin (see Part I) used kites in their research work it was not really understood that these fragile toys made of silk or paper could teach them the secret of heavier-than-air flight.

Yet every little boy flying his kite knows that he can get it off the ground by pulling it by its cord against the wind so that the pressure of the rushing air gives it a lift; he also knows that a kite with a tail will keep a better balance in the air than a kite without one. In fact, there are four forces in action when an aeroplane flies: the lift, or upward force of the moving air acting on the lower surface of the aircraft wing; the drag, or backward pull, caused by the resistance of the air; the weight, due to gravity, which pulls the aircraft down; and the thrust, which pulls it forward: in the kite this is the function of the cord, in an aeroplane it is done by the propeller, the jet or rocket engine. It is clear that the thrust must be stronger than the drag, and the lift greater than the weight, to allow the aircraft to move forward.

If the innumerable inventors who tried to tackle the problem in past centuries had studied the kite they would have understood the action of at least some of these forces. Yet nearly all of them, including Leonardo da Vinci (who, however, made a valuable

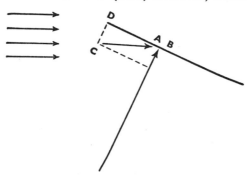

How a kite stays in the air: diagram of wind
force and string pull

contribution to the theory of the helicopter, which we shall describe later), believed that the solution lay in 'flapping-wings' flight, in imitating the birds. But Man's muscles—and these were the only 'engine' available in those days—are just not strong enough for the job of flapping artificial wings capable of lifting his heavy body into the air; besides, the birds have an intricate mechanism for altering the angle at which their wings attack the air, a mechanism which even today would be extremely difficult to construct artificially. Yet flap-wing machines are still being built and tried out by inventors although the principal development of aeronautics has been in a different direction.

The first man to break away from the flap-wing idea was an English scientist, Sir George Cayley, who may be regarded as the true father of the modern aeroplane. His contemporaries, however, called him 'crazy as a tight-rope walker'.

In 1799, at the age of 26, Cayley engraved on a small silver disc the diagram of forces involved in heavier-than-air flight, and on the reverse side the sketch of a glider aircraft. This disc, now at the Science Museum in South Kensington, London, was the result of Cayley's basic research work on aerodynamics, and the whole development of mechanical flight stems from his brilliant efforts. He followed his theoretical work up with the construction of a model glider, which has been called the first proper aeroplane, in 1804. Later he built and flew the first man-carrying glider, and in 1809 he wrote a paper in which he clearly defined the principles of heavier-than-air flight. The basic design, he said, must be that of a bird with rigid wings; then he continued: 'A new era of society will commence from the moment of realization [of mechanical flight]. I feel perfectly confident that it will be possible to transport persons and goods more securely by air than by water, with a velocity from 20 to 100 miles an hour. It is only necessary to develop a suitable engine. Boulton-Watt's steam-engine might be a possible source of power, but as lightness is of so much value, there is the probability of using the expansion of the air by sudden combustion of inflammable powders or fluids.'

Cayley's prophecy proved to be completely correct—but nearly a hundred years passed before the internal combustion engine provided the source of power which he had foreseen.

Due to Cayley's pioneer work, the idea of the fixed-wing aircraft took root in England and France. But as there was no other prime mover besides the steam-engine, the 'winged locomotives' which were built from 1840 onwards never had a great chance of becoming airborne. Otherwise some of these aeroplanes—such as those made by William Samuel Henson and John Stringfellow in Britain—showed very promising designs. In France, Alphonse Pénaud produced a model incorporating such advanced notions as the control column and a glass dome for the pilot; it would, no doubt, have become the prototype of the first practical aeroplane if Pénaud had lived long enough to see the introduction of the petrol-engine. But he killed himself, his health and spirits undermined, at the age of 30, only a few years before Daimler and Benz built their first motor-cars.

After him, it was again an Englishman who came to the forefront of aeronautic research. Percy Sinclair Pilcher, a lecturer at Glasgow University, began by designing a steam-propelled aircraft, then discarded the idea and experimented with gliders. He

Chanute's glider (1890)

Langley's petrol-driven aeroplane, which crashed on its first flight (1890)

was already building a 4-h.p. petrol-engine when he was fatally
injured as his glider crashed near Standford Park. Another
pioneer who tried out steam propulsion was Sir Hiram Maxim,
the Anglo-American inventor of the machine-gun. He built two
enormous steam-engines of 150 h.p. each into an aeroplane which
he set on rails at the Vickers works at Erith; it crashed after
leaving the rails, and the experiments were abandoned.

A Frenchman, Octave Chanute, tried out a number of gliders,
from monoplanes to six-wingers, on Lake Michigan, and an
American university professor, Samuel Pierpont Langley, built a
petrol-driven single-seater for the American Army; it was to be

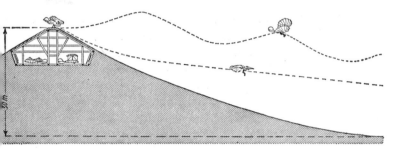

Diagram of Lilienthal's gliding experiments

catapulted from a ship, but at the first test flight it fell into the
Potomac, and the pilot had to be rescued by fishermen.

Clément Ader, a French engineer, succeeded in building a very
light steam-engine, of 65 lb. weight and 30 h.p. performance; the
French war ministry backed his experiments. His third machine
actually flew for 300 yards, but a gust of wind sent it crashing to
earth, and the authorities refused to spend any more money on
his invention.

All these attempts took place in the 1890's. So did the famous
gliding experiments of Otto Lilienthal, a most gifted German
engineer, who built a number of sailplanes with the help of his
brother, Gustav. Otto Lilienthal was already 43 when he began
his strenuous and dangerous trials. After jumping from a spring-
board in the garden of his house in Berlin, he bought a small
piece of land in the neighbourhood of the town, with a 50-foot
hillock. He strapped himself to his gliders made of plywood and
canvas, and made the rising air-current carry him gently down

from the hilltop. Encouraged by his successful flights he continued his experiments with larger gliders and from higher hills, running against the wind until it began to carry him.

In the course of five years he made over two thousand flights, the last series from a 100-foot hill, sailing through the air for distances up to 1,000 feet; his brother timed the flights with a stop-watch. Once he even succeeded in returning to his starting point.

One morning in August 1896, however, a sudden gust caught his machine; it crashed and he was fatally injured. 'We have to make sacrifices', were his last words as he lay dying.

Far from deterring the other pioneers of heavier-than-air flight, Otto Lilienthal's tragic death spurred them to greater efforts. This was particularly true of the brothers Orville and Wilbur Wright, the sons of an American cleric, who ran a bicycle shop in Dayton, Ohio. They had no desire to risk their lives by trying out flimsy contraptions like Lilienthal's gliders, but began by systematically collecting all the available data from flying-machine tests in Europe and America, and studying them carefully to see what mistakes had been made. Lilienthal, for instance, had failed to provide lateral stability, and that had cost him his life. They decided to incorporate in their aircraft design a means of warping the wings with wires which could be pulled by the pilot.

It took them years of studying and experimenting before they felt that the time to build a full-sized, man-carrying machine had come. They tested many small models and made several large gliders to try out all the details of their design; they even built a wind-tunnel to test wing shapes. Eventually they made their own petrol-engine at the back of their bicycle shop. It weighed 152 lb. and developed 12 h.p., which was even more than they had expected. They calculated the most efficient design of the propeller,

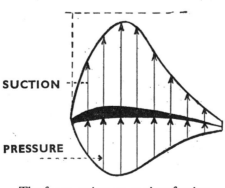

SUCTION

PRESSURE

The forces acting on an aircraft wing

which was the trickiest job of all. The aeroplane itself was designed as a biplane with a wing span of 40 feet, an 'elevator' rudder in front, and a tail rudder with two movable vanes; the two wings were 6 feet apart, and the engine was placed right of the centre on the lower wing, while the pilot had to lie flat on his stomach to the left of the centre to keep the machine in balance. The two propellers were arranged behind the wings so that they should 'push' the aircraft forward like ship's screws.

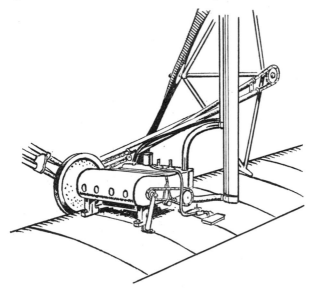

The Wright brothers' 4-cylinder aero-engine (1903)

In the late autumn of 1903 this machine was at last ready for its first flight on the beach of Kitty Hawk, North Carolina, where the Wright brothers had carried out their many glider tests in previous years. The first attempt was a failure, and the aeroplane suffered some damage. After this had been repaired, the machine was pulled out of its shed and set on the start-rail on the morning of 17 December 1903. There was a cold wind of 24–27 m.p.h. A few local people, four men and a boy, assembled to watch the great event.

Ten years later Orville Wright wrote: 'With all the knowledge and skill acquired in thousands of flights in the last ten years, I would hardly think today of making my first flight on a strange

machine in a 27-mile wind, even if I knew that the machine had
already been flown and was safe. After these years of experience,
I look with amazement upon our audacity in attempting flights
with a new and untried machine under such circumstances. Yet
faith in our calculations and the design of our first machine, based
upon our tables of air pressures, obtained by months of careful
laboratory work, and confidence in our system of control
developed by three years of actual experiences in balancing
gliders in the air, had convinced us that the machine was capable
of lifting and maintaining itself in the air, and that, with a little
practice, it could be safely flown.'

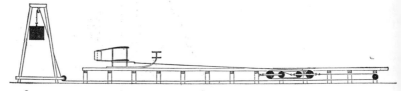

Start rail used by the Wright brothers during their experiments

On that historic morning, Orville climbed into the machine,
lay on his stomach, and gripped the controls. The engine was
started and made to run a few minutes to warm up. Then Orville
released the wire which held the machine to its starting-rail, and
it shot forward into the wind. Wilbur ran along with it for a few
seconds, holding the wing to keep it on the rail. After gliding for
forty feet along the rail, the aircraft lifted. It was an uneven flight;
the wind pressed it now up, now down. One hundred and twenty
feet from the point at which it had risen into the air it landed, after
a flight of twelve seconds.

'Nevertheless', wrote Orville Wright, 'it was the first flight in
the history of the world in which a machine carrying a man had
raised itself by its own power into the air in full flight, had sailed
forward without reduction of speed, and had finally landed at a
point as high as that from which it started.'

Probably the five spectators did not realize what revolutionary
event they had witnessed. They were treated to a few more
flights; the last of them, with Wilbur at the controls, lasted nearly
one minute, and covered a distance of over 850 feet. After the
landing, however, the keen December wind caught hold of the
machine and damaged it seriously.

Oddly enough, the great news of these successful trials did not get farther than to a local newspaper, which published a rather garbled version, too fanciful to be believed. Only a month later did the *New York Herald* publish a short account under the heading 'The Machine That Flies', but it was not much more accurate than the report in the local paper.

The Wright brothers were not yet interested in publicity. Their main concern was now the construction of a new machine, larger and sturdier. Only after its completion did they invite the Press to a demonstration. Unfortunately there was some engine trouble and the flight had to be cancelled. Now the newspapermen left the Wright brothers in peace, and they went on testing their machines.

Three years went by before the leading popular magazine, the *Scientific American*, published the true story of their achievement. 'In all the history of invention', wrote the magazine, 'there is probably no parallel to the unostentatious manner in which the Wright brothers of Dayton, Ohio, ushered into the world their epoch-making invention of the first successful aeroplane.'

In 1908 they decided to show their latest machine in France. After the first flight at Le Mans, Wilbur, the pilot, was mobbed by enthusiastic spectators who all wanted to kiss him. Meanwhile, Orville demonstrated another machine to United States government officials and journalists at Fort Myer, near Washington. The American newspapermen and the crowd 'went crazy' when the machine left the ground, as Theodore Roosevelt Junior put it. Hardened reporters were seen to weep with excitement. The Wright brothers were proclaimed national heroes.

Now, within an incredibly short time, aeroplanes were built and flown in almost every country in the world, with France in the forefront. In 1909 there was already a 'School of Aeronautics' in Paris, frequented by designers, constructors, and pilots of aircraft. The curriculum, which was somewhat vague, did not include any flights, because most machines were still single-seaters and there were no facilities to take students up in the air. Flying was then first and foremost a sport, and few people believed that it would ever become a means of passenger transport.

The early pioneers, like the Wright brothers piloting their own machines, improved the aeroplane quickly and considerably. Santos-Dumont gave up airships in favour of aeroplanes; his

Igor Sikorsky's pre

first monoplane, of a box-type design and made of bamboo and silk, flew with great success, and in 1909 he set up a speed record of 60 m.p.h. The Anglo-French sportsman Henry Farman, the Frenchmen Voisin and Ferber, Blériot and Delagrange built and tested one machine after another, spending great sums of money and risking their lives in aircraft which, as a rule, ended in a heap of tangled metal, wood, and canvas. Perhaps the most surprising thing is that there were few fatal accidents.

Louis Blériot, a lamp manufacturer, invented the aileron—a small, subsidiary plane hinged to the wing edge to achieve lateral stability, superseding the Wrights' system of 'warping'. He survived almost as many accidents as Santos-Dumont. In one of them his machine burst into flames in mid air, and he was pulled out of the wreckage with a severely burnt foot. But this did not stop him from attempting to win the *Daily Mail* prize of £1,000 for the first flight across the English Channel.

He succeeded on 25 July 1909, with his *Blériot XI*, a monoplane with a large tailplane with the elevator and vertical rudder, a wing span of 25 feet 6 inches, and a 25-h.p. Anzani engine slung under the wing and driving a two-bladed tractor airscrew. It took him half an hour to cover the 24 miles from Calais to Dover. 'England has ceased to be an island', warned the London newspapers, and the military authorities on both sides of the Channel began to study seriously the possibility of using aeroplanes in warfare.

Blériot's competitor in this venture was Hubert Latham, a young Anglo-French engineer; his machine fell into the Channel, and he had to give up. But a few months later he set up an altitude record of 3,300 feet. This was broken within less than a

ngined airliner (400 h.p.)

year by a French airman, Legagneux, who reached a height of
10,230 feet.

One of the few aircraft designers who recognized the need for
large, powerful passenger aircraft even in those early days was a
23-year-old Russian, Igor Sikorsky, who persuaded a reluctant
industrialist at St Petersburg to let him create such a prototype in
1912–13. It was the largest machine ever built until that time: the
first aircraft with four engines, each of 100 h.p., with a span of 92
feet and a total weight of 9,000 lb., a closed cockpit for the pilot
and co-pilot with double controls, a luxuriously decorated room
for sixteen passengers, and even a toilet. Two of these machines
were successfully flown up to the outbreak of the First World
War, and as a result Sikorsky was commissioned to build a whole
fleet of four-engined bombers based on this design. They were
the only machines of that size taking part in the First World War.

In Western countries, too, aircraft development during the war,
when government money and resources became readily available,
was rapid and helped to turn the flimsy sports machine into a more
reliable means of transport. The beginnings of the military aeroplane, however, were modest; at first its use was restricted to
reconnaissance work. Then a few commanding officers had the
idea of arming their airmen with revolvers to shoot at enemy
machines until the designers incorporated machine-guns in the
cockpit. The first type with a built-in machine-gun in the nose
was a British Vickers fighter.

Bombing began with airmen throwing hand-grenades at enemy
aircraft, and with home-made bombs—empty meat tins filled
with powder and shrapnel, exploded by fuses. For some time,
steel arrows were dropped on enemy troops; if they hit a man

they went through him from head to toe. But soon there were bigger bombs and bigger bombers available. The biplane was the favourite design. Between 1914 and 1918 speeds rose from 70–80 m.p.h. to over 150 m.p.h., and air-cooled engines developed from 4 lb. weight per h.p. to 1·9 lb. per h.p. while the flying 'ceiling' increased from an average 7,000 to 30,000 feet. The British Royal Flying Corps, later to become the Royal Air Force, began its activities in 1914 with 179 machines and the Royal Naval Air Service with 93; at the end of the war the R.A.F. had over 22,000 aircraft.

Passenger and postal air services began soon after the war; even in 1920 they flew a total of nearly three million miles. The first all-metal planes, which owed their designs to a better understanding of aerodynamics, were built by the German engineer Professor Hugo Junkers and the Dutch designer Anton Fokker, while Igor Sikorsky, who had emigrated to America, worked on the same lines in 1924. A few years later, 200-m.p.h. airliners made their appearance in America. Flying soon became big business and a serious rival to transport by boat and rail.

After a few unsuccessful attempts, the Atlantic was first crossed in an aeroplane by two Britons, Capt. John Alcock and Lt Arthur Whitten-Brown, in a Vickers machine in June 1919 from Newfoundland to Ireland, a distance of 1,880 miles, in 16 hours and 12 minutes. No other west–east flights across the Atlantic were made until May 1927, when Capt. Charles Lindbergh made his famous solo flight in his 220-m.p.h. monoplane, *Spirit of St Louis*, from Long Island to Le Bourget in a little over 33 hours; the distance was 3,000 miles. A year later two Germans, Hauptmann Köhl and Baron Hünefeld, and a Briton, Fitzmaurice, made the first successful east–west crossing. Another eleven years passed before an American airliner, a flying-boat, carried the first transatlantic passengers from Baltimore to Europe via the Azores; but regular commercial traffic between Europe and America began only after the end of the Second World War.

Basically, flying with heavier-than-air machines remained the same during the first half of our century. True, there were immense improvements; aircraft dimensions increased ten times, carrying capacity a hundred times as compared with the first machines; engine power, speed, passenger comfort developed to an extent undreamt-of by the early pioneers of flight. But in principle, the airliner of 1950 had the same kind of propulsion, and moved through the air in the same way, as the Wright brothers' first machine.

Only then, largely due to war-time developments, there emerged two entirely new systems of motive power and flight: jet propulsion and the vertical-lift aircraft. Both inventions, however, go back a long way in technical history.

Hero's little steam turbine (see Part I) was, in fact, a jet engine. Steam, air, or some other gas being squirted out from a nozzle propels the object from which it emerges. It is a common error to believe that the jet propels that object, such as an aircraft, by pushing against the surrounding air. In fact, it works like the recoil of a gun according to Newton's famous third law of motion: that to every action there is an equal and opposite reaction. A French engineer, René Lorin, stated the basic principles of jet propulsion in 1913, and took out patents for it; rocket propulsion, in many ways similar, is of course much older, including the idea of using it for aircraft: a Chinese, Wan Hoo, is said to have joined two large kites together, and propelled them with forty-seven rockets, around 1500 (he lost his life in this experiment); Sir William Congreve invented a rocket gun which was used in several battles of the Napoleonic wars; Professor Tsiolkovsky in Russia, Hermann Oberth in Germany, and Robert H. Goddard in America published extensive studies of rocket propulsion in the first quarter of this century. But the rocket—to which we shall return later in this chapter—has certain characteristics which make it suitable for other tasks than the jet engine; both, however, are based on the reaction principle.

Thus the principle of jet propulsion was well known a long time before it became a reality, but technological development was lagging behind. First of all, jet propulsion cannot be effective unless very high speeds are reached, and it was not until aircraft capable of withstanding speeds of over 400 m.p.h. had been designed that it acquired practical interest. Secondly, it works at very high temperatures, and it was first necessary to develop alloys which could stand great heat.

A young English airman by the name of Frank Whittle, however, was convinced that the time had come to have another look at the problem. He was a 20-year-old flight cadet in the R.A.F.

College at Cranwell in 1927 when he chose as the subject of his
fourth-term thesis, 'Future Developments in Aircraft Design'.
In this he wrote about speeds of 500 m.p.h., at a time when the
top speed of R.A.F. fighters was less than 200 m.p.h.; of air
travel at very great heights; and of the necessity to supplant the
conventional piston engine by some other power plant such as a
rocket engine or a gas turbine driving propellers. The idea of
using a gas turbine for jet propulsion did not occur to him then,
but within a few months he was already working out such an
engine. Instead of individual explosions driving pistons in
cylinders, there would be a continuous burning of cheap fuel oil
in a combustion chamber; the expanding gases would press
against the blades of a turbine and make it turn. Then the hot,
compressed gases would rush out of a jet pipe at the rear at many
times hurricane speed, forcing the aircraft forward according to
Newton's third law of motion. The turbine had the job of
operating a compressor which would draw in the air from the
front of the aircraft, and compress it before it would go into the
combustion chamber.

The patent was filed in 1930, published in 1932, and in 1934 it
lapsed—Whittle had no money to invest in an invention which
no one seemed to want, neither the Air Ministry nor private
firms. Two more years passed before Whittle found support;
capital for a development company was dug up in the City of
London, and eventually the Air Ministry agreed reluctantly to
grant him leave so that he could carry out his plans. But only
when the clouds of war gathered in 1939 did it give him a contract
for a prototype jet engine.

It was built in secrecy by a group of only sixteen men, most of
them in their twenties. Meanwhile, an experimental aircraft—the
first to be powered by the new engine—was being built at the
Gloster works, and in May 1941, the E 28, as it was called by its
code name, was taken up for the first time. It was the most
uneventful test flight imaginable: everything went according to
plan, and aircraft as well as engine worked with the utmost
perfection. 'Frank, it flies!' cried someone enthusiastically, and
slapped Whittle on the back. 'Well', replied the inventor, who
could not bring himself to feel the drama of the moment, 'that
was what it was designed to do, wasn't it?'

The secret of the new plane was so well kept that even those

R.A.F. officers who saw it fly had no idea what it was all about. One of them, puzzled, talked over his tea in the canteen about a strange machine 'going like a bat out of hell', and added, 'My God, chaps, I must be going round the bend—it hadn't got a propeller!'

In Germany, developments had taken a similar course. Here the outstanding figure in jet-engine research was Hans von Ohain, a young engineer, who persuaded the Heinkel aircraft works to build a demonstration model from his designs in 1936. Three years later, shortly before the outbreak of the war, a Heinkel machine—the world's first jet aircraft—started for a test flight. The performance, however, does not seem to have come up to expectations because there was no further development of this prototype. The other big aircraft works took up research, which was hampered by a shortage of skilled personnel and heat-resisting raw materials. However, a number of Me 262 twin-engined jet fighters, built by Messerschmitt, went into service in the autumn of 1944, while Whittle's Gloster machines came too late to play any part over the battlefields. Germany's defeat cut short the further development of her jet aircraft, and Whittle's engine had the whole world to itself.

Within a few years after the end of the war, the jet engine began to conquer every field of aviation, military and civil, in all countries. Air speeds went up by leaps and bounds. In 1947 an American jet plane, the Bell XS-1, broke through the 'sound-barrier', which many experts had believed to be impenetrable. The speed of sound near the ground at freezing-point is 760 m.p.h. If a body, such as an aircraft, travels at a speed much lower than this, the air ahead of its path is 'warned' by pressure waves that it is coming; the air—which is an elastic matter—then flows round the aircraft with relatively gentle changes in pressure, and its density does not alter very much in the process. But when the speed of the aircraft approaches that of sound there are no more 'warning' waves travelling ahead, but a sudden change of air density as it is compressed by the aircraft. This results in a drastic increase in drag and decrease in lift; a 'stationary compression wave', or shock wave, forms on the aircraft body.

Breaking through the 'sound-barrier', however, proved not only possible but simpler than expected, though only for suitably designed jet aircraft; even if a propeller-driven plane could

H

achieve such a speed it would be wrecked in the process. The fast airliners of today are, therefore, jet-propelled; the first of them was the British 'Comet', which flew in 1950, but the original type had to be withdrawn after some accidents, which were never fully explained. Since 1958 British, American, French, and Russian jet airliners have taken over from the piston-engined machines on most long-distance routes.

What is the speed limit of the jet liner? Although the sound-barrier has been pierced, the 'heat-barrier' is still there, and it may restrict the speed of an aircraft in the atmosphere to Mach 3, which is about 2,000 m.p.h. At this speed the 'skin' temperature of an aircraft, produced by friction with the air, is in the region of 280° centigrade (water boils at 100° centigrade). Steel and titanium structures can be made to withstand such temperatures, and so we may see, some time between 1970 and 1980, the first Mach 3 jet airliner flying from London to Los Angeles in $3\frac{1}{2}$ hours.

But the jet engine has also been adapted to power propeller-driven aircraft. In the so-called turbo-jet system, which we have described above, the turbine is so designed that it extracts from the expanding gases no more power than is necessary to drive the compressor; very considerable energy, therefore, remains in the exhaust gases which are expelled at high speed from the jet nozzle, and due to the momentum of these gases a corresponding forward thrust makes the aircraft move. The higher the speed, the more effective is the turbo-jet system. At more moderate speeds, say up to 400–450 m.p.h., the propeller is a better means of propulsion, and this is where the 'turbo-prop' system has been found extremely efficient.

Here the turbine extracts the entire power of the expanding gases and is made to turn a conventional propeller (the turbine speed of 12,000–15,000 r.p.m. is brought down to about 1,000 r.p.m. at the propeller by way of reduction gearing). In this field, too, Britain was the pioneer country; already in the 1940's turbo-prop aircraft were flying on the commercial routes, and they are still extremely efficient and economical on short and medium-length flights and as freighter planes. We shall deal later with the gas turbine in helicopter design.

Apart from propelling aircraft, the gas turbine has found a number of useful applications as a new prime mover in other fields. We have already mentioned the gas-turbine-driven motor-car and ship. In 1949 a gas-turbine locomotive made its trial run in England. The advantages of the gas turbine are that it can use all kinds of fuel such as low-grade oil (paraffin) and even coal dust, and that it needs less space than the steam turbine (which requires a boiler for raising steam). In our energy-hungry age it will have a very useful part to play also as a stationary engine; the first gas-turbine power station was started up—by telephone from a distance of 100 miles—on Dartmoor in 1959.

Somewhere between the jet engine and the rocket lies the ram-jet. It achieves propulsion by ejecting a powerful stream of gas from the rear jet pipe like the turbo-jet; but it is much simpler in construction because it has no compressor or other moving parts —it is, in fact, just a combustion chamber (and has been nick-named 'flying stovepipe' for that reason). In order to compress the air for combustion, the ram-jet relies on its own very rapid forward movement. This means that it cannot start from speed zero as the other propulsion systems can but needs either an auxiliary engine or a carrier aircraft to accelerate it to such a speed (over 600 m.p.h.) that the compression of the scooped-up air is sufficient.

Apart from this disadvantage it is difficult to control, and its operation is affected by the shock waves which tend to form at the air intake. But it has the advantages of having no moving or delicate parts, of being able to operate at great altitudes, and of requiring less fuel than any other aircraft engine with a com-parable performance. There may be some practical applications of the ram-jet for special types of aircraft; one of them which uses it is the 'coleopter', constructed by an Austrian designer, Helmut von Zborowski, for the French aircraft research authority, and tried out first in 1959. This machine has a circular wing around its body; it starts and lands almost vertically but goes into a horizontal position at cruising altitude. Passengers and crew have swivel seats so that they remain in an upright position throughout the flight.

American aircraft designers believe that it would be com-mercially possible to build a 2,000-m.p.h. ram-jet liner using conventional jet engines to take off, climb to altitude, and pick up speed; then the pilot would shut off the turbo-jets and turn on the ram-jets. At a cruising height of 60,000 feet the ram-jet produces 3–4 times more thrust per pound of engine weight than the turbo-jet, which would save about 20 per cent in fuel costs. Thus the extra expense of having two kinds of propulsion engines may be justified.

Vertical take-off aircraft are, as a technical idea, at least as old as bird-shaped aircraft. Helicopter toys (*helix* and *pteron* are

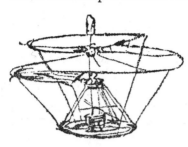

Greek words meaning screw and wing) were known to the ancient Chinese. The 'Chinese top', a little propeller on a rod with a screw thread, which would start turning quickly when pushed up and then shoot into the air, was a popular toy in nineteenth-century European nurseries. Around 1500 Leonardo da Vinci examined its possibilities; in his notebooks he

Leonardo's sketch of a helicopter

had drawings of helicopters based on the Archimedean screw, and he may have built small-scale models. 'If this instrument fitted with a helix is well constructed', he wrote, 'and the helix is turned with great speed, it should be able to screw itself up in the air and rise high.' But at Leonardo's time there was no machine that could have provided the motive power for turning the screw.

Sir George Cayley, too, experimented with the helicopter about 1800; he built a small, hand-operated model which 'rose as high as 90 feet in the air', according to his notes.

Throughout the nineteenth century inventors tried to make helicopter aircraft fly: two Frenchmen, who attempted to operate it by hand-cranks; an Italian, who is said to have succeeded in making his steam-driven machine rise 40 feet into the air; an American, who wanted to use it as a bomber in the Civil War; another Frenchman, who fitted his model with an electric motor; a German, an Austrian, and even the great Edison, who thought of supplying the driving power from gun-cotton explosions.

The twentieth century began with the demonstration by a Berlin inventor, Hermann Ganswindt, of a helicopter powered by two men working bicycle-type pedals. It rose slightly from the Tempelhof Airfield and fell back to earth. In 1907, the French inventor Cornu in Lille actually lifted himself and a passenger

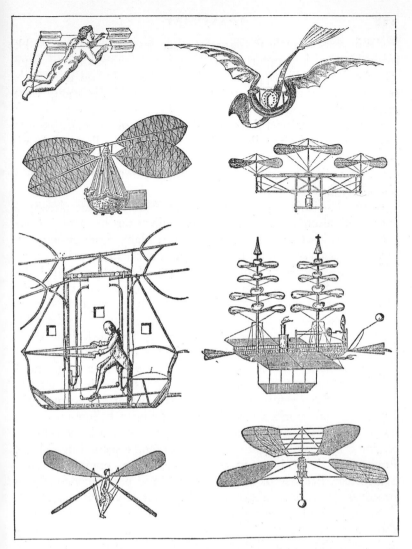

Some eighteenth- and nineteenth-century helicopter ideas

five feet into the air, where they remained for over a minute, in a two-rotor helicopter powered by a 24-h.p. petrol motor, the whole structure of metal girders weighing 450 lb. In the same year another French engineer, Louis Bréguet, built a four-rotor helicopter, but it did not fulfil his expectations and he turned to fixed-wing aircraft.

Two years later Igor Sikorsky, then less than 20 years old, made his first helicopter at his home in Kiev, a kind of large wooden box with the petrol-engine on one side and the pilot's seat on the other. Two rotors, with two blades each, were arranged one above the other, with a diameter of 15 feet, turning in opposite directions. But the lifting power of the machine was found to be only 350 lb. while it weighed 450 lb.: so young Sikorsky had to accept the disappointing fact that it would never fly, and built his second model a few months later. It could almost fly, but not quite.

More than thirty years later, when Sikorsky was already a successful aircraft designer and manufacturer in America, he returned to his first love, the helicopter. Many more attempts at perfecting such an aircraft had been made in the intervening years; another Russian-born inventor, George de Bothezat, had designed one with six enormous, four-bladed rotors with the money of the American Government in 1921, but it was controlled more by the wind than by the pilot. A useful contribution to the solution of the problem came from a young Spaniard, Juan de la Cierva, and his 'autogyro', which had a conventional power-driven propeller for its forward flight as well as a large, non-powered rotor instead of fixed wings to sustain it in the air and control its movements. At last, in 1938, a German team at the Focke aircraft works succeeded in building a helicopter which could really lift itself in the air and fly; powered by a 150-h.p. engine it reached a height of 11,500 feet, and a second model, the Focke 223, built in 1940 with a 1,000-h.p. engine, reached 23,400 feet. Because of the war, design and performance of that prototype remained unknown outside Germany until 1945.

Sikorsky had a very distinct notion of what his helicopter should be even before he began to design it: a 'pack mule of the air', as he put it, an all-purpose vertical-lift machine. It was to have neither fixed wings nor thrust propeller, but a power-driven rotor which would not only lift the machine up but also drive it forward, steer it, balance it, and keep it hovering. The rotor should have three blades, whose pitch—the angle at which they 'bite' into the air—would be controlled by the pilot, with a movable axis to control the 'tilt' of the machine; pitch and tilt would decide the vertical and horizontal movements of the helicopter. It must also have a small vertical propeller, the 'auxiliary rotor', at the tip of its tail to counteract 'torque', that is, the tendency of the machine to turn with its rotor.

This 'pack mule of the air' was such a tempting task for Sikorsky, as it had been for so many designers before him, because it was to be the only aircraft which can hover at any point in mid air, and which would need no more than a few square feet of taking-off and landing space—on a roof-top or in a back-yard, in a jungle clearing or on a mountain plateau, on an ice shelf or (when fitted with floats) in water.

Juan de la Cierva's 'autogyro'

Sikorsky's XR-4, the prototype he built for the United States Army, carried out its test flights in December 1941 on the airfield of the Sikorsky aircraft works at Bridgeport, Connecticut. It was a complete success, and the officers who had assembled to watch the machine were treated to a few astonishing stunts: its pilot picked a brass ring from the top of an 8-foot pole, made it place a bag with a dozen raw eggs gently on a prearranged spot, lowered a rope ladder so that a man could climb up to the hovering helicopter, and landed in exactly the same grooves which the wheels had dug in the ground before the start. 'If I hadn't seen this with my own eyes', said one of the onlookers, 'I'd say it's impossible.'

From that day on the helicopter extended the usefulness of the aeroplane in innumerable fields, bearing out Sikorsky's prediction that it would soon prove to be 'a faithful servant of the peaceful progress of humanity'. Helicopters—American, British, and continental—have carried sick people from ships at sea to hospitals on shore; they have rescued marooned people from floods, laid pipes in mountainous country, and carried materials for oil derricks into the jungle; they are in daily use for crop spraying, geological prospecting, mapping, and surveying work—to mention only a few of the great variety of tasks which only these machines can perform with speed, accuracy, and efficiency.

In the sphere of regular passenger service, however, helicopters have not fulfilled the expectations of many transport experts who believed that there would be an incessant stream of helicopters connecting city centres with city centres, thus eliminating the tedious journeys from and to the airports which often take up much more time than the actual flight from airport to airport. The reasons for this disappointment are technical as well as economic.

The helicopter is not an efficient means of horizontal transport; it cannot go much faster than 150–200 m.p.h. with its rotor. Although the rotor needs relatively very little power for lifting, it is rather uneconomical in forward flight. The small, one-rotor machine, seating half a dozen or a dozen passengers—the type which began to operate between Belgium, Holland, and the Rhineland in the 1950's—is a very expensive vehicle to convey people over short distances. It is also noisy, and wherever plans are made to build heliports people living in the area protest against this attack on their ears and nerves. Larger, two-rotor machines seating 40–50 passengers would be more economical but also still noisier, and they would need more landing space. Thus the idea of the rooftop heliport has not quite come off. Heliports on jetties built into rivers, away from populated areas (as in London), are a better solution.

Russia is the country that has made more use of the helicopter as a passenger aircraft than any other. It had 200 regular lines in 1961, serviced by 11-seater MI-4's; they have been found to be of great value, especially in Siberia, where they provide links between the taiga areas of Khabarovsk, Komsomolsk on the Amur, Petropavlovsk, and Yakutia. Helicopter services are also used extensively in the health resort regions of the Crimean and Black Sea coasts.

From the technical point of view, the most efficient helicopter type is that whose rotor is not driven by a gas turbine in the aircraft body, but by small jets on the tips of the rotor blades. This gives the aircraft greater and cheaper power, although it adds to the noise. A new, most successful type is a cross between a helicopter and a fixed-wing machine. The British-built Fairey Rotodyne was the first of this kind; it has been flying since 1957, and will operate commercially from 1963. It has a large rotor with pressure jets at the blade tips as well as short, fixed wings with two conventional turbo-prop engines for forward flight. It ascends by means of the rotor; at cruising altitude the turbo-prop engines take over and drive the machine forward. It is then rudder-controlled and therefore needs no tail propeller; the rotor is free-wheeling, and its jets go into action again only for the vertical descent.

The first model of the Fairey Rotodyne was able to carry forty-eight passengers; its range was 400 miles. The French Bréguet 940, also first shown in the late 1950's, has no rotor but a jet engine which blows air over the fixed wings, thus giving the machine an almost direct lift so that it needs no more than 50 yards runway. Perhaps the nearest thing to the 'family helicopter' which was once the dream of the designers is the Dutch 'Kolibrie', a very small helicopter with blade-tip jets on its rotor, which can achieve a speed of 60 m.p.h.

Several types of VTOL (Vertical Take-Off and Landing) aircraft using direct jet lift have been tried out. As early as 1953 Rolls-Royce built an experimental 'vertical thrust-measuring rig', an unmanned steel structure with vertical jet engines which lifted it off the ground. Then came the famous Rolls-Royce 'flying bedstead', based on the same system, and controlled by a pilot. These and other 'airframes' which were built later are more interesting for military than for civil aviation purposes, but the principle has beeen developed into a take-off and landing aid for large jet airliners, which normally require excessively long runways. In some types part of the thrust of the jet engines can be diverted downwards to achieve quicker lift and to brake the descent; others have extra batteries of small jets mounted under the wings, which are in operation only at take-off and landing.

The star of the 1960 Farnborough Air Show, Britain's annual display of new aircraft types and flying techniques, was the Short SC-1 VTOL prototype. This experimental machine, shaped like a triangle, started from a 40-foot by 40-foot metal platform by firing its four downward-facing Rolls-Royce R.B.-108 jets; it

*H

rose from the platform like a helicopter to a height of about 50 feet, where it hovered motionless for a few seconds. Then the pilot tilted the jets until they pointed back at a 30-degree angle, and the conventionally mounted R.B.-198 jet engine drove the aircraft forward. A moment later it was already flying at over 300 m.p.h. It circled the airfield, and then slowed down and stood still in mid air before gliding gently down to its platform. It is always, of course, a long and weary way from a prototype to serial production of a new model—anything up to ten years' research and development may be necessary—but many of the onlookers at Farnborough felt that the SC-1 could be the forerunner of a future jet airliner able to manage with a 'runway' no larger than a football pitch for taking off and landing.

Another interesting and even more radical solution of the VTOL problem seems to be the one adopted by Dr Barnes Wallis, probably the most ingenious of Britain's aircraft designers, in his 'Swallow'; large-scale models of this type were flown under radio control in 1958, and work on the first man-carrying machine was begun in 1960, backed by British and American money. The 'Swallow' can fold its wings like a bird; they are extended for take-off and landing, but swept back for high-altitude cruising at speeds of 1,800 m.p.h., giving the aircraft almost the shape of a rocket. It has no tailplane, elevators, or rudders; their tasks are carried out by the two pairs of jet engines, mounted above and below the wings, which are pivoted to pitch up and down and swivel. Thus they can achieve a steep take-off, and also act as brakes on landing. Dr Barnes Wallis expects that a 'Swallow' airliner could cross the Atlantic in $2\frac{1}{2}$ hours, and fly from London to Australia without refuelling.

Yet another promising type is the tilt-wing machine, which resembles a conventional fixed-wing aircraft in forward flight, but the wings can be tilted through 90 degrees at take-off and landing so that the propellers of jet-engines mounted on the wings give a vertical thrust. This is an efficient alternative to the coleopter, which we have described earlier.

One does not have to be a romantic dreamer in order to regret that Man's age-old longing to be able to fly like the birds has not really been fulfilled. The giant airliners of our time, in which you sit as comfortably as in the easy chair of a hotel foyer, do not make that dream come true; everything is so designed that you feel as little as possible of the actual flight. Only in a glider do you get that feeling of weightless soaring.

But engineless gliding—a sport which has never succeeded in becoming truly popular—is restricted to landscapes which offer certain suitable features and air currents—and as a rule a motor-car is needed for towing the glider until it becomes airborne. Soaring in the wind is beautiful, but you can't fly wherever you like: the wind won't let you.

For this reason there appear every now and again inventors who want to use muscle power for making gliders rise and for controlling their flight. One of these systems is, of course, that of the flap-wing plane. Another is the 'flying bicycle', in which the airman powers a propeller with his leg muscles. In 1936 two German engineers of the Junkers works succeeded in making a 20-second flight with such a machine.

In 1959 a senior officer at the British Ministry of Aviation developed his flying bicycle at Cardington airfield, and at the same time a lecturer in aeronautical engineering at Queen's College, Belfast, worked on similar lines. The first believed that a single 'cyclist' would be capable of lifting the 90-lb. machine with himself in it into the air, the other put two men on a tandem frame in his machine and made them turn a propeller at the tail. For the start, which requires especially much power, he used auxiliary power in the form of the energy stored in twisted elastic bands, as in toy aeroplanes. The airmen themselves wound the elastic band up by pedalling before the start so that the principle of muscle power was preserved.

The road back to Icarus may perhaps bring us the fulfilment of that old dream, which modern air transport has not given us yet.

Atomic energy (see Part I) has made a promising start in shipping, and to the layman it seemed only a matter of time before it would be used for aircraft propulsion. Nuclear bombers were built and flown in the 1950's in America and Russia; a United States B-36 bomber was equipped with a reactor which took over from the conventional turbo-prop engines at altitude over uninhabited areas. But when President Kennedy moved into the White House in 1961 he decided to scrap the further development of the nuclear bomber. Some weeks later there was an unconfirmed story, which appeared in a leading American aviation magazine, that the Russians had successfully tested a nuclear-powered bomber, which flew for twenty-one days without refuelling, cruising at 2,500 m.p.h., with a top speed of 3,500 m.p.h.! But although the word 'impossible' does not exist in technical matters, the atomic airliner must be regarded as impracticable, to say the least.

Nuclear power is extremely 'heavy' and comes into its own only where considerations of weight are of minor importance, such as in electricity-generating power stations and at sea. Just as steam-engines proved impracticable in air transport, atomic reactors are not suitable for propulsion in this sphere where the economics of weight and performance play such an important part. And there is a special problem: the necessity to protect passengers and crew from dangerous radiation by massive shielding means that many tons of 'unproductive' steel and/or concrete have to be lifted and carried by the aircraft.

Another problem is that of the possible failure of an airborne reactor; if one of the four or more gas turbines or jet engines of an airliner fails, the others can get the aircraft safely down to earth, but a nuclear airliner could certainly not carry a second or spare reactor or an auxiliary power plant such as a turbo-jet engine for safety's sake. The weight would be forbidding. Also, the crash of a nuclear aircraft would endanger large areas as a result of radiation escaping from the smashed-up reactor.

Still, we have witnessed so many unexpected and astonishing developments in our century that any day might bring the solution of the problem of the nuclear airliner: it may be the discovery of some new, light-weight material for 'biological shielding', or the emergence of some revolutionary method of conveying people—such as the application of the nuclear-tug system, which has been suggested for shipping (see Chapter 4), to air transport.

Technically and economically, there is no reason why we should look for new systems of generating power in the air and propelling aircraft; and one of the machines we have now at our disposal can produce speeds and cover distances far beyond any foreseeable requirements in everyday transport: the rocket engine.

Earlier in this chapter we have mentioned some of the pioneers of propulsion by reaction, which is the same in jet and rocket

engines. But there is one essential difference, which was first
expounded by the Russian scientist and schoolmaster, Tsiolkovsky, in 1903. He suggested rocket propulsion for vehicles
leaving the earth's atmosphere because the rocket carries within
itself all the chemicals necessary for combustion and for the
generation of the gases which drive it through space. It does not
need oxygen from the air.

Germany was the leading nation in this field in the 1920's and
1930's. Hermann Oberth set the ball rolling with his book, *The
Rocket into Interplanetary Space*, published in 1923. A few years
later the motor-car industrialist Fritz von Opel tried out a rocket-
propelled car near Berlin, and a rail vehicle of similar construction ran along a test track near Brunswick. Max Valier, another
rocket pioneer, built a car which achieved a speed of 235 m.p.h.
on a frozen Bavarian lake in 1929, using ethyl alcohol and
liquid oxygen as a fuel. Valier was killed in this experiment;
one of the rocket tubes exploded, and a piece of metal pierced
his lung.

Hitler banned all non-military rocket development work, and
set up the enormous Peenemünde research station where the
flying bomb, called V 1, and the V 2 rocket were created as
secret 'revenge' weapons against Britain. The man responsible
for the Peenemünde station was General Dr Walter Dornberger,
with young Dr Wernher von Braun as his chief assistant; much
of the theoretical work was contributed by the Viennese scientist,
Dr Eugen Sänger.

The first V 2, prototype of all modern rockets, lifted from its
test bed on a disused artillery range somewhere in the Branden-
burg heath on 3 October 1942. It had a total weight of 27,500 lb.,
including a ton of payload, at the start. Its rocket engines developed a thrust of 55,000 lb., carrying the vehicle up to an
altitude of 60 miles and over a distance of about 650 miles. The
top speed of the V 2, reached at a height of 15 miles, was nearly
3,700 m.p.h. Its propellent fuel consisted of alcohol and liquid
oxygen (later V 2's were propelled by nitric acid and hydrazine,
a nitrogen-hydrogen compound). It was controlled by gyroscopes
and a radio beam from the ground.

From this beginning stemmed most of the post-war development in the field of rocketry in America, Russia, and Britain
(many of the German scientists and technicians were induced to

work for the victorious nations). A great variety of guided weapons and space rockets have been developed; but let us first examine the use of rockets for transport in the air.

Propeller, jet, and rocket engines all have their limits within which they develop their best performances. The first of them operates most efficiently in the lower layers of the atmosphere where there is enough 'thick' air to bite into. The jet engine, which achieves much greater speeds, does not need air to thrust the aircraft forward, but it is an 'air-breathing' machine; in fact, it needs quite a lot of air, especially the so-called by-pass type in which some of the sucked-in air by-passes the compression and combustion parts of the engine and goes directly to the jet tube at the rear end. One problem in raising the speed of the jet-propelled aircraft, as we know, is that of the heat barrier, or, to be more precise, that of the 'boundary layer', a thin layer of air which is carried along with the moving body and rubs against the surrounding air. This produces friction, and friction produces heat; therefore, especially heat-resisting materials—including ceramics—must be used in aircraft construction where the speed of sound is greatly exceeded.

But if we want to avoid the 'heat barrier' there is only one way: that of getting out of the atmosphere altogether. This is possible only with the rocket engine which needs no air to operate. We know that in principle the rocket moves exactly like the jet aircraft: its forward movement depends on the hot gases which are thrust out at the rear end. The efficacy of the rocket exhaust depends, in its turn, on two factors, the rate at which the gases—which are 'mass'—are thrust out (so many pounds of exhaust gas per second), and the speed at which this goes on. The question of what fuel should be used is therefore of primary importance; next comes the design of the exhaust nozzle, or nozzles, which must ensure that the gases come out with the maximum speed.

The fuel mixture of hydrogen and oxygen has the greatest exhaust velocity, over 13,000 feet per second, but because of its low density—in other words the space which the fuel tanks take up in the rocket—it is uneconomical in rocket aircraft. Penta-borane, a compound of boron and hydrogen, in combination with oxygen has an exhaust velocity of only about 10,000 feet per second, but a much higher density; still higher is that of kerosene and oxygen, with a correspondingly lower exhaust velocity. The temperatures at which these various compounds burn are another important consideration; if an elaborate cooling system has to be installed to keep the rocket aircraft from going up in flames this would affect the weight of the payload and therefore the economy of the vehicle.

This is also the particular problem of the American Pratt and Whitney rocket motor, one of the most advanced types, which uses liquid hydrogen and oxygen. These fuels, however, are extremely cold and must be kept at these very low temperatures until they go into the combustion chamber. There is also the problem of designing moving parts such as engine valves and turbine pumps which are able to work efficiently at temperatures approaching the 'absolute zero'.

But these problems have been solved in principle, and it is only a question of time before the first long-distance rocket liner will take off. The most efficient speed range seems to be over 3,000 m.p.h., and the most practical shape that of a seagull with its wings folded back; for its flight through the atmosphere it would extend its wings. The American experimental rocket plane X-15, with an engine of 57,000-lb. thrust, reached a record speed of 3,140 m.p.h. in 1961.

Rocket liners are expected to accelerate to speeds of 9,000– 12,000 m.p.h., and then coast—like satellites in an orbit—just outside the atmosphere for the main part of the journey. By this route, the crossing from London to Sydney would take no more than an hour.

Space exploration began in October 1957, when a Russian rocket carried a small, man-made 'moon' 560 miles up into space, where it began to circle the earth at a speed of 17,000 m.p.h. Since then many more Russian and American *sputniks* (satellites) have been shot out of the earth's atmosphere, fitted with automatic instruments which record temperature, radiation, magnetism, and so on, and radio these data back to earth. In September 1959 a Russian rocket hit the moon, and a month later another Russian space vehicle called *Lunik III* circled it, photographed the far side of the moon, which we never see, and radioed the pictures back to earth. Other rockets have been shot past the moon, and become satellites of the sun, revolving around it like the earth and the other planets. Even now the earth satellites are already fulfilling

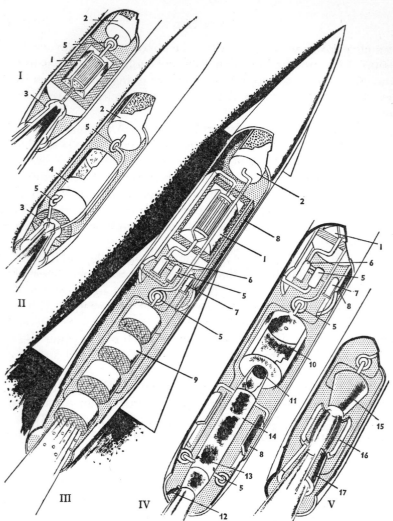

Five Soviet ideas for nuclear space rockets. *Left to right:* I. The propellent passes through an atomic reactor which heats it. II. The propellent is mixed with radio-active matter which heats it. III. The reactor generates current for electric fields in which ions are accelerated. IV. The propellent is burnt at a temperature of 2,500° C. in a high-pressure combustion chamber, the pumps being activated by energy generated in a reactor. V. The reactor produces an electric arc in which the propellent is heated. *Key to figures:* 1, reactor; 2, propellent container; 3, nozzle; 4, tank with radio-active matter; 5, pump; 6, steam tube; 7, electric generator; 8, low-pressure steam system; 9, electric fields for ion acceleration; 10, high-pressure combustion chamber; 11, combustion-chamber valve; 12, nozzle valve; 13, cooling-system valves; 14, ram-jet valve; 15, arc anode; 16, stabilizer; 17, arc cathode some important tasks. They are a great help in weather fore-casting; they can take pictures of cloud formations and give early warnings of hurricanes and blizzards. And they can also serve as celestial telephone exchanges; with the help of miniature com-puters, recording and transmitting equipment they can relay telephone conversations, radio, and even television programmes, thus providing a telecommunications link between the continents of the earth. Three such satellites, orbiting around the globe at an altitude of 22,000 miles so that they appear to be standing still above the earth, could serve as permanent links between Europe, America, the Far East, and Australia. The first of these communi-cations satellites, called Telstar, began its operations by relaying —or rather receiving and retransmitting—television programmes from America to Europe and *vice versa* in the summer of 1962, circling the globe at a height of 600 to 3,500 miles once every 160 minutes at a speed of 11,000 to 18,000 m.p.h.

On 12 April 1961 a Russian $4\frac{1}{2}$-ton space vehicle carried the first man, Major Yuri Gagarin, into orbit and around the earth in eighty-nine minutes at a speed of 18,000 m.p.h., and brought him safely back. It is only a question of time before the first man-carrying rocket will start on a round trip to the moon—with visits to other planets such as Mars and Venus to follow. What will these interplanetary rockets be like? Many experts believe that only nuclear propulsion can provide the answer, for in space travel the problem of fuel weight is even more important than that of engine weight. Landing on a distant planet—after a journey through empty space, which needs little fuel—is not nearly as difficult as starting back to earth again, which even the most intrepid space travellers will probably want to do. The mass of chemical fuel that a space-ship would have to carry for that purpose may be prohibitive as the propellent—usually a gasified liquid—will have to be ejected from the nozzle at very high speed and temperature.

Both the Russians and the Americans are therefore working on nuclear space rockets. The Soviet scientists are developing several types: in one of them the propellent passes through an atomic reactor where it is heated; in another radio-active matter is mixed with the propellent and heats it; a third type works with a reactor which generates current for a series of electric fields in which charged particles, ions, are accelerated; a fourth type

operates like a ram-jet with a high-pressure combustion chamber
in which the propellent is burnt at a temperature of 2,500°
centigrade—the pumps are activated by reactor-generated
current; and there is a fifth type in which the reactor produces the
current for an enormous electric arc in which the propellent is
heated before rushing out of the nozzle. Russian scientists believe
that these systems of nuclear propulsion in space can produce up
to fifteen times more thrust than chemically fuelled rockets.

At the Nevada test site of the U.S. Atomic Energy Commission, experiments with reactors of the KIWI type (named
after the flightless New Zealand bird) were begun in the late
1950's. Here the propellent is liquid hydrogen, which is squirted
through the reactor heat and rushes out of the nozzle, developing
a thrust of 50,000 lb. or more. Another American type is an ion
rocket engine in which caesium ions are accelerated by reactor-
generated electric fields to velocities up to 200,000 miles per hour
before being released through the nozzle.

The race to the planets is on between the two great powers—
a rivalry in space for the sake of prestige which future historians
may call childish, considering the vast amounts of money and
labour it costs, and the more pressing tasks that require our
attention and energy on our own planet.

# III

# Communications

# I

◇◆◇◆◇◆◇◆◇◆◇◆◇◆◇◆◇◆◇◆◇

# The Printed Word

THREE TIMES the great library of Alexandria was destroyed:
during the siege of the town by Julius Caesar; in A.D. 390, when
the books were dispersed by Theophilus, Patriarch of Alexandria;
and finally in A.D. 642, when the Muslims conquered the town and
the Caliph Omar ordered that it should be burnt.

Altogether 400,000 volumes must have fallen victim to the
folly and malice of Man. They contained all the wisdom and
knowledge, the literature and folk-lore of the ancient world. Most
of these manuscripts—for these books had been written by hand
by scribes, slaves, and scholars—were irreplaceable; only very
few of them existed in other libraries as duplicate copies. The
destruction of the major library of antiquity robbed us of a great
wealth of information, learning, and art.

A catastrophe like the one which befell the library of Alexandria is unlikely to happen ever again. Even if the British Museum
in London, the Library of Congress in Washington, and the
Bibliothèque Nationale in Paris were burnt to ashes, most of the
printed books they possess could be traced in other libraries. As
long as civilized life continues on this planet, the printed word
will preserve all that is worth preserving (and a good deal more
besides). Among the innumerable inventions made, and arts
learnt, by mankind, that of printing may be the one that had the
most far-reaching influence; for it has affected not only people's
way of life but their minds and hearts.

How was that invention made? There are some conflicting
stories about this. Again, the Chinese seem to have been the first
to cut the characters of their written language in wood, assemble

243

them, ink them, and press sheets of paper on them to get im-
prints (paper-making, too, is an old Chinese invention). The
Chinese written language consists of syllables, not of individual
letters; thus the printing with movable type, which began in that
country in the thirteenth and in Korea in the fourteenth century,
was a development from the 'block printing' of pictures, which
had been in use in Far Eastern countries for several centuries.

In Europe, too, printing began with pictures; images were cut
in wooden blocks or stamps, especially for the making of playing-
cards for which there was a great demand. The Church began to
campaign against the vice of card-playing, and had pictures of the
saints printed in large quantities. The idea of adding words was,
therefore, not very far-fetched, but cutting long texts into the
wood blocks was a tedious job. A number of people in western
Europe seem to have thought around the same time of making
letter types of wood or metal and assembling them to form words
and sentences for printing; paper was now available for this
purpose since the Arabs had brought that invention from China
and Japan to Spain, where the first paper-mill had been set up in
the twelfth century.

In Haarlem, Holland, there are two monuments in praise of a
man called Laurens Coster, who is said to have printed the first
book with movable letters. The little Italian town of Feltre has
another monument in honour of a doctor who is supposed to have
made the same invention, and Strasbourg and Prague have also
such monuments in memory of their citizens for whom the same
claim is made. The idea of the movable type was certainly in the
air; all those who had acquired the art of reading and writing
were longing for books, but the few handwritten ones were
available only to the monks in the monasteries, the church dignitaries, and the professors at the universities. The ordinary
citizen's desire for information, for ideas in black and white, was
not satisfied.

Who, then, should be honoured as the true inventor of the
movable type? The controversy has been on for five hundred
years. It appears that Laurens Coster, who was an innkeeper by
profession, produced a book printed with movable type some
time in the first half of the fifteenth century, but we have to
acknowledge that Johann Gutenberg, of Mainz, Germany,
perfected the art of printing by a series of inventions.

Gutenberg came from a wealthy family of burghers. Born a few years before 1400, he went to Strasbourg as a young man, and learnt the art of block-printing; he also tried his skill at cutting gems and polishing mirrors. He made several inventions in these crafts, and was involved in a lawsuit concerning a new type of printing-press for woodcuts. It may have been at Strasbourg that he first thought of using movable letter types to compose words, sentences, and whole pages.

An early printing press

All we know is that he returned to his native Mainz at the age of 50, and began to put his idea into practice: to make moulds, one for each letter of the alphabet, from which to cast little metal types, all of equal length so that they could be assembled to form lines, and the lines assembled to form pages. To this end, Gutenberg had to design a new alphabet suitable for casting because the handwritten letters of the period were much too ornate. He accomplished this job beautifully by striking a happy medium between practical requirements and artistic form. He invented a type-founding system to produce letters with great accuracy so that they would fit well together, devices for inking the composition evenly, and a hand-operated press for applying just the right amount of pressure—to mention only the most important tasks that had to be done before he could start printing. He completed them with much trial and error.

His first experimental printing job was the reproduction of an old German poem. The system worked. Now he proceeded to turn out his masterpiece, the whole Bible in Latin, 1,282 pages of 42 lines each—an enormous undertaking for such a small and largely experimental enterprise. After many years of work he completed it in 1456.

By that time, however, he had no money left, and his partner, who had financed him, demanded repayment. There was nothing Gutenberg could do but get out of his house and workshop, leaving all his printed volumes behind. The partner moved in, and soon the world's first printing works grew into a very prosperous enterprise.

Little is known about the rest of Gutenberg's life, except that ten years later a church dignitary made him an honorary member of his household so that he could spend the rest of his life—only two more years—in peace.

After Germany, the first countries to introduce printing were Italy and France, where German printers established presses, and England followed at a short distance. William Caxton, a merchant born in Kent, was also a man of 50 when he took up the new craft. Appointed governor of the Company of Merchant Adventurers, he was sent to the Continent to negotiate commercial treaties with the dukes of Burgundy. The Duchess Margaret, sister of Edward IV and wife of Charles the Bold of Burgundy, made him her commercial adviser, and when he happened to be in Cologne in 1471 he saw one of the printing-shops there. He decided to become an apprentice in this art, and when he had learnt it he printed his first book at Bruges: his own translation from the French of Homer's *Iliad*. This book, the first to be printed in English, appeared in 1474. Two years later he opened a printing-works in Westminster, starting with a book of philosophical quotations.

Caxton never regretted having given up his career as a merchant and courtier comparatively late in life to become England's first printer. When he died in 1491, at the age of 70, he had the satisfaction not only of having printed about eighty books, thus bringing many important works of world literature within the reach of his countrymen, but also of having standardized the English language, whose spelling and grammar were then in a constantly changing, chaotic condition.

Perhaps the invention of printing more than any other event or development brought the Middle Ages to an end. Formidable forces of the human mind were liberated with it. Ideas—those mighty weapons which are feared by the powers of reaction, ignorance, and oppression—spread far and wide. Through the

A printing-shop of the time of Gutenberg

medium of the printed word, the common people heard about the scientists' new concepts of heaven and earth, about the new lands discovered beyond the oceans. Words in black and white flashed like lightning in the mental darkness in which the rulers of the world wanted to keep their subjects. Pamphlets and broadsheets prepared the greatest popular uprising in German history, the peasants' revolt; with Martin Luther's treatise *On the Liberty of a Christian Man*, the opening shot of the Reformation rang throughout the Holy Roman Empire.

Books, news-sheets, and later newspapers became inseparable from civilized life, and literacy a reliable indication of the degree of maturity reached by a nation. The technique of printing, however, remained more or less the same for three and a half centuries after Gutenberg. Letter type was composed by hand, and prints made by hand-operated presses. It was a combination of slow, leisurely jobs, not very well suited for the printing of topical publications. Yet the need for quick information by the printed word grew. The first newspaper-type of broadsheets were published by the frightened Viennese authorities when the Turks appeared at their gates in 1529; in these news-sheets the whole Christian world was implored to come to the aid of the besieged city. A century later, in 1622, an Englishman, Nathaniel Butter, published the first periodical as a commercial enterprise, the *Weekly Newes*. During the Civil War and the Cromwell Commonwealth a great number of periodicals appeared, but they had to be licensed first by the Star Chamber and after its abolition by the Long Parliament: kings and dictators had become aware of the dangerous power of the printed word. Ever since then the great battle between the Press and those who want to suppress information and opinion has been going on, now in this country, now in that; when the first daily newspaper, the *Daily Courant*, appeared in England in 1702, the Press was at last free of Government censorship, but soon the British authorities invented another efficient means of strangling it—the Newspaper Tax. It survived in the form of the Stamp Act until 1855.

By that time, however, the power of the Press had increased enormously, mainly because it had been given a new machine for mass production, the steam-operated mechanical printing-press. One day in 1812, John Walter II, the son of the founder of *The Times*, was asked by a friend to come to a workshop in Whitecross Street, in the City of London, to see the greatest advance in the art of printing since Gutenberg's days.

Mr Walter went, and was introduced to the machine and its inventor, Friedrich König, a printer from Germany who had come to England where the patent laws protected inventors much better than in his homeland—a country then divided into dozens of small principalities, so that a patent taken out in one of them was without value in the others. König, his chief mechanic, another German by the name of Friedrich Bauer, and his financial backer, Thomas Bensley, concluded an agreement with John Walter for the delivery of two double machines for

*The Times* and the *Evening Mail*. Their completion took two years.

König's idea was simple. Until then, every single sheet to be printed had to be positioned on top of the composed type by hand; the inking of the type was done by hand-operated rollers, and the press bar was swung round, or pushed down, by hand or foot. The quickest printers managed to produce about 300 sheets per hour. Surely the thought of applying steam-power to printing must have occurred to many technical minds, but it seemed difficult to adapt these varied movements to the reciprocating or rotating action of the steam-engine.

König found the solution. He made the 'forme' with the type move forward and back under a large inking cylinder; all that had to be done by hand was the 'feeding' of the paper sheets to the machine, which put them mechanically on top of the forme; then another cylinder pressed them against the type which moved under it, and they were delivered into the printer's hands at the other end of the machine while the forme moved back again to receive another coat of ink. Thus, 1,000 to 1,200 sheets could be printed in an hour, with much less labour.

The printers had, of course, heard of the machines that were to be set up, and feared for their livelihood. They gathered around the van which was to take the machines to *The Times* office, and prevented the coachman from delivering them. Walter resorted to a ruse; he installed the machines in another building, and printed the morning issue of 29 November 1814 there secretly.

The leading article explained the revolution that had taken place. 'Our journal of this day', wrote Walter, 'presents to the public the practical result of the greatest improvement connected with printing since the discovery of the art itself. The reader of this paragraph now holds in his hand one of the many thousand impressions of *The Times* newspaper, which were taken off by a mechanical apparatus. A system of machinery almost organic has been devised and arranged, which, while it relieves the human frame of its most laborious efforts in printing, far exceeds all human powers in rapidity and dispatch. . . .

'Of the person who made the discovery we have little to add. Sir Christopher Wren's noblest monument is to be found in the building which he erected: so is the best tribute of praise which we are able to offer to the inventor of the printing machine comprised in the description of the powers and utility of his invention. It must suffice to say further that he is a Saxon by birth, that his name is König, and that the invention has been executed under the direction of his friend and countryman, Bauer.'

John Walter paid the wages of the printers whom the machine had displaced until they found other jobs. Soon it became clear that what at first seemed to endanger their bread and butter was in fact a great boon for the whole printing trade. Mechanical production of newspapers, and later of periodicals and books, made reading much cheaper, and the demand for printed matter grew by leaps and bounds.

König and Bauer made little money out of their success; Mr Bensley had seen to it that he received the lion's share. After paying their debts to him they had just enough money left to return to the Continent. A few years later they set up a factory for mechanical printing presses in a former monastery in Bavaria, and trained peasant lads as mechanics. They succeeded in building up a flourishing business, which is still in existence.

Fifty years after König's invention came another major improvement in printing—the rotary press. The first machine of this kind was built by an American, William Bullock, in 1863; he lost his life soon after in an accident with one of his presses. The rotary press, which is still the standard machine in newspaper printing, has large rolls of paper which are printed in a continuous process so that the 'feeding' of individual sheets is unnecessary. The rotary machine works not with a 'flat bed' of type but with a cylindrical forme—paper, ink, and type are all on rotating cylinders, which makes the printing of hundreds of thousands of newspaper copies per hour possible. A modern 24-cylinder press can print up to 1,200,000 copies per hour. These giant machines also cut, fold, and—where necessary—deliver the copies in bundles of so and so many copies. Needless to say they can also print in more than one colour, and not only letter type but also pictures. The type and picture blocks are composed in a flat frame, then a mould of the page is made in 'flong', or papiermâché, and from this a curved stereotype plate is cast, which is then fixed to the type cylinder.

Another German who had gone abroad was responsible for

the liberation of the type-setting process from its slow manual drudgery. Ottmar Mergenthaler, the son of a schoolmaster in Württemberg, was a young mechanic in a Baltimore workshop when, in 1876, a group of inventors asked him to help them with the development of a machine with which a printer should be able to set type mechanically—merely by operating a typewriter-like

Mergenthaler's Linotype machine (1900)

keyboard. These inventors had been working on their idea for years, spending a great deal of money and energy but getting nowhere.

Mergenthaler took up the challenge. He designed, constructed, scrapped, and rebuilt machine after machine until at last, in 1886, he succeeded in solving the main problems with his 'blower machine', so called because it worked with an air blast device; later the trade name of the invention became 'Linotype', under which it is still known.

The Linotype produces lines of metal called slugs, each of them of the same length according to the width of the newspaper column. When the operator presses a key on his keyboard a matrix is released from a magazine above. A matrix is a flat metal plate with the die of a letter, or 'character', on its vertical edge. The matrix falls down on a constantly revolving belt into a little composing-box: in the old 'blower' machine, this journey was made with the help of an air blast. The spaces between the words are adjusted automatically by little wedges so that the line has just the right length.

As soon as the line is completed the operator pulls a handle, and the line is carried off to be cast: the row of matrices is filled with molten metal, which solidifies quickly. The cast line, the slug, is then ejected to the front of the machine while the matrices are lifted up to its top to be distributed back to their places in the magazine. Each matrix has a series of little teeth, almost like a key, which makes it fall into its appropriate container in the magazine, one for each character. It is this automatic distribution principle of Mergenthaler's invention which enables the Linotype operator to produce slugs continually; as the matrices return to the magazine instantly it becomes a literally inexhaustible fountain for new type.

Mergenthaler's machine was an immediate success. Thirty 'blowers' were installed in the *New York Tribune*, twenty in the Louisville *Courier-Journal*, about the same number in the *Chicago News*, and some in the *Washington Post*. One important question, however, remained to be answered. So far, all matrices for these machines had been made by hand—a very costly and slow process, quite apart from the difficulty of finding enough skilled craftsmen. An ingenious American inventor, Linn Noyd Benton, came to the rescue with his mechanical punch-cutter for type-setting machines, working on the pantograph principle.

For other type-setting jobs which may necessitate many corrections—especially books—the Monotype has been found more suitable. Tolbert Lanston, born in Iowa, a poor young man who served in the American Civil War and later became an official in Washington, invented it in the 1880's. It consists of two separate parts: a keyboard machine, which perforates rolls of paper in certain patterns, each of them representing a character; and a caster in which the perforations release matrices from which the characters are cast in single metal types (not as complete line 'slugs' as in the Linotype). The lines are automatically assembled from the types and the spaces adjusted. A Monotype keyboard permits the setting of over 300 characters, roman and italic, large and small capital letters, figures, and all kinds of special characters and signs.

Although Mergenthaler's Linotype is still doing its job magnificently in countless printing workshops all over the world, there have been some important improvements in type-setting. One is the Teletypesetter, which makes it possible to operate a Linotype at a distance by wire or radio. The operator in Town A types the lines on a tape-punching machine, very much like that of a Monotype; the hole pattern of the tape is then trans-mitted automatically by wire or wireless to Town B, where a receiver unit, the 'reperforator', repeats the punching on another tape. This is then 'fed' into the Teletypesetter unit attached to a standard Linotype keyboard and operates the machine without any help from a human operator. The system is especially useful where large national newspapers have to be printed in two or more towns, each of them serving the readers in its region. The speed of the Teletypesetter is twelve lines a minute.

Photocomposition is an entirely new concept in printing. The equipment consists of a keyboard unit, photo unit, tape editor, corrector, and composer. The operator types the copy on a key-board, again with a roll of tape to receive patterns of holes; he has at his disposal 18 'founts', or letter types, in sizes from 6 to 36 point (the operator sees his work before him in the form of a typed sheet; should he make a mistake he can cancel the line and retype it). Punched tape from several keyboards can be sent to a single photo unit, which looks like a large wardrobe; here the punch holes are changed into type on film or paper, which is then checked by the printer's reader. Any corrections which have to be made are done in the corrector: a new line to replace the faulty one is set on the keyboard and turned into galley form by the photo unit; this correction galley is then placed in the corrector, which cuts out automatically the error line and replaces it with the new one on the film or paper.

The make-up of the whole page from the film negative is done in the composer, an electro-photographic machine. Here a news-paper or magazine page is made up with all the type in the required position and size—for this machine can enlarge or reduce any type from 4 to 216 point. The composer produces the page also on film or paper; then the pictures are inserted, and the page is ready for the engraver or platemaker.

Then there is the Protype system for setting big type—for headings, advertisements, posters, and so on—photographically. Individual letters, words, lines, or complete pages can be composed on sensitized paper or film. This is done by contact printing with a small ultra-violet lamp from a wide range of characters in all sizes. The result can be used immediately for block-making, litho, or gravure.

We shall later describe some of the more recent reproduction systems. But now we have to mention the all-important typewriter, one of the truly indispensable tools of our age. Over fifty inventors in many countries tried to solve the problem of a writing-machine in the eighteenth and nineteenth centuries, beginning with an Englishman who was granted a patent as far back as 1714; but none of them proved practical.

Christopher Latham Sholes, who had begun his career as a printer and worked successively as a postmaster, duty-collector, editor, and inventor, became interested in the problem when he was already 48 years old and a senator in Milwaukee. Together with Carlos Glidden, an attorney and son of an Ohio ironmonger, he built the first experimental model of a typewriter in 1867, a clumsy monster with a piano keyboard, a tripod, and many wires, one for each key. It was the first of over four dozen models; and the last one—roughly looking like a present-day typewriter, though much higher and lavishly decorated with flower designs—got him a contract with the Ilion Arms Manufactory. The first thousand machines were built in 1873; the model was called 'Remington'.

The typewriter, though a simple piece of machinery compared to other technical devices in our daily lives, is a little miracle of mechanical perfection. What the first Remington prospectus said of it still holds good: 'Its advantages over the pen—legibility, rapidity, ease, convenience, economy. . . . No fear of pen paralysis, loss of sight, or curvature of the spine from using the machine. . . . Persons travelling by sea and rail can write with it when pen writing would be impossible.' The 'Machine to supersede the pen' was especially recommended to reporters, stenographers, lawyers, authors, playwrights, clergymen, merchants, bankers, and 'all men of business' for their correspondence.

What neither the inventor nor the makers of the first practical typewriter could foresee was the tremendous importance of this

*Top:* Parsons's *Turbinia*, the first steam-turbine ship, making 34½ knots on a trial run in 1897.

*Bottom:* The prototype of the 'hovercraft' during a test on the Solent in 1959.

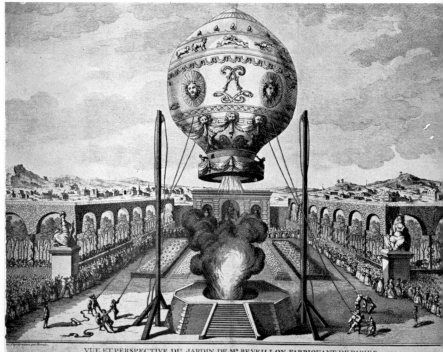

VUE ET PERSPECTIVE DU JARDIN DE M.ˢ REVEILLON FABRIQUANT DE PAPIER,
Fauxbourg S.ᵗ Antoine, à l'ancien Hôtel de Titon, où se sont faites les expériences de la Machine Aérostatique de MM. Montgolfier freres, dans le courant de l'Eté, en l'année 1783 à la satisfaction d'un concours immense d'amateurs.

DEDIÉE A M.ˢ LES PHYSICIENS.

*osite, top:* Professor Charles ascends in his
rogen balloon at Versailles on 1 December 1783.

*osite, bottom:* Testing of a captive Montgolfier
-air balloon, made of cotton lined with
er, in a garden in Paris in 1783.

*:* The famous British dirigible R 34 which
ceeded in crossing the Atlantic by air for
first time in July 1919.

*tom:* The German airship *Graf Zeppelin* in 1928.

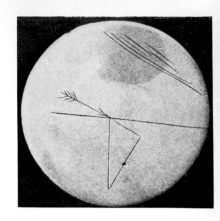

*Top:* Front and back of a silver disc engraved by Sir George Cayley in 1799. The front shows a design for a glider, the back a diagram of forces involved in bird flight.

*Left:* Otto Lilienthal during a flight in one of his biplane gliders in 1896.

*Opposite, top:* The first flight with a heavier-than-air machine: Orville Wright lying in the machine, Wilbur running after it (Kitty Hawk, North Carolina, 17 December 1903).

*Opposite, bottom:* The British 'Rotodyne', combining the features of a turboprop plane and a helicopter.

*Top:* Aboard the cable-laying ship *Faraday*
in the 1860's.

*Bottom:* The coiling of the Atlantic cable
on board H.M.S. *Agamemnon* in 1857.

*Top:* Alexander Graham Bell's experimental telephone (1876).

*Bottom:* Philipp Reis's telephone (1863). *Left,* the transmitter; *right,* the knitting-needle receiver.

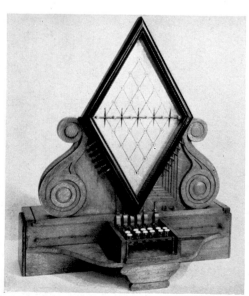

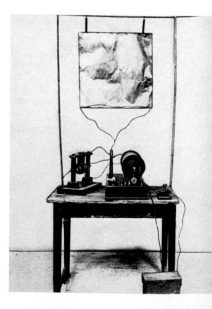

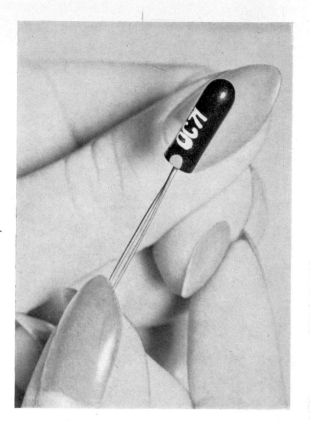

*posite, top:* Morse's first tele-
aph, made from an easel
35).

*posite, bottom: left,* Cooke
d Wheatstone's 5-needle
egraph (1837); *right,*
arconi's apparatus used in
ly in 1895.

*p:* Heinrich Hertz.

*ght:* A transistor, compared
h a thumbnail for size.

*tom:* Marconi in 1902 with
transmitter (right) and
eiver.

*Opposite, top:* Thomas Alva Edison and his phonograph (1888).

*Opposite, bottom:* A commercial Daguerre camera (1840).

*Top:* A photographic studio in the 1840's.

*Left:* An early calotype by Fox Talbot, 'The Chessplayers'.

*Top:* The 'Zoetrope', an early Victorian toy based on the inertia of the human eye.

*Right:* The first cinematographic pictures. *From top to bottom:* Lumière's 'Lunch Hour at the Lumière Factory' and 'Arrival of a Train' (1895), R. W. Paul's 'Derby 1896', 'Bank Holiday in Leeds' (1896), and 'The Gordon Highlanders leaving for South Africa' (1899).

*Top:* An early American sound-film studio. Note the sound-proof camera booth and the microphone suspended from a string.

*Bottom:* Film-making for television (BBC production of *Women of Troy*). The camera is mounted on a 3-ton crane movable in all directions; there are two microphone 'booms'.

*Top:* John L. Baird's original television transmitter of 1925.

*Bottom:* Baird's first commercial receiver, with Nipkow disc, of 1936.

*Top:* The 'image orthicon' television camera with 4-lens turret.

*Bottom:* TV Camera without cameraman, used by the BBC for interviews to preserve an intimate atmosphere in the studio. The interviewer holds the 'shot-box' and selects the camera angles by pressing buttons. The camera adjusts pan, tilt, zoom, and focus automatically.

*Top:* At the Saratov glass factory, a woman engineer operates the conveyor of the grinding and polishing section from a central control panel.

*Bottom:* An electronic process-control computor. Input and recording is effected by magnetic tape, output can be transcribed on an electric typewriter.

machine in freeing the girls and women of the poorer and middle classes from their subordinate role in Victorian family life. The typewriter, by offering them independence through paid work, did more for their emancipation than all the movements, organizations, and publications which demanded equality for women in society. It is interesting to record that in 1885 Count Leo Tolstoy became the first European author to use a typewriter. He made his daughter practise on it, and dictated to her many of his works and all his correspondence. She was Europe's first girl typist, the forerunner of a vast army of women who found congenial and independent careers at the keyboard of the typewriter.

Around 1880 hardly a girl was to be seen in the business quarters of the great cities; women never as much as visited them. Today they heavily outnumber the men among the commercial and administrative employees. The typewriter was the most important factor in bringing about this social change of fundamental importance.

# 2

‹⋄–⋄–⋄–⋄–⋄–⋄–⋄–⋄–⋄–⋄–⋄–⋄–⋄–⋄–⋄›

# Messages by Wire

TELEGRAPHY is a very old idea. Darius, King of the Persians around 500 B.C., is said to have put some of his subjects with especially loud voices on mountain tops to shout royal orders and news to one another. The Greeks developed an optical telegraph working with torches on hill-top ramparts; combinations of torches were used to transmit the letters of the alphabet. The Carthaginians and the Romans had similar systems. In his *Bellum Gallicum*, Julius Caesar reports that the assassination of a number of Romans at Senacum, the modern Orléans, became speedily known all over Gaul because 'if there is an important event the Gauls convey the news to one another by shouting'. In Africa the ancient bush telegraph is still widely used; messages are transmitted by striking 'drums' made of hardwood trunks with cavities of various sizes so that a number of different notes can be produced. The South American Red Indians in the Amazon region have an acoustic telegraph, also made of tree trunks, which is said to cover a range of a mile. The 'code' consists of long and short notes. Mountain-top fires of damp wood, which gives off a great deal of smoke, were used in many countries to convey messages by smoke signals.

Until the end of the eighteenth century there was not much development in acoustic or optical telegraphy. In 1792 a French mechanic, Claude Chappe, demonstrated his optical telegraph to the French National Convention. It was based on a suggestion made over a century earlier by the English scientist Robert Hooke, a friend of Sir Christopher Wren. The French Government, then engaged in fighting various invasion armies, accepted the idea eagerly, and the first Chappe telegraph line was set up between Paris and Lille in 1794. It was followed by other lines in western and central Europe, the most elaborate system being installed in Prussia between Berlin and Koblenz on the Rhine.

These optical telegraphs worked with semaphores, pivoted signal arms on high poles, equipped with lamps at night; the arms were bent into various positions, thus forming code signals which indicated the letters of the alphabet, punctuation marks, and numbers, altogether 70 to 90 different positions. Telegraph posts were spaced out at about six miles' distance, and manned by operators equipped with telescopes who repeated the observed signals. The system worked surprisingly well; a signal from Paris, for instance, arrived at Lille, 130 miles and 22 posts away, within two minutes.

Napoleon's military and administrative authorities used the Chappe telegraph extensively, and many of his swift strategic movements were due to the rapid information he received and the orders he dispatched in this way. When the Austrians occupied Munich in 1809 he heard the news the same day in Paris, and retook the town only six days later in a quick counter-attack. Napoleon led his ally, the King of Bavaria, back to Munich, and this prince was so impressed by the telegraph to which he owed his speedy restoration that he asked the Munich scientist, Samuel Thomas von Sömmering, in what way the Chappe semaphores might be improved.

Sömmering's answer was to begin work on an electric telegraph. Some experiments had already been carried out in this field; the Scottish physician Charles Morrison had suggested the transmission of signals by electricity as early as 1753. Sömmering decided to use electrolysis, the splitting-up of water into hydrogen and oxygen, for his telegraph. Powered by a voltaic pile (see Part I), his transmitter worked with two dozen metal pegs, one for each letter of the alphabet; when the circuit was closed by connecting the pile with one of the pegs, a little column of air bubbles rose from a corresponding peg in the receiver—a glass tank filled with acidified water. Sömmering needed two dozen wires connecting transmitter and receiver: it was a complicated system, but it worked.

The discovery of the deflection of a magnetized needle by an electric current, made by Professor Oersted in Copenhagen in 1819 (see Part I), opened a new road to scientists experimenting with telegraphy. The director of the Göttingen observatory, Carl Friedrich Gauss, saw the Sömmering telegraph in Munich, which prompted him to take up the idea. With a colleague, Wilhelm Weber, physics professor at the University of Göttingen, he installed a telegraph line from the observatory to the physics laboratory, over a distance of more than two miles, in 1833 (they had some difficulty in getting permission from the authorities to fix their wires on the roof-tops). The impulses coming from the transmitter deflected a large iron bar, which was used instead of a magnetized needle, in the receiver; the deflection was observed by means of a mirror galvanometer, an invention by Gauss, a little mirror attached to the magnetized bar, which could be watched through a short-range telescope with a calibrated scale so that even the slightest deflection could be measured accurately. The two scientists agreed on a 'deflection code' representing the letters of the alphabet.

Although their intention was merely the exchange of scientific data between the observatory and the laboratory, this was the first electrical telegraph system which permitted the transmission of messages over an appreciable distance. The first 'telegram' read: 'Michelmann is coming'—that was the mechanic who had helped the scientists to install their apparatus. Forty deflections were required for this message.

'I believe that, provided suitable wires are used, messages could be sent in this way from Göttingen to Hanover and from Hanover to Bremen', wrote Gauss. But neither he nor Weber did much about the development of their system, and it remained unknown outside a small circle of scientists. Shortly before his death twenty-two years later, when the electric telegraph was already well established in Europe and America, Gauss described his system in a letter to the English scientist, Sir David Brewster (inventor of, among other things, the kaleidoscope), adding that the practical application of his idea never occupied his mind. Weber, however, mused: 'If the globe were covered with a network of railway lines and telegraph wires, this would carry out services comparable to those of the nervous system in the human body, partly as a means of transport, partly as a means for transmitting ideas and emotions with the speed of lightning.'

Once, however, Gauss advised a former student of his, Carl August Steinheil in Munich, that he should develop his telegraph for everyday use. Steinheil used two magnetized needles instead of the heavy magnet bar, and made them move two nibs with little ink containers; the nibs printed dots on a moving paper band. The first Steinheil telegraph was installed between the Royal Academy and the observatory in Munich in 1837. Meanwhile, the first German railway line had been built between Nuremberg and Fürth, and he was asked to set up a telegraph line alongside.

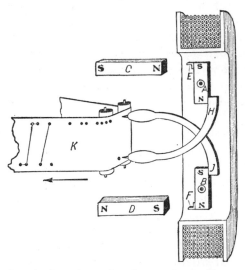

Steinheil's telegraph: the receiver. *Key to letters:* A to D, electro-magnets; E and F, swivel armatures; H and J, writing-arms; K, moving paper tape; N and S, north and south poles of the magnets

Steinheil intended at first to use one wire only, and carry the current back through the rails. But their connections were not good enough for the purpose. However, during these experiments Steinheil suddenly discovered that the earth itself was a first-class conductor! All you have to do to make the moist earth take over the function of a second wire is to sink two metal sheets to subsoil-water level, wired to the transmitter and receiver respectively, and the soil will close the circuit.

A scientifically minded diplomat attached to the Russian legation in Munich, Baron Paul Schilling, had seen Sömmering's electrolytic telegraph and took a model with him to Petersburg in 1812 to show it to the Tsar. But Alexander I, although a ruler with liberal leanings, was afraid that the improvement of communications in his empire might weaken his absolute powers, and forbade Schilling to build a telegraph line, or even to write about the invention in scientific journals.

Schilling, however, continued to work on the telegraph, and demonstrated a system operating with five magnetic needles at a scientific congress in Bonn in 1835. A professor from Heidelberg borrowed the apparatus from Schilling, and showed it to his students during his lectures. A young Englishman, William Fothergill Cooke (later Sir William Cooke), who studied medicine at Heidelberg, was most impressed, and when he returned to England he teamed up with Sir Charles Wheatstone, professor at King's College, London, to improve Schilling's system.

The Cooke-Wheatstone telegraph also worked with five needles, arranged on a lozenge-shaped panel with the letters of the alphabet and the numbers from 0 to 9 on it; the positions of the needles indicated the transmitted letter or figure.

The two scientists built England's first telegraph line—with five wires—along the London–Blackwall Railway. This was so successful that the Great Western Railway had a 19-mile line installed from Paddington to Slough. It was opened in 1844, and posters invited the public to use it and watch its operation.

At first people did not know what to do with this 'wonder of the age' except watch the operators with their needles and wires. Soon, however, the power of 'instantaneous communication' was to be demonstrated in a most impressive way. On 1 January 1845 the operator at Paddington received this telegram:

a murder has just been committed at salthill and the suspected murderer was seen to take a first class ticket for london by the train which left slough at 7.42 a.m. he is in the garb of a kwaker with a brown greatcoat on which reaches nearly down to his feet. he is in the last compartment of the second first class carriage.

The operator could not make out what was meant by 'kwaker', and sent a query back to Slough. He was told that 'kw' stood for the letter 'between p and r'; there was no 'q' on the telegraph

---

Opposite: Advertisement of the Paddington–Slough telegraph (1844)

panel. He hurried to the police station and delivered the message. When the train arrived at Paddington, two plain-clothes police-men were on the look-out for the 'kwaker'. They shadowed him across London on a horse-bus, and finally arrested him.

The murder trial of John Tawell was the sensation of 1845. The policemen gave evidence how the telegraph delivered the suspect into their hands. Tawell confessed and was executed, and Londoners said: 'Them cords [the telegraph wires] have hung John Tawell!'

The Cooke-Wheatstone needle telegraph—it was eventually reconstructed to work with only one needle—survived for a long time in Britain; some lines were still in operation in our century. Meanwhile, however, a better system had been developed in America.

It was not a scientist but an artist who perfected the telegraph and launched it on its triumphant course over the whole world. Samuel Finley Breese Morse, the son of a village parson in Connecticut, began his career by drawing portraits of his school-mates for a few cents, but by the age of 30 he had already risen to great fame and popularity as a painter. Some of his portraits of historical personalities, including President Monroe and Lafayette, are still displayed prominently in public buildings in Washington and New York. But when he lost his beautiful young wife he felt unable to continue his work, and went on a long journey to Europe. He was over 40 when he returned to America on board a sailing ship in 1832. That crossing was to be the turning point of his life.

One of the people on board, a young American doctor, enter-tained his fellow-passengers with some scientific conjuring tricks. He had seen Professor Ampère in Paris demonstrate an electro-magnet, and had brought one along, complete with voltaic pile and wires. He showed that a piece of soft iron would become a temporary magnet if a current was sent through a length of wire wound around it, but that it would become non-magnetic again when the current was stopped.

Samuel Morse was the doctor's most attentive spectator. An idea had suddenly crossed his mind—in his own words: 'If the presence of electricity can be made visible in any part of an electrical circuit closed by an electro-magnet, I see no reason why intelligence may not be transmitted instantaneously by electricity.' With that idea, the artist turned inventor.

Morse knew nothing of all the various attempts by earlier inventors to transmit signals by electricity. What he realized was that the time was ripe for a modern instrument of international communication. England's Industrial Revolution had changed the country socially and economically almost out of recognition, and America was following suit. Steam power was superseding the horse in land transport, and the sail on the seas; mass production was taking the place of slow manual work; more and more capital was being invested in industry, demanding profit from a rapid exchange of goods among the countries and continents. Everywhere the pace of daily life was quickening. Only the transmission of news and messages was still as snail-like as it had been thousands of years ago—to be sure, there was the Chappe telegraph, but this was such an expensive method that only governments could afford it: a medium-length telegram would have cost something like £10. Besides, anybody could get to know the semaphore code and read the messages.

Throughout the crossing Morse worked on his idea, covering the pages of his sketchbook with technical drawings. Back in New York he did not seek any new commissions for pictures, but kept body and soul together by giving art lessons while tinkering with his invention day and night. An old easel served as the basis and framework for the telegraph; other parts were a crude electro-magnet which he had wound himself, the wheels of a played-out wooden clock, a single-cell galvanic battery, and other odds and ends.

After some weeks the inexperienced Morse had put his apparatus together. It worked, though not too reliably and only over very short distances. When he closed the circuit between the electro-magnet and the battery, the electro-magnet attracted a small piece of iron—the armature. A pencil was attached to it; underneath ran a strip of paper, pulled by a weight and clockwork gear, and the pencil made slanting lines on the paper.

For two years Morse wrestled with this primitive model. He knew that the principle was sound, but he could not get the signals to travel over more than forty or fifty feet of wire: the current was too weak, even from a multi-cell battery. He wondered what to do, and finally conceived a brilliant idea. He called it the 'relay'—a device which was to grow to great importance in all branches of electrical engineering. 'Relays' were, in the days of the mail-coach, post stations where the tired horses were replaced by fresh ones. Morse translated this principle into technical terms: the weak current arriving at the end of its range was not required to do more than operate a very small electro-magnet; as it attracted the armature, a fresh circuit, powered by another battery, was closed. Thus the incoming signal was able to continue over another length of wire—and another and another, for there was no reason why a chain of relays should not carry the telegraphic signals over any distance.

Morse had in the meantime found a job as an art professor at the New York City University. He showed his invention of the relay to some students; one of them, Alfred Vail, the son of an ironworks owner, offered to help him perfect the telegraph with his mechanical talent and with a few thousand dollars lent by his father.

On 4 September 1837 Morse and Vail invited the whole university to witness the first demonstration of the new model built by the young man; he had also added an invention of his own, a 'key' for closing and opening the circuit easily and rapidly. We call it the 'Morse key'. The message transmitted across the Hall of the university read:

SUCCESSFUL EXPERIMENT WITH TELEGRAPH SEPTEMBER 04 1837

—transmitted with the use of the United States Navy code. Both Morse and Vail, however, realized that another, simpler code, more suitable for the movements of the armature, was essential if the Morse telegraph was to be introduced to the general public.

Morse had the idea of composing it from dots, short signals, and dashes, long ones. He and Vail counted the letters of the alphabet according to their frequency in a newspaper, and allotted the code signals to them—starting with a dot for the most frequent one, the 'e', and a dash for the 't'. Thus they went through the whole alphabet, the numbers and punctuation marks. The 'Morse Code' was put up on the blackboard of the university on 24 January 1838.

Morse had hoped that his struggles would now be over, and the world hail his invention as the new means of communication it had been waiting for; but the most difficult part of the road lay still before him. He submitted the telegraph to Congress, and a Bill for the appropriation of $30,000 for the construction of the first telegraph line from Washington to Baltimore was to be tabled at the next session. Morse, unaware of the fact that the General Postmaster and all the other postmasters, who feared for their livelihood, were his enemies, sailed for Europe, where he wanted to interest other governments in his invention.

The journey was a failure. Cooke and Wheatstone's system had been adopted in Britain. France granted him patent rights, but under conditions which made them practically worthless. In Russia, Tsar Alexander's successor, Nicholas, tore up the agreement which his Chancellor had already signed with Morse. 'As soon as I have these telegraph poles put up', he said, 'my loyal subjects will pull them down, either because they want to chop them up for firewood, or because they think the devil's in those wires.'

When Morse returned to the States he learnt that an economic crisis had begun and his Bill had been quashed at the demand of the General Postmaster. New proposals which he submitted to Congress were ignored. Even Alfred Vail, his faithful young friend, advised him to stop worrying about his invention and take up painting again. The years passed. Morse made a last, desperate appeal to Congress: 'If I cannot get a satisfactory reply I shall return to my brushes and have nothing more to do with the telegraph!'

At last, in March 1843, the 'Morse Bill' was put on the agenda again. It was a dramatic session, extending into the early hours of the morning. Morse, unable to face his final defeat, left the Congress gallery from where he had been watching the debate, and travelled home to New York by the midnight train. He had 27½ cents left after paying for his ticket.

The next day a friend burst into his room. 'You've won! The Bill has been passed by 89 to 83 votes!'

Work on the Washington–Baltimore line began at once; a travelling salesman, Ezra Cornell, supplied the copper wire, which was difficult to get (he ended up as a telegraph tycoon and founded Cornell University at his home town, Ithaca, N.Y.). The General Postmaster did his worst to make things difficult; his men cut the wires at night, pulled the poles down, and even fired pot-shots at the workers. Morse and Vail organized groups of watchmen to end this sabotage, and submitted evidence of it to the president, who forced the General Postmaster to resign.

The first telegram—'What hath God wrought'—was tapped out on 24 May 1844. But the general public took no notice of the

Morse telegraph for post office use (*c.* 1890)

invention. As in England, a chance event helped the telegraph to gain popularity overnight. At that time the Democratic Party held its convention in Baltimore to nominate its candidates for the forthcoming presidential election. James Knox Polk, who was to become the eleventh President of the U.S.A., was put up by the convention, and Silas Wright as the candidate for the vice-presidency. Vail telegraphed the news to Washington, where Wright was attending Congress. Morse brought him the message, but Wright declared that he would not stand. Morse sent the news at once to Baltimore, where it was received with incredulity—after all, no more than half an hour had passed since Wright's nomination. But when a special courier of the Democratic Party arrived from Washington many hours later and confirmed the news, Morse and his miraculous telegraph were the talk of the day. Twelve years of drudgery, privation, and disappointment were at last justified and rewarded by fame and success: dot and dash, the new language of the telegraph, set out on their conquest of the world.

Most European countries followed America's example by accepting the Morse telegraph after all. Here, the first Morse telegraph line was built in 1848 between Hamburg and Cuxhaven; three years later, the first underwater cable—insulated with gutta percha—was laid under the Channel, and in 1858 the first transatlantic cable connected Britain and America. The English scientist, Professor Thomson (later Lord Kelvin), helped in this venture; but after three weeks the cable failed, and another one was laid by the famous *Great Eastern* (see Part II). Thomson superintended the manufacture of the new cable, organized the difficult job of paying it out from the ship, and at last, in 1866, the first dependable and permanent telegraphic connection between Europe and the New World was established.

Samuel Morse reaped the full benefit of his invention. When he died in 1872, at the age of over 80 years, his finger rested on the telegraph key on his table, which connected him with thousands of operators in the language he had created. Other inventors and engineers took over, improving the Morse telegraph—Edison in America, Werner Siemens in Germany, and his brother William in England. Another Siemens brother, Karl, succeeded in overcoming Russian resistance and suspicion towards the telegraph. The Tsar consented to having a private line laid at his palace in St Petersburg, but he made the condition that the wires must be invisible from the outside. Karl Siemens ran the wires along the drain-pipes. This impressed the Tsar so much that he permitted the construction of telegraph lines all over Russia. The firm of Siemens even acquired a copper-mine in the Caucasus to provide the raw material for the production of telegraph wire.

Sir Charles Wheatstone was responsible for one of the most useful improvements in telegraphy with his high-speed automatic system, invented in 1867. It works with a perforating machine with which the operator punches holes, representing the Morse signals, in a paper tape; this is fed into the actual transmitter, which converts the holes into electric impulses at the rate of 300 words a minute. In the receiver, the process is reversed, and the signals come out in Morse code.

But the electric current can accommodate more than one stream of signals. A French telegraph official, Baudot, invented the first system of multiplex telegraphy in 1874; it permits the transmission of several telegrams simultaneously over the same circuit.

A London-born Kentucky music professor, David Edward Hughes, invented the letter-printing telegraph, which did away with the job of 'translating' Morse signals into ordinary letters, in 1854. This miracle of an instrument, which can transmit fifty-two different letters, figures, and signs, is operated by a piano-type keyboard with black and white keys. As soon as one of them is pressed at one end of the line, the corresponding letter is printed at the other end. The modern teleprinter, now the standard means of telegraphic communication in postal, newspaper, and business offices, is the direct descendant of the Hughes machine, which was one of the most ingenious (and complicated) instruments created in the nineteenth century.

What the telegraph did for civilization, what far-reaching changes it brought about in all walks of life, is part of mankind's history. The world drew closer together, news was now really new, time and space dwindled to fractions of seconds. For better or worse, the nations of the earth were tied together by the wires and cables of the telegraph.

'I succeeded in inventing an apparatus that enables me to convert audible sounds into visible signs, and with which, moreover, sounds of every sort may be reproduced by the galvanic current at any distance. I called it the "Telephone".'

The man who wrote these lines around 1860 was a poor young physics teacher at a private school near Frankfurt-am-Main, Germany. Philipp Reis had a little workshop in the schoolyard where he spent every free minute tinkering with all kinds of models and devising experiments for the boys. The mechanics of hearing and speaking interested him specially. He made a replica of a human ear, for he recognized that the first step towards his goal—the transmission of sounds by electricity—was a thorough study of the working of that organ. His wooden ear was fitted with hammer, anvil, and tympanum like a human one, but in place of nerves he used electric wires. When he connected two such ears by wire, with a battery in between, he could hear faintly in one of them what was spoken into the other.

He realized that 'transmitter' and 'receiver' had to be designed differently. He abandoned the ear form, bored a hole in the bung of an old cask, and stretched an animal bladder over it to act as a membrane. This was the first transmitter. He tried to devise an instrument for the reproduction of sounds by fixing a knitting-needle, wound with insulated wire, in the body of a violin.

One day he brought this receiver into the class-room and went back in his shed, where he played a few musical instruments and sang into the 'microphone'. At the other end of the wires, the boys were able to hear some chirping sounds.

In October 1861 he ventured to give a lecture and demonstration before an audience of scientists at the Physics Association in Frankfurt. His subject was: 'Telephony by means of the galvanic current'. 'Every sound and every combination of sounds produces in our ear vibrations of the membrane, which can be represented by a graph', he said. 'It is these vibrations which produce in our brains the impression of the sounds of which they are composed. If we can reproduce these vibrations artificially we will, therefore, hear them just as though they were natural sounds. This is what I have attempted with my apparatus. Since the length of the conducting wires can be extended in the same way as in electric telegraphy, there is no reason why we should not be able to transmit sounds over any distance. You will now hear music which is being played and sung in a house a hundred yards away, with the doors and windows closed. I should like to add that we are, of course, still a long way from the practical use of the telephone, as I have called my instrument.'

If Reis had hoped that the demonstration, which went very well, would cause a sensation, he was disappointed. The savants listened to the sounds emerging from the knitting-needle, smiled indulgently, and went home. Only a single report of the lecture appeared in the *Annals of the Physical Society*; the writer expressed the opinion that the telephone was no more than 'a trifle'. Some enthusiastic amateurs, however, asked him for sets of the instrument, and he had about a dozen of them made by a Frankfurt mechanic.

Two years after the physicists' meeting a popular German magazine, *Die Gartenlaube*, published a description of the Reis telephone under the heading, 'A Toy for Clever Boys', with directions how to build it at home. Another year later, in 1864, Philipp Reis achieved a little more recognition when he exhibited his instrument at the Natural History Congress in Giessen. Some of the younger scientists among the audience congratulated him, and the *Annals* now asked him to write an article on the telephone. He replied, peevishly, that it was 'now too late', and that his invention would become known to the world 'even without a report in the *Annals*'.

It was indeed too late: a few years later he died, only 40 years old, after a long illness which eventually robbed him of his voice —the voice he had hoped to send across the lands with his instrument. 'I have given a great invention to the world', he whispered to a friend shortly before his death, 'but I must leave it to others to develop it.'

Somehow one of the Reis telephone sets had found its way to the natural science department of Edinburgh University, where a young Scottish-American, born in Edinburgh but brought up in Boston, Massachusetts, studied in 1862–3. His name was Alexander Graham Bell. He took a special interest in the instrument because he wanted to devote himself to the speech-training of deaf-mutes. He visited Wheatstone in London, who told him that the German scientist, Helmholtz, had succeeded in making tuning-forks sound by electro-magnetism. Sir Charles and the young man had a long talk about the possibilities of 'musical telegraphy'.

After his return to Boston, Bell took up work as a teacher of the deaf-mute, but went on experimenting with the 'musical telegraph' in his spare time. He had become engaged to one of his students, a beautiful deaf girl, and her father helped him with money for his experiments.

He discovered that when an iron diaphragm was made to vibrate close to a permanent magnet with a coil of wire wound around it, a weak current was induced in the coil, varying with the rhythm of the vibrations. This, Bell realized, was the key to the transmission of sounds. For two years he worked with the help of a mechanic, Thomas Watson, zigzagging along a road which led through virgin technical territory. There were many setbacks and disappointments, and no encouragement at all from the outside world. 'Fearing that ridicule would be attached to the idea of transmitting vocal sounds telephonically', he wrote later, 'I said little or nothing of this plan.' Even his future father-in-law had come to the conclusion that it was all 'a wild dream'.

One day in June 1875 Bell and Watson were testing a transmitter and receiver in adjoining rooms of the workshop when suddenly one of the diaphragms got stuck to its magnet. As Mr Watson tried to pluck it free, Bell noticed that the diaphragm in his own instrument vibrated too. He held his ear to it—and heard a faint sound every time Watson plucked the iron disc in the other room.

'For a long time that day there was little done but plucking and observing the effect', recalled Bell. He realized that chance had shown him the right way; the diaphragm had to be so close to the magnet that it almost touched it, though not quite.

For a few more months Bell and Watson worked hard to build the first practical telephone with an efficient membrane to convert sounds of all kinds into electric impulses in the transmitter, and the impulses back into sounds in the receiver. This early model did not need a battery; it worked solely with the induction currents produced by the moving membrane in the transmitter.

In January 1876 it was to be tried out for the first time. The transmitter was set up in the attic of Bell's house, the receiver on the ground floor. The first words which Bell spoke into his instrument have become famous: 'Mr Watson, please come here, I want you.'

A minute or two later, Watson stood before him, panting from running up the stairs. 'I could hear you!' he cried. 'It works!'

Bell obtained his patent a few weeks later, on his twenty-ninth birthday. In the summer of that year he showed the telephone at the Centennial Exhibition in Philadelphia. At first it attracted no attention at all; but chance helped the inventor again. Pedro II, the young Emperor of Brazil, visited the exhibition and recognized Bell; he had attended one of his speech classes at Boston University a few years before. Bell hastened to demonstrate the telephone to him. When Dom Pedro heard Bell's voice coming from the receiver he jumped from his chair and cried: 'Great Heavens—the thing talks!'

From this moment the telephone was the sensation of the exhibition. After his visit, Professor Thomson (Lord Kelvin), the English physicist, reported: 'I was astonished and delighted. . . . This has been obtained by appliances of a quite homespun and rudimentary character. With somewhat more advanced plans and more powerful apparatus, we may confidently expect that Mr Bell will give us the means of making voice and spoken word audible through the electric wire to an ear hundreds of miles distant.'

Bell and Watson decided to demonstrate the telephone to the general public by going on a lecture tour, starting with Salem. Using the telegraph line they established a telephone connection between the two towns over a distance of fifteen miles. Watson in Boston played some musical instruments and sang as best he could, and Bell in Salem let members of the audience listen: it was, in fact, the first broadcast.

In the summer of 1877 Bell went on his honeymoon trip to England, and took a set of his instruments with him, combining business with pleasure. He spoke before scientists, held telephone conversations with divers in water tanks, and demonstrated the apparatus to Queen Victoria, who took a great liking to the telephone. She had a private line laid between Osborne House, Isle of Wight, and London via Cowes and Southampton. Bell also installed a telephone in the gallery of the House of Commons, and for the first time part of a parliamentary debate was dictated from Westminster to a stenographer in Fleet Street.

Quickest off the mark to introduce the telephone as a permanent means of communication were the Germans. Heinrich Stephan, the go-ahead Postmaster General in Berlin, founder of the Universal Postal Union and inventor of the postcard, had heard rumours about attempts to 'speak through the electric wire' but could get no technical details. When the *Scientific American* published a description of the telephone as its front-page feature in October 1877, Stephan wrote at once to America for a set. Before he received a reply, however, the manager of London's Telegraph Office happened to visit Berlin and brought a pair of telephones with him. On the same day Stephan had them installed in his headquarters and in Potsdam, sixteen miles

away. Werner Siemens attended the trials and realized two things
—first, that there was some scope for improvement of the
instrument, and secondly, that Bell had not yet taken out a
German patent. Within a week he began to mass produce telephones in his own factory, and installed the first permanent line
between the General Post Office and the Telegraph Office in
Berlin early in November 1877. The Berliners went crazy about
the new invention, and bought telephones as toys for their homes
as fast as Siemens could produce them.

Combined speaking and listening telephone (*c.* 1900)

The first central switchboard, without which no local or
regional network could operate, was set up in New Haven,
Connecticut, in 1878; a year later telephone exchanges were
opened in London, Manchester, and Liverpool, with fifty, eighty,
and forty subscribers respectively. They were private enterprises,
and only in 1911 did the General Post Office take over the entire
telephone service in Britain.

Originally, Bell's speaking-tube and listening-tube were
identical instruments. You had to shout a good deal to make your-
self understood at the other end. The voice currents were weak,
and long-distance communication would have been impossible
without the invention of an amplification device by David
Edward Hughes, which he called microphone.

In 1878, a quarter of a century after his invention of the type-printing telegraph, Hughes constructed a simple device for amplifying the voice currents in the telephone transmitter. It consisted, in its original form, of two bars of carbon on which he laid a third bar. The bottom bars were connected with the speaking-tube (via a battery) so that the current had to cross the two points at which the top bar rested on the bottom bars. This produced oscillations of the current according to the sound impulses coming from the speaking-tube. Eventually the carbon bars were replaced by carbon granules, packed immediately behind the diaphragm, and years later the microphone was combined with the listening-tube. It is in this form that we know the small, handy telephone receiver. For sound recording in broadcasting, television, film production, on tape and disc, however, the microphone has had to remain separate.

For thirty, forty or even more years, the big cities of the world depended for their telephone connections on human operators, girls who proved most efficient in these jobs which, like those at the typewriter, helped them to achieve social independence. For the subscriber, however, the manual operation of the telephone exchange was an incessant source of annoyance. When he was in a hurry the operator was often busy and had to let him wait; wrong connections—erring is only human—were frequent; subscribers carrying on an important conversation found that they had been cut off; and there was always the possibility that a third person, the operator, might have eavesdropped on some private talk.

An ailing, highly strung American, Almon B. Strowger, one of the early telephone subscribers, had one row after another with the operators until he felt his nerves could not stand it any longer. He decided to invent an automatic telephone exchange. He did so, and took a patent in 1889; he demonstrated the model of such a switchboard without human operators in an office in Kansas City. One of the directors of the Bell Telephone Company watched it working and declared that the whole system of manually operated exchanges was a mistake; no telephone network should have been installed before the perfection of the automatic switchboard. As it was, the telephone companies hesitated to scrap their manual exchanges which had cost them so much money, and install automatic ones which would cost even more.

For these reasons the coming of automation in telephone communication took a long time. La Porte, Indiana, was the first town to install an automatic switchboard, in 1892. The apparatus was shown a year later at the Chicago Exhibition, but there was not much interest. Again it was Germany, where the telephone had been a State-run enterprise right from the start, which led the way.

Europe's first automatic exchange was installed in Munich in 1909, built by Siemens. A dial, with ten holes for the subscriber's fingers, and marked with the numbers 0 to 9, was attached to the front of the telephone box, and by turning it the subscriber could select the number he required. All the early automatic systems were based on Strowger's 'step-by-step' principle, which is still widely in use today: the dialled digits 'route' the call through several switching stages, which select the exchange, the group of lines, and finally the called line, at the same time switching on the ringing current or the 'engaged' signal.

There are also other systems: the 'panel' system, which is used in many American areas including New York, and in which the switching is done by motor-driven units; the 'crossbar' system, developed by the Bell Company, which works with relays; the 'rotary' system, which has motor-driven shafts and electro-magnetic clutches; and the modern electronic system which establishes the required contact in a gas-filled valve within two thousandths of a second. It can offer several new kinds of service; for instance, numbers which the subscriber wants frequently can be rung up by dialling only 2 digits instead of 6 or 7, and third and fourth subscribers can be included in a telephone conversation. The electronic exchange can repair itself—if a circuit develops a fault, a spare one is switched on automatically.

In long-distance telephone communications the so-called co-axial cable has been found most effective because it can carry hundreds of calls at the same time: it consists of a copper tube as the outer conductor, and a copper wire, the inner conductor, extended along its centre. A great number of transmitters, similar to those used in short-wave radio telephony, and as many receivers are fitted at either end of the cable, each pair of transmitters and receivers working on another frequency (see the chapter on radio). Co-axial cables are especially useful where long-distance connections from town to town are to be made automatically by dialling, without the help of an operator.

But the dial as we know it is on its way out. The telephone of the future will have push-buttons for the digits, arranged on a small panel; and as you can press a button much more quickly than dial a number the pace of putting through telephone calls will be speeded up considerably. The push-button telephone requires an electronic system of routing calls. Perhaps even the familiar sound of the telephone bell will be replaced by another alarm signal if the engineers have their way; they want to find a sound that can be produced by the speech wires so that no extra pair of bell wires has to connect the subscriber to the exchange. It may be a high-pitched chirrup or a low whistle.

The revolution in human communications which was started by the telegraph has been completed by the telephone. The 'personal touch' of a direct conversation over many miles, from town to town, and from continent to continent has intensified and speeded up men's activities in all spheres of life. Of all the innumerable inventions to which we are accustomed the telephone is perhaps the one we could dispense with least of all. There are some staggering figures about its use in our time. The United States has about sixty-five million instruments, roughly one for every three inhabitants; Los Angeles has one for every 1·5 and New York one for every two people. Next comes Britain with nearly eight million telephones, one for every seven inhabitants. The greatest talkers seem to be the Canadians, with 480 calls per head a year; the inhabitants of the U.S.A. make an average of 425. Britain lags far behind with only 80.

Alexander Graham Bell never boasted of his brilliant technical achievement. 'I am sure that I should never have invented the telephone if I had been an electrician', he used to say. 'What electrician would have hit upon so mad an idea? I must confess that to this day I don't understand how it is possible that someone can speak in Washington, and someone else hear him at the foot of the Eiffel Tower.'

# 3

# Radio

WHEN the Duke of Devonshire endowed the University of Cambridge with a new research institute for experimental physics, to be called the Cavendish Laboratory, in the 1860's, James Clerk Maxwell was unanimously elected as its first head. Few of the great scientists who honoured him in this way, however, believed that there was something in Maxwell's theories on electricity and magnetism, and fewer still shared his conviction that the light waves were, in fact, waves of electric and magnetic forces.

Maxwell died ten years before the truth of this theory was proved by a German physicist, Heinrich Hertz, by an ingenious experiment in his laboratory at the Polytechnic in Karlsruhe. In November 1887 Hertz set up an electric induction machine in one corner of the laboratory, and in the other what he called a 'resonator': a wire ring broken by two small metal balls with a gap of a fraction of an inch between them. The inductor had unusually large metal plates, which increased the frequency of the electro-magnetic oscillations produced by it. Between these two machines, the inductor and the resonator, there was no connection at all, just air.

Hertz started the inductor up. To his great satisfaction he found that his—and Maxwell's—theory was correct: electro-magnetic waves travelled from one corner of the room to the other with the speed of light. While they were given off from the metal plates, the gap between the metal balls of the resonator was bridged by tiny sparks. For the first time electro-magnetic waves had been systematically produced and picked up—we might call Hertz's apparatus the first wireless transmitter and receiver.

He never attempted to put his discovery to any practical use. When he died seven years later, at the age of only 37, the seed he had sown was just beginning to sprout. Physicists had to admit that these 'Hertzian waves' and light were essentially the same thing, both electro-magnetic phenomena which differed only in their wavelengths—and in the way we receive them. We can see the light, but we need complicated instruments to make the presence of the other electro-magnetic waves known to our senses.

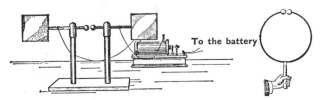

To the battery

Hertz's experimental inductor (transmitter) and resonator (receiver)

Hertz's simple wire ring with the two metal balls was not sensitive enough as a receiver for any practical purposes. In Paris, Edouard Branly, physics professor at the Catholic University, observed in 1890 that metal filings, when subjected to 'Hertzian waves', behaved very strangely. Normally, filings do not transmit an electric current because there are air spaces between them; but when placed within the range of electro-magnetic waves, the filings fuse a little together, enough to offer a conducting path to an electric current. The filings remain a conductor until they are disturbed by shaking or tapping.

Branly called the little glass tube in which he placed his filings 'coherer'; it was the first form of a 'detector' for electro-magnetic waves. Other scientists contributed various ideas and instruments towards the utilization of these waves. Lord Kelvin suggested using them for conveying telegraphic signals. A Russian, Professor Popov of Kronstadt, discovered that the range of the waves could be extended appreciably if they were received by means of wires at roof-top level; with the help of the 'aerial', as we now call his discovery, he was able to make a Morse telegraph receiver register all the flashes of lightning within a range of many miles during thunderstorms in 1895.

Thus a good deal of preparatory work had already been done when a young Italian, the 20-year-old student Guglielmo Marconi, achieved the wireless transmission of signals for the first time, in December 1894. Prompted by his teacher, Professor Righi of the University of Bologna, the young man had worked for many months in his little laboratory in the attic of the Villa Griffone, near Bologna, where he lived with his well-to-do parents. In the middle of the night he woke his mother and asked her to come up and watch an important experiment.

Guglielmo pressed a Morse key, sparks crackled, and at the other end of the attic, twelve feet away, an electric bell rang. Signora Marconi realized only much later that she had watched an historic event—the first transmission of a signal by wireless.

Young Marconi moved his equipment into the garden of the villa; assisted by his brother, he extended the range of the signals, and succeeded in transmitting them across a little hill. Each time a signal arrived, the brother climbed up the hill and did a Red Indian dance to inform Guglielmo that the experiment had been successful. Early in 1896 the transmitting distance had grown to almost two miles, and Marconi's mother—who came from Ireland—suggested to him that he should take his invention to Britain, which was bound to have the greatest interest in the new means of communication: it was just what her ships at sea and her lightships needed.

The first thing Marconi did in London was to take out a patent for his invention. An introduction to the Engineer-in-Chief of the General Post Office, Mr (afterwards Sir) William Preece, got him an offer to demonstrate his apparatus on the roof of the Post Office building, with another set installed in a house on the Thames Embankment. Marconi wondered anxiously if his crude home-made equipment would work well enough to satisfy the critical audience of scientists, post office engineers, and business men who assembled on the roof to watch the tests, but they were completely successful. The next demonstration took place on Salisbury Plain by invitation of the Army and Navy authorities; Marconi achieved transmission over distances of up to eight miles.

In May 1897 the world's first wireless telegraph station was set up at Lavernock Point, near Cardiff, with a 100-foot mast for the aerial, to find out how the signals would travel across water. At first the signals from the island of Flat Holme, in the middle of the Bristol Channel, would not arrive at all. Marconi, unruffled, tried to find out what was wrong, and made a number of improvements. Then the signals came, but weak and distorted. Marconi lengthened the aerial considerably, and started a new series of tests.

A German expert, Professor Adolf Slaby, and his assistant, Count George Arco, had been sent over by the Berlin authorities to watch Marconi's experiments. 'I shall never forget', wrote Professor Slaby, 'how we were huddled together, five men, in a large wooden box to escape the strong wind, eyes and ears strained to the utmost, watching the receiver. Suddenly the flag went up on the island, and there came the first tapping, the first clear Morse signals, carried silently and invisibly from the rocky coast over there, which we could hardly see in the haze. . . . It was the Morse letter *v* which came across as agreed.'

Marconi turned and smiled at the men in the box. '*Ecco*', he said, 'there you are!' He had never doubted that his system would work.

Within a short while the story of his success spread all over Europe, and Marconi was the hero of the day. The mocking and spiteful voices in England who had called the young Italian an 'organ-grinder without a monkey' were silenced once and for all. It was clear even to the most primitive minds that now, for the first time, there was a possibility of communicating with ships on the high seas.

While Slaby and Arco returned to Berlin and began with their own wireless experiments (which included lifting aerial wires to an altitude of 1,000 feet by balloon), Marconi succeeded in increasing the range of his signals with amazing speed. In the summer of 1898 a Dublin newspaper employed Marconi, himself a keen yachtsman, to 'cover' the Kingstown Regatta for its readers; he did so by following the boats in a tug equipped with a wireless transmitter, and tapped his report straight into the Morse key. It was received by a shore station, from where it was telephoned to the newspaper office. It was the first Press report sent by wireless. Perhaps more important, though less spectacular, was the installation of transmitters in two isolated lighthouses off the Irish coast, commissioned by Lloyd's.

Shortly afterwards the Prince of Wales, later Edward VII, fell ill on board his yacht off the Isle of Wight. Queen Victoria, who was staying at Osborne House on the island, was anxious to be kept informed of her son's progress. Marconi offered to set up wireless communication between the Prince's yacht and Osborne House; for sixteen days contact was maintained without a break or hitch, and 150 telegrams were sent in both directions.

A few months later, in March 1899, human lives were saved for the first time by wireless telegraphy. A patrol boat, one of the few British ships which had already been equipped with Marconi's apparatus, happened to discover a steamer stranded on the Goodwin Sands, and informed the South Foreland lighthouse by wireless. Lifeboats were sent out, and everybody on board the steamer was saved.

The next step was the opening of the first cross-Channel communication by wireless. The twenty-odd miles were bridged with the greatest ease; yet only three years before Marconi had been quite happy to achieve a range of a few hundred yards. He had increased the range fifty-fold within this incredibly short time by constant experimenting and improving. But the greatest test was yet to come.

A few dozen miles of land or water presented no difficulty to the wireless telegraph—this had been proved. But what about a few thousand miles? It was not only a question of increasing the power of the transmitter and the sensitivity of the receiver. The fundamental question was this: did the electro-magnetic waves, as some physicists believed, travel out into space in a straight line, or did they follow the curvature of the earth? In the former case, all hope of bridging the great oceans by wireless would have to be given up.

There was no other way of finding out but by experiment. On 12 December 1901 Marconi and a few of his assistants squatted in a derelict wooden hut near St John's, Newfoundland. The temperature was well below freezing-point, the storm blew in from the cracks in the walls, and the rain seeped down through holes in the roof. There was no nourishment except some cocoa and a bottle of whisky. Outside, a kite from which the aerial was suspended fluttered 400 feet high in the gale.

At noon, East American time, the transmitter at Poldhu, Cornwall, 2,170 miles away, was to start sending the Morse letter *s*. But there was nothing to be heard in the headphones except 'atmospherics'. 'It was still my opinion that electric waves would not be stopped by the curvature of the earth', Marconi said later, 'and therefore could be made to travel any distance separating any two places on our planet.'

At 12.30 Marconi's companion, who was listening, suddenly lifted his hand and grinned. 'It's here', he said. Marconi took the headphones and strained his ears. There it was, the signal from the other side of the ocean: three pips, repeated over and over again. The wireless waves had crossed the ocean.

Marconi had to pay dearly for his fame and success. Some, among them Edison, said that he had been a victim of his own imagination when he believed he had heard the signals from Poldhu. Others called him a cheat. An American telegraph company threatened to sue him because he had infringed their monopoly of telegraphic communication in Newfoundland. Other groups of business men and politicians accused Marconi himself of trying to establish a world monopoly in wireless communication, and German ships, equipped with Professor Slaby's transmitters, were forbidden to communicate with those using the Marconi system. There developed what was called the 'Marconi scandal' in which the inventor was declared guilty of all kinds of evil intentions and manœuvres.

Yet his invention continued to prove its immense value in incident after incident. In 1909 two ships collided, and 1,700 passengers and crew would have lost their lives if rescue vessels had not been called by wireless. Shortly afterwards a murderer trying to escape from England, the notorious Dr Crippen, was recognized on board a liner, and the captain informed Scotland Yard by wireless; on his arrival in Canada he was arrested.

The first international wireless conference at the beginning of the century agreed on the letters S O S as a distress signal. It is not, as popularly interpreted, an abbreviation of 'Save Our Souls', but was chosen for the simplicity of the Morse signals: three dots, three dashes, three dots. It played a dramatic part in the disaster of the *Titanic*, which struck an iceberg on her maiden voyage in April 1912. Thanks to the S O S signals ceaselessly sent out by the liner's heroic wireless operator, who sank with the ship, 700 people were saved.

The miracle of wireless telegraphy had hardly materialized

when people began to ask how long it would be until the wireless waves could be made to carry voices and music as well, not only Morse signals—perhaps even into private homes. But there were formidable technical obstacles.

Early wireless telegraphy stations used high-frequency generators, which produced a 'train' of waves, or electric arcs which generated intermittent pulses, in their transmitters. For reception, Marconi had replaced Branly's primitive coherer by a magnetic detector of incoming waves; the signals closed a relay circuit, which amplified them enough to make them audible in the headphone or to work a writing telegraph. So far, so good; this system was quite adequate for simple Morse signals, but it was unable to transmit and receive the complicated sounds of

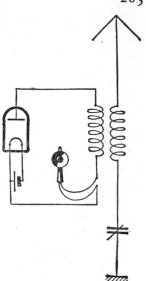

Fleming's thermionic-valve circuit for telephone amplification

speech and music. Radio telephony had to wait until a new piece of equipment had been developed.

Three men worked on it independently from each other—an Englishman, an Austrian, and an American. Professor (later Sir) Ambrose Fleming, a Lancastrian, who had helped Marconi with the building of the Poldhu station, discovered in 1904 that a vacuum tube with two electrodes, one heated and one cold, has the effect of a detector of alternating wireless waves; it allows them to pass in one direction only, with the electrons that are emitted from the heated cathode. This rectifying effect makes the tube a detector. He called it 'thermionic valve'.

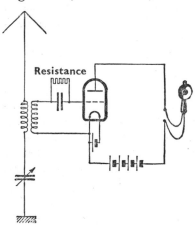

Lee de Forest's amplifier-valve circuit

Two years later Robert von Lieben in Vienna and Lee de Forest in America, who had both realized the great possibilities of Fleming's thermionic valve, improved it decisively so as to make it an instrument not only for detecting waves but also for amplifying them. Both were originally thinking only of creating a relay for telephony by wire. They placed a third electrode, a perforated 'grid' between Fleming's two; it was supplied with the sound impulses coming from the microphone, and these modulated waves acted as an invisible brake on the stream of electrons between the cathode and the anode, regulating it very finely. In this way the weak microphone impulses could be amplified as much as required, with complete accuracy. And that was not all: a few years later several research workers discovered that the thermionic valve could also be used to generate high-frequency, continuous-wave oscillations for the transmitter.

Lieben died young, too soon to take part in the development of radio telephony and broadcasting. But Lee de Forest extended his system for the purposes of transmission as well as reception; his 'audion' valve stands at the entrance to the vast field which we now call electronics.

Here, then, was the instrument which made the transmission of modulated microphone waves possible. A continuous 'carrier wave' is sent out by the transmitter, with the impulses coming from the microphone superimposed on it; the superimposition is done by the thermionic valve. In the receiver, the carrier wave is 'filtered off', the modulated waves are amplified by another set of thermionic valves, and translated back into sound in the headphone or loudspeaker.

In 1907 technicians in the British Navy transmitted a band performance of 'God Save the King' from ship to ship during a world cruise. In 1909 Lee de Forest installed a microphone in the New York Metropolitan Opera, and transmitted Caruso's voice to his laboratory. During the First World War, Marconi experimented with wireless telephony; he was able to establish contact between a shore station and a warship thirty miles out at sea. In 1917 German technicians succeeded in transmitting speech and music between two stations on the western front.

In the autumn of 1919 Dr Hans Bredow, a Telefunken director, gave a demonstration lecture in Berlin; speech and music were received from the Königswusterhausen transmitter near the capital. The reproduction by loudspeaker, however, was distorted, and when Dr Bredow told the Post Minister that one day he would be able to speak from his desk without wires to every post official in Germany, the minister patted Dr Bredow on the back as if he were a madman who must be humoured. Only one of the journalists present wrote enthusiastically: 'A perspective worthy of Jules Verne—the future political orator speaking into the wireless transmission apparatus, and being heard at the same time in a thousand different halls all over Germany by a million people!' He never dreamt that his estimate was on the conservative side. Two years later Bredow was appointed Secretary of State for wireless telegraphy and telephony at the German General Post Office.

Marconi attended the Paris Peace Conference as a delegate, but he got away as soon as possible to his new yacht *Elettra*, which he had equipped as his laboratory for wireless telephony. He set up a shore station near Lisbon, and succeeded in carrying on a conversation over a distance of 300 miles. A few months later, on 2 November 1920, the world's first broadcasting station, in Pittsburgh, started its regular service with a report on Harding's election as President of the U.S.A.

England was the first European country to take an interest in broadcasting. But while in America there were no legal restrictions to setting up transmitters and broadcasting anything one fancied, the law in Britain hampered technical progress very much. The amateurs, who were the pioneers of wireless research (especially in the field of short-wave communication), were severely handicapped by the ban on transmitters with more than 10-watt power. It took many months to persuade the authorities that a 100-watt station could do no harm, and eventually the Marconi company was allowed to set up such a station at their laboratory in Writtle, near Chelmsford. It began a once-weekly service in February 1922; this went on for half an hour only, and of that short time part had to be used for Morse signalling. After each seven minutes there had to be a three-minute interval during which the station was tuned to the telegraphy frequency of a Government transmitter—in case the authorities should suddenly decide to prohibit any more broadcasting. The entertainment programme of the station was rather poor; no artist of repute was prepared to travel into darkest Essex for a few minutes' performance; only Dame Nellie Melba came once.

In May 1922 London was allowed to have its first station, also of 100-watt power, called 2 LO. The studio was on the top floor of Marconi House. At first it was forbidden to broadcast music; but when this absurd restriction was removed the station became a great success, and letters from enthusiastic listeners came from all over Britain and France. Popular demand for the introduction of a regular, well-organized, technically efficient broadcasting service with a nation-wide network of transmitters grew daily stronger, and in November 1922 the British Broadcasting Corporation was formed as a public body by half a dozen manufacturers of wireless equipment. It was given a Charter granting it the sole right of broadcasting in the United Kingdom. On 14 November the London station started with its daily programmes; the next day Birmingham followed, and shortly afterwards Manchester.

On the Continent, four-year-old Czechoslovakia was the first country to start regular programmes (May 1923), after President Masaryk had expressed his great interest in the new means of entertainment and information for the people. Germany followed in October 1923; the first item was a concert by a cellist and a pianist (during which a rectifier valve burnt out), given in the makeshift studio of a gramophone company near the Potsdamer Platz in Berlin.

Those were the modest beginnings. Enthusiasts listened with uncomfortable headphones clamped over their ears, by means of crystal detectors whose 'cat's whiskers'—thin wires touching a sensitive spot in the crystal—needed constant adjustment. But even in those days it was clear what tremendous part the radio was going to play in every walk of life once the technical teething-troubles were overcome. Later in the 1920's modestly priced, fool-proof loudspeaker receivers with amplifier valves began to appear in the shops, and innumerable pieces of new equipment in the broadcasting studios; the old carbon-granule microphone, for instance, gave way to the 'ribbon' type, in which a very light ribbon of aluminium foil is suspended between the poles of a permanent magnet so that it vibrates with the sound waves and induces voice frequency currents in the magnet. The reverse process takes place in the 'ribbon' loudspeaker.

At first, broadcasting was carried out exclusively in the medium

(100–550-metre) and long-wave (1,000–2,000-metre) bands, but the general tendency among wireless technicians has always been the utilization of shorter waves—for the longer the wave, the more space it needs in the wave-band, and as an increasing number of stations appeared on the air they began to disturb one another, despite international agreements not to step on each other's toes. In the short-wave region (16–75 metres), however, there is much more room. It is widely used where long distances have to be covered (among other things, for political propaganda from one country to another), because short waves can be received when they are reflected by the 'Heaviside layer' of the upper atmosphere around the earth.

But where we want no more than a first-class, disturbance-free reception of our local or regional transmitter, ultra-short waves are the answer. We know this system as 'V.H.F.', Very High Frequency, for the shorter the wavelength the greater the frequency of the electro-magnetic oscillations generated by the transmitter valve. It would be equally correct to call this system, as it was done in the beginning, 'F.M.', Frequency Modulation. Thanks to the research work by an American, Edwin H. Armstrong, in the 1930's, it was introduced not only in sound broadcasting but also in television for high-quality transmission of signals at short range. Normally, sound broadcasting is done by the 'amplitude modulation' system: the amplitude, or lateral flow, of the carrier wave is modulated by the microphone current, but the frequency remains constant. In frequency modulation, the amplitude does not change, but the frequency of the carrier-wave is modulated by the microphone current. This system lends itself especially to transmission in the very short wavebands between 1- and 10-metre length; and here a great number of stations can be accommodated without interfering with each other. But the greatest advantage of the V.H.F. system is that it can transmit the whole range of sounds and notes from the lowest to the highest, which is impossible with amplitude modulation.

Frequency modulation has also enabled the wireless technicians to realize an old ambition of theirs: stereophonic, 'three-dimensional' transmission of sound. This requires not only two microphones placed at a certain distance from each other in the studio, but also two 'channels' carrying separately their oscillations to two transmitters, and two receivers and loudspeakers in

K

the listener's home; this, at least, was the arrangement during the first experimental transmissions. A system tried out in Britain in 1960, however, makes it possible to transmit both channels over a single station to a single transmitter with two loudspeakers. We shall return to the technique of stereophony in connection with the gramophone disc.

In radio reception, no fundamental changes took place between the introduction of the valve receiver and the early 1950's. Then, however, an entirely new development began in the entire sphere of electronics with the invention of the transistor.

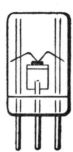 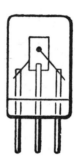

*Left:* Point-contact transistor; black rectangle is the crystal. *Right:* Junction transistor; thin wires lead to two points on the crystal

It is a brilliant achievement of the period after the Second World War, although its origins go back to the early days of radio, of the 'cat's whisker' receiver. The detector crystal, usually a piece of the lead sulphide, galena, rectified the incoming radio signals by turning the alternating electro-magnetic waves into a direct current which could operate the headphones. Such a crystal is called a semi-conductor, that is, half conductor and half insulator.

When the amplifier radio with loudspeaker came into use, research into semi-conductors almost ceased; the thermionic valve seemed so much more efficient for detecting radio signals and amplifying them. The war, however, reawakened the interest in these crystals when scientists looked around for alternatives to the fragile valves, which required high-voltage current for heating the cathode.

In 1948 a group of research workers at the Bell Telephone

Laboratories in America—John Bardeen, Walter H. Brattain, and William Shockley—demonstrated their first transistor. It does the job of the thermionic valve: it controls electrons. The main part of the transistor is a piece of germanium or silicon, both of which are semi-conductors; by introducing certain 'impurities' into the crystal it is turned into a kind of miniature racecourse for electrons. If an incoming radio signal injects, say, one million electrons into the crystal, fifty million electrons will start to flow in it in a closed circuit. The result is that amplification is achieved

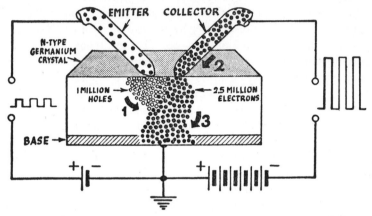

Enlarged point-contact transistor. 'Holes' are impurity atoms lacking an electron, flowing in direction 1, and attracting to themselves other electrons, setting up a flow in directions 2 and 3

with a minimum of power—in fact, a loudspeaker radio with transistors instead of valves can work for many months on a torch battery.

This miraculous little gadget, which is shorter than a match-stick and not much thicker, found one of its first applications in portable radio sets. Apart from its obvious advantages—that it is so small, that it needs no high-voltage power, that it operates 'cold', that it is unbreakable and has a very long life—it lends itself excellently to insertion in 'printed' circuits, another important development in the manufacture of receivers: this makes the laborious wiring and soldering of the set by hand unnecessary. In a series of automatic processes a copper surface is first laminated to the plastic chassis of the receiver, then the pattern of the circuit is outlined in acid-resistant ink on the copper foil, and finally the copper surface which is not protected by the ink is washed away by another chemical. This leaves the circuit 'printed' in copper. This technique overcomes the problem of assembling very small parts, such as transistors, which are just clipped in.

The use of transistors in radio sets was only a start; soon they began to replace the thermionic valve in many products of electronic engineering, from hearing-aids to guitars, from instruments in space rockets to electronic computers. We have also mentioned (see Part I) that solar and atomic energy can be changed directly into electricity by the use of semi-conductors.

Short-wave radio-telephony—as distinct from broadcasting for entertainment—has conquered many fields. It has largely superseded wireless telegraphy at sea. It is indispensable in ship-to-shore and aircraft-to-ground communication. Traffic control policemen, explorers on mountain tops and in polar wastes, ambulance and taxi drivers, workers in nuclear power stations and on large construction projects, and of course all branches of the armed forces (where the 'walkie-talkie' was first introduced) are making much use of the radio-telephone. In some areas you can even call any ordinary telephone subscriber from a moving car; doctors in hospitals and employees in large factories or office buildings are kept in touch with the switchboard by means of minute 'personal-call' sets; and international conferences are conducted with the members listening to the proceedings by means of pocket-size receivers which can be tuned to pick up one of a number of languages into which the speeches are translated by interpreters, each with his own microphone and transmitter. The transistor has made this great variety of applications possible.

# 4

✦✦✦✦✦✦✦✦✦✦✦✦✦✦✦✦✦✦

# Sounds Preserved

ONE OF THE problems which Thomas Alva Edison began to tackle in his new laboratories at Menlo Park, New Jersey, into which he had moved in 1876, was a recording machine for telegraphic signals: a wax cylinder into which a needle imprinted the dots and dashes of the Morse code. As he was talking to an assistant, a sound coming from his lips made the needle jerk and prick his finger.

The average technician would not have paid much attention to this incident, but would have licked the drop of blood from his finger and gone on experimenting with the machine. But Edison —the man who once said that genius was 98 per cent perspiration and 2 per cent inspiration—turned his mind immediately to the question why the needle had pricked him. If the vibrations caused by the human voice were powerful enough to make it jerk, then there was a possibility of recording sounds on some suitable surface, and of reproducing them by reversing the process—by making the needle skim over the marks it had made on that surface.

Edison drew a rough sketch of the machine he had in mind and had it built at once by his mechanics: a brass cylinder mounted on a horizontal spindle with a handle for turning it, and a kind of ear-trumpet with a piece of parchment as a membrane and a needle attached to the narrow end of the trumpet, mounted on a pivot above the cylinder. It was completed within a day. Edison wrapped a sheet of soft tin foil tightly around the cylinder, turned the handle, and spoke into the trumpet the first thing that happened to come into his mind, a nursery rhyme: 'Mary had a little lamb, its fleece was white as snow. . . .'

Then he put the needle back to the point where it had started, and turned the handle again; and out came the faint but distinct words: 'Mary had a little lamb . . .'

'I was never so taken aback in my life', Edison confessed. 'I was always afraid of things that worked the first time.'

The phonograph, as Edison called his talking machine, created a sensation. Visitors who wanted to see and hear it crowded the laboratories; special trains were run to Menlo Park; Edison was invited to Washington to demonstrate his machine to senior government officials and record the voices of politicians. 'The Wizard of Menlo Park' they called the inventor all over America. Some people did not believe their own ears, and suspected that they were being tricked by a ventriloquist.

Before long Edison realized that he had made a mistake by demonstrating a machine that was far from perfect. The recording material, tin foil, was difficult to handle; the recording quality was poor, and after a few repetitions the sound was too faint to be heard. Within a few months the public lost all interest in the phonograph, and Edison turned his attention to other technical problems.

Ten years later, in 1888, he took it up again. Working for five days and nights, he improved the machine in every way. The tin foil was replaced by wax cylinders, the handle by a clockwork mechanism. In its new form the phonograph became the favourite nickel-in-the-slot machine of the fun arcades, netting Edison a fortune. As a dictation machine for offices and other places where speech recording had to be done quickly and replayed without special processing it outlived its inventor by many years—until the tape recorder took over.

Other inventors tried to improve sound-recording in the 1880's. Alexander Graham Bell, assisted by an Englishman, Charles S. Tainter, produced his 'graphophone' machine, which had a cardboard cylinder coated with wax and a sharp, flat-fronted stylus for recording while the reproduction was done by a round-ended stylus which did not damage the wax too much. As with the Edison machine, the sound vibrations were cut into the wax vertically, forming grooves with little 'hills and dales'.

The decisive step was made by a German-American inventor, Emile Berliner, in 1887, when he replaced Edison's cylinder by a flat disc, and the 'hill-and-dale' recording system by a horizontal, 'lateral' one; later he introduced the copying of records, similar to the way in which photographic pictures are reproduced. The sound was recorded on a wax disc, from which a 'negative' metal matrix was made, and from this as many copies as required could be moulded in a press in a plastic material. Much of this process is still being used in the production of discs—although, of course, enormous strides have been made in sound recording and reproduction since Berliner's days, the most important of them being the introduction of electrical recording, by means of microphone and amplifier, in the 1920's, which superseded the mechanical recording in which the sounds were spoken, sung, or played into the horn of the machine. Some time later, mechanical reproduction was largely replaced by the electrical 'pick-up' system. Further improvements in disc recording and reproduction came after the Second World War: the 'long-playing' record—invented by Dr Peter Goldmark of the Columbia Broadcasting System and marketed in 1948—has up to 300 grooves per inch and revolves at only $33\frac{1}{3}$ or 45 revolutions per minute instead of at the 78 revolutions introduced by Berliner, making it possible to accommodate a whole symphony on one disc; 'high-fidelity' recording and reproduction, which gives the whole range of sounds, not just a sector of all the vibrations produced by the human voice and musical instruments (this is not so much a matter of a basically new system but of high-quality electronic equipment); and 'stereo' sound, which works with two microphones and two loudspeakers representing our two ears, which hear the same sound at slightly different times, so that we have the impression of space and depth (this entails the cutting of two sound tracks, one for each microphone and loudspeaker, on the same disc).

The principle of the 'gramophone'—this was the trade name given to Berliner's system when the Gramophone Company was formed in 1898—has remained unchanged. It was his great idea to turn the Edison wax cylinder, which could not be copied, into the flat disc of which any number of copies can be made. In this way the gramophone became a practical instrument, and our century is fortunate to have the voices of its great contemporaries, the performances of its best artists recorded on disc matrices for us and for posterity.

In the next chapter we shall deal with the history of sound

recording on film, but now we have to trace the development of another technique of recording which has grown to major importance in many branches of entertainment and communication. It goes back to 1899 when Valdemar Poulsen in Copenhagen, one of the pioneers of wireless telegraphy, invented what he called the 'Telegraphone'. It was a little box with two drums winding and unwinding a length of steel tape or steel wire which was pressed against the poles of an electro-magnet as it moved from one drum to the other (Poulsen also described the use of some material such as paper tape covered with a magnetizable metallic dust). The sound impulses converted into electric modulations in a microphone acted on the electro-magnet, which magnetized the steel accordingly; these recorded impulses could be converted back into sound by moving them again past the electro-magnet, which was then switched to receiving them and making them audible by the action of a membrane. Or, to quote Poulsen's own description in his patent specifications:

'The invention is based on the fact that, when a body of magnetizable material is touched at different points and at different times by an electro-magnet included in an electric circuit, which carries electric currents varying in accordance with the vibrations of sound, its parts are subjected to such varied magnetic influences that, conversely by the action of the magnetizable body upon the electro-magnet, the same sounds are subsequently given out in the telephone (or loudspeaker) as those which originally caused the magnetic action upon the magnetizable body.'

Poulsen went on to describe this apparatus as a new kind of machine for phonographic recording and for recording telephone messages automatically when the subscriber was not at home—it might, he said, even answer the caller with a message such as: 'Ring me again at three o'clock!' Poulsen emphasized, quite rightly, one of the most important advantages of his system: that the recording could be 'wiped' from the steel by passing a steady current to it through the electro-magnet so that the same wire or tape could be used over and over again.

The invention was far ahead of its time and of technical developments at the turn of the century. For nearly twenty years it remained forgotten. From 1918 American technicians took it up again, and a German engineer, Kurt Stille, produced a practical wire-recording system for use in broadcasting. Another German inventor, Pfleumer, worked from 1929 on the development of a magnetic tape in which a soft-iron powder was mixed with some organic binding medium. But another six years passed before this idea took practical shape in the form of the German 'Magneto-phon' system, the first of all the systems using plastic tape coated with ferrous oxide, which has become the standard material in tape recording. Even before the Second World War, entire programmes of the German broadcasting network were assembled from such recordings, and the quality was good enough to make even the experts believe that the sound was 'live'. The machines, however, were large and heavy, but during the war lighter models were made for the use of the German forces in the field. At the same time, some American models were developed, also for war purposes such as recording in aircraft; much of this work was done by a young engineer, Marvin Camras, at a research laboratory in Chicago after 1940.

It was only after the war that the small, practical, all-purpose tape recorder came into being in Britain, America, and Germany, ready for use in the homes and offices, and easy to work; large models, with a tape speed of 30 inches per second, are made almost exclusively for broadcasting stations, film, television, and gramophone studios. Here the fact that tape recordings can be copied on disc, film or other tape without any loss of quality, is of the greatest value; so is the ease with which they can be cut and edited like film. If during a disc recording anything goes wrong, the whole disc has to be recorded again; on tape, any part of the performance—even a syllable—can be cut out; what is imperfect can be wiped, and re-recorded. There is also less background noise and distortion on tape, and the plastic reels can stand up to much rougher handling than discs.

A great variety of these machines have been developed for innumerable purposes, from the big 30-inch console for the recording studio down to the pocket-size dictation model with a tiny reel of tape, running at a speed of only 3¾ inches per second. For the amateur 7½ inches is sufficient; 15 inches permits perfect musical recordings. Apart from its use as an instrument for home entertainment, the tape recorder is extremely practical in its portable, battery-operated, transistorized form for reporters; it helps actors and singers to hear themselves and improve their

* K

performances, and public speakers to rehearse their speeches at home; dramatic training, music appreciation, foreign-language practice, speech therapy, announcements over public-address systems, continuous recording of important business conversations and of ground-to-aircraft communication at airports—in all these fields the tape recorder has already become quite indispensable. In television, as we shall see later, it plays a very special part.

But there are yet other uses for this versatile instrument, perhaps even more important ones, in industrial automation: these uses, too, shall be dealt with in a later chapter.

# 5

━◇━◇━◇━◇━◇━◇━◇━◇━◇━◇━◇━

## Pictures

WHAT made our primitive forefathers, tens of thousands of years
ago, draw and paint men, beasts, and objects of their everyday
lives on the walls of the caves that were their homes? Did they
believe that to possess the pictures of their enemies or their quarry
would give them magical powers in fight and pursuit? Were there
some early Rembrandts and Picassos among the cavemen, keen to
exercise their art? Did they want to preserve the scenes they had
watched and experienced as a kind of pictorial record, or perhaps
for sentimental reasons?

We do not know. But we know that although the art of drawing, painting, and sculpturing goes back very far in human
civilization, there has for a long time also been a feeling that somehow Nature might be persuaded to record its own picture. Many
legends tell us of such happenings; tradition has it, for instance,
that the picture of Christ remained imprinted on the kerchief with
which St Veronica wiped His face on the road to Calvary.

In the eighteenth century the vague idea that such pictures
might be made by the action of the sun on some chemical substance seems to have ripened. In 1760 a Frenchman, Tiphaigne de
la Roche, published a book in which he described the effect of
light on a surface covered with silver nitrate, and discussed the
possibility of using that effect to make an 'artificial painting'.
The Swedish chemist, Karl Wilhelm Scheele, studied the dis-
coloration of silver salts by sunlight, and Professor Charles, the
inventor of the hydrogen balloon, tried to make silhouettes—
which were then the great fashion—with the help of silver salts.

Much scientific interest was aroused by the discovery, in 1799,
of several perfect reproductions of paintings in the possession of

the Duke of Hamilton. Lady Anne, daughter of the ninth duke, decided to freshen up some small family portraits in window recesses which had not been renovated since the 1670's. On the original mount paper behind them she found excellent impressions of the pictures in tones of blue and lilac. She gave eight of these papers to scientifically minded friends; one of them, showing a portrait of the Duke of Hamilton painted in 1678, has survived and is in the possession of the Royal Society in London.

Systematic experiments began before the turn of the nineteenth century. In 1802 Thomas Wedgwood, son of Josiah Wedgwood the famous potter, published an account of his studies and those of Sir Humphry Davy: they tried to find a method of copying paintings on glass, and of recording profiles by the action of the sunlight on paper soaked in silver nitrate. But they found no way of fixing these images by removing the affected part of the chemical coating. In a famous experiment, Wedgwood put some plant leaves on the paper with the chemical on it; the part of the paper which was not covered turned black after being exposed to sunlight, while the portion under the leaves became only grey, with the stems and veins standing out in white.

In 1811 an ex-officer who had fought in Napoleon's army, Nicéphore Niepce, took up experimenting with light-sensitive chemicals. He did two things which secured him a place of honour in technical history although he never reached the goal to which he aspired. First, he created the term 'photography'; secondly, he thought of using the 'camera obscura' for recording pictures (though some sources say that Thomas Wedgwood did this in 1794).

Leonardo da Vinci had described the camera obscura in his notebooks, but the principle may have been known much earlier: when the light rays enter a small hole in a dark box, they throw an upside-down and reduced picture of the scene outside the hole on the opposite wall of the box. A German monk, Zahn, improved the camera obscura by fitting an optical lens into the hole; now the images were upright and much sharper. In 1569, the Italian physicist, Giambattista della Porta, built the first large-size camera obscura of the type which can still be seen in operation in a museum on Edinburgh's castle rock. The hole with the convex lens is at the top of a dark chamber, and above it is a mirror fixed at an angle of 45 degrees to the horizon so that the light rays are reflected vertically downwards, producing an image of the town on a large, round, white table. It is said that della Porta built his camera obscura to allow the ladies to watch what was going on in the streets without being seen themselves.

Niepce, an ardent inventor though not a scientifically trained man, tried out innumerable substances for capturing and retaining the light rays in a little camera obscura, eventually hitting on asphalt varnish. If asphalt is exposed to the sun for a long time,

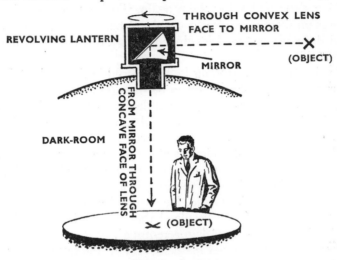

Camera obscura

the exposed part becomes soluble in vegetable oils. After exposure, Niepce etched the asphalt-covered plates and then printed them. It was a lengthy and complicated process, and it produced no more than the contours of a picture.

At the end of nearly twenty years of work, chance brought Niepce in touch with another man whose mind was occupied by the same problem, Louis Jacques Mandé Daguerre, a decorator, artist, and diorama showman. The two inventors signed an agreement to pool their efforts and share the proceeds, if any. Daguerre had been using silver nitrate, but without spectacular success. After two years' collaboration with Niepce, in 1831, he found that silver iodide was much more suitable. Meanwhile, Niepce had perfected his photographic camera obscura: a neat, oblong box measuring six inches from the back wall with the sensitive plate to the lens, which he had fitted into a tube that could be telescoped for focusing. Another two years later Niepce died, almost on the eve of what modern research workers call the 'break-through'.

Daguerre worked on; four more years passed until, in the autumn of 1837, chance intervened again to reward his patient labours. He had put a few plates, which he thought were spoilt because he had not exposed them long enough, in an old cupboard. After a few weeks he took them out with the intention of washing them and using them again. To his utter surprise the pictures on them were clearly visible. What had happened? How could these plates have 'developed' all by themselves in the old cupboard?

He cleared out everything he had stored in the cupboard until it was completely empty—or so he thought at first. But then he discovered, in the narrow fissures at the bottom, a number of tiny, glittering balls of mercury, which had run out of a broken bottle.

So that was the secret! The silver iodide plates had been developed by the chemical action of the mercury vapour. Daguerre tested his theory, exposed a plate for a short time, and held it over a heated bowl of mercury in a dark room. The picture appeared as though by magic. He fixed it by bathing the plate in sodium sulphate, which dissolved the silver haloids. At last he held in his hands the first 'daguerreotype'.

Daguerre demonstrated his discovery to the famous physicist and astronomer, François Arago, secretary to the Academy of Science, who called a meeting of the Academy for August 1839 at which he personally introduced the inventor and his system of making the light reproduce Nature. Arago also announced that this invention was not to be kept secret, but that France offered it as a gift to the whole world. Daguerre and Niepce's son were granted State pensions by an Act of Parliament. 'One day', declared the member who introduced the bill, 'it will be possible to reproduce Nature at any place not only on the surface of the earth, but also high up in the air and deep below the sea.'

Daguerre's success surpassed all his expectations. The people of Paris nearly went out of their minds with enthusiasm, just as they had done over the first balloon ascents; but this time there was a chance to take part in the miracle, for everybody could afford to spend a few francs to be 'daguerreotyped'. They did not mind sitting motionless for half an hour in the sun if they could only take home a small metal plate with their likeness on it. Amateurs scrambled for cameras, plates, and equipment. The craze spread to America. As early as April 1840 a Boston dentist used the first Daguerre camera; Samuel Morse, the inventor of the telegraph, bought one in Paris from Daguerre himself, and set it up on the roof of New York City University.

By one of those curious coincidences which we find so often in the history of inventions, the photographic system which was to supersede that of Daguerre was discovered in the same year—1839—in which the daguerreotype craze started in France, by the Englishman, William Henry Fox Talbot, a scientist and gentleman of leisure. During a sketching-tour in Italy, he wrote later, 'the idea occurred to me—how charming it would be if it were possible to cause these natural images to imprint themselves durably, and remain fixed upon the paper!' Working in his splendid old home, Lacock Abbey in Wiltshire, he laid the foundation stone on which most modern photographic systems rest by inventing the negative-positive process. On Daguerre's plates, a positive image was produced directly, and there was no possibility of making more prints or of enlarging it. Fox Talbot produced first a negative picture, with darks and lights reversed, on paper; then he made a positive print on another sheet of sensitized paper by letting the sun shine through the negative, and fixing it with hyposulphite of soda as suggested by the astronomer, Sir John Herschel. He called his process 'calotype'.

Although he patented his system in 1841 and received the Royal Society medal for it a year later, it remained comparatively unknown while Daguerre was being celebrated in France and abroad. Even the publication of the first photographic book by Fox Talbot, 'The Pencil of Nature', in 1844, with twenty-seven pictures of buildings, still-life, and works of art, caused no sensation. 'It is, of course, an effect of sunshine, and sets at nought the work of human hands', said one reviewer. Only when, in 1848, a nephew of Daguerre's collaborator, Niepce de St Victor, had the idea of using glass plates instead of paper for negatives did the art and craft of photography develop more quickly.

It was to be expected that artists everywhere, especially those who lived on portrait-painting, feared that photography would put them out of business. Many of them therefore bought cameras, learnt to use them and to develop pictures, and turned themselves into photographers. This is the explanation for the surprising artistic quality of those early pictures, daguerreotypes as well as calotypes. Pictures by artists such as David Octavius Hill in England or Blanquart-Evrard in France—who founded the first art publishing house in Lille in 1851—are visual documents of the period as well as works of art.

But there were already the beginnings of other uses of the new technique than those of photographing people and landscapes. As early as 1846 it was applied in meteorology by an English scientist who devised a system of recording automatically the readings of magnetometers and other instruments on calotypes. Ten years later photography was already being used in astronomy and microscopy. At the same time there was a new fashion in France—photographic visiting cards. Disderi, a French photographer, mass produced as many as 1,800 pictures a day by using a camera with several lenses and making up to a dozen different poses of the sitter on one negative, which were then printed on small cards. The craze swept to England and later to America, where it reached its heyday during the Civil War.

Friedrich Voigtländer, of Brunswick, made the world's first metal camera for daguerreotypes as early as 1840; the lens, scientifically calculated, had the astonishing light sensitivity of 1 : 3·4, which reduced the time of exposure to one or two minutes.

Although the 'autotype' process by which photographs could be reproduced in newspapers (invented by two Germans, Meisenbach and Schmädel, in 1881) was still a long way off, photographic reporting took shape in the 1850's and 1860's. The first war pictures were made in the Crimea by an English photographer, Roger Fenton, and during the American Civil War a wagon with a complete dark-room installation went with the supply columns of the Northern Army. At about the same time the first 'photographic feature' was made at Munich, showing the successive phases of the erection of the giant statue of Bavaria high above the town.

Born out of war-time necessity, a new photographic technique was invented in Paris during the siege of 1870–1: a system by which written messages could be photographically reduced to very small size and printed on collodion medals, which were then flown out of the beleaguered city to unoccupied France by carrier-pigeons.

Until the 1870's photography was a complicated and dreary business. When a portrait or family group was to be taken the photographer first seated his customers on chairs with head supports which helped them to keep absolutely still; after focusing he had to rush to the dark room with the plate-holder, coat the glass plate with a wet mixture of collodion and light-sensitive salts, rush back to the camera, insert the plate-holder, pull out the slide and take off the lens cap to expose the plate—still wet—to the light for a minute or two, during which time the people had to remain completely motionless. Then the photo-grapher had to rush back to the dark room and develop the plate at once.

At last in 1871 two Englishmen, Dr R. L. Maddox and Sir Joseph Wilson Swan (who later invented an incandescent electric lamp prior to Edison's), produced dry, 'rapid' photo-graphic plates in which the sensitive silver-bromide salts were held by a gelatine emulsion. With this achievement the greatest obstacle to the further progress of photography was removed, and the number of people who took it up as a profession or hobby grew rapidly. The most important benefit of the dry plate was that there was no longer any need to carry about a portable dark room when taking pictures out of doors.

A few years later, in 1884, another great advance helped to make photography easier and simpler. An American, George Eastman, invented the photographic film, using celluloid—the first man-made 'plastic' material, invented by the Birmingham chemist, Alexander Parkes, in 1856—instead of glass as the basis for the light-sensitive emulsion. In 1891 Eastman and his collaborator, Hannibal Goodwin, introduced a roll film that could be loaded into the camera in daylight. This was the begin-ning of photography as a truly popular pastime.

Many more improvements followed. Eastman brought out the first small-size amateur camera, the 'Kodak' box; lenses and emulsions of greater sensitivity and with better definition made it possible to reduce the size of the film and camera considerably (the Leica, the first camera using 35-millimetre film, and the panchromatic emulsion, giving more accurate black-and-white values of natural colours, were marketed in the 1920's). New shutters permitted speeds of very small fractions of a second, cheap enlargers gave the amateur a chance to 'compose' his pictures at home, reflex cameras enabled him to see the scene he was 'shooting' in full size on a horizontal focusing-screen. Some modern cameras have not only built-in exposure-meters but relieve the photographer of all the little jobs of adjusting speed,

Early photography: clamps immobilized
the victim's head during exposure

aperture, and focus so that all he has to do is press the trigger. Flash bulbs or electronic flashes coupled to the trigger provide artificial light where there is not enough daylight (Sir Joseph Wilson Swan used arc-lights in his Newcastle studio for the first time about 1880); the blinding, smoke-belching, evil-smelling flashlight powder became a thing of the past.

The paragon of perfection, an achievement of the 1950's, is the American 'Polaroid Land Camera', which produces a black-and-white or even a colour print within one minute of shooting it. Invented by Dr Edwin Land, this camera contains the necessary dry chemicals and two paper rolls, one for the negative and the other for the positive picture, within a minimum of space. Of course, complete automation in photography may not be to every amateur's taste, and many will no doubt prefer the old system of 'do-it-yourself' to achieve a picture of artistic merit, not just a snapshot.

Scientific and industrial requirements have made it necessary to design new types of cameras such as the huge Baker-Nunn satellite-tracking camera with its intricate system of lenses; it follows an orbiting satellite as it speeds across the sky, with a tracking error of less than 1 per cent. 'Big Schmidt', the 48-inch Schmidt telescope at the Mount Palomar Observatory in California, was used to make the photographs for a new sky atlas for the National Geographic Society; they show stars up to one thousand million light-years away.

At the other extreme there is the camera built by an American, Dr Harold E. Edgerton, for taking pictures in the 24,600-foot Romanche Trench, the deepest part of the Atlantic, between Brazil and West Africa. Piercing the utter darkness of the ocean bed with electronic flashes, the camera took a number of pictures before the $1\frac{1}{2}$-inch-thick lens cracked under the tremendous water pressure; fortunately, no water seeped into the camera.

The 'evaporograph' camera can take pictures of the proverbial boxing match between two negroes in a tunnel at midnight. It needs no light at all but photographs the extremely weak heat radiations given off by any object. It focuses these radiations on a thin oil film so that the oil molecules evaporate to a varying degree according to the heat impulses.

The United States Bureau of Standards has developed a research camera with a microscopic optical system, which could photograph the entire Bible on a film the size of one square centimetre. There are cameras which can expose 35-mm. film at the rate of 15 million frames per second—and in colour!—or photograph shock-waves from explosions travelling at a speed of five miles per second.

A variety of photographic processes are used in printing (q.v.) and in copying documents, drawings, and so on. In the latter field, some compact and fast-working machines for the office, producing 'photostats' of the original on sensitized paper—either negative or positive—have been developed, but they are not essentially new inventions. One process, however, may claim to be really revolutionary: xerography. Invented by an American scientist, Chester Carlson, in the 1930's—he had grown up in poverty, and the success story of Edison and other inventors influenced him greatly—xerography has three main advantages over conventional photographic processes: the negative plates can be used repeatedly, the prints can be made on any type of paper, and it uses no liquids. It employs a plate which consists of a thin photo-conductive coating on a metal sheet. Photoconductivity is a photo-electric effect in which the electrical conductivity of certain substances such as selenium increases with the intensity of the light which falls on them. The coating of the plate is electrically charged in the dark, and when it is exposed to an image and then dusted with powder, the electrostatic image which has been formed by the powder can be transferred to any sheet of paper.

Carlson had at first no success with his invention; only in 1946 did a New York photographic firm acquire his patents, and four years later the first xerograph machine was marketed. The system has since been introduced in offset-lithographic printing, in industrial firms with a large output of pictorial printed matter, in X-ray photography of welds and castings, for the enlargement of microfilms, and—last not least—for the high-speed printing of the results coming from electronic computers. Three thousand lines per minute, about the length of an average novel, can be printed by the xerographic process.

Probably the most difficult photographic process ever carried out was that by which the Russian space vehicle, *Lunik III*, took and transmitted the first pictures of the far side of the moon in October 1959. The assembly contained a camera with two lenses, a developing and fixing unit, a miniature cathode-ray tube, and numerous electronic devices such as scanners, automatic controls, timing mechanisms, and a wireless picture transmitter. The moon photographs were taken when *Lunik III* was about 40,000 miles from the moon, the lenses being focused on the target by a series of automatic actions. Gyroscopes guided by a small electronic computer stopped the vehicle spinning around; two light-sensitive cells 'homed' on the sun and the earth to point the cameras at the moon; a master-cell, by now beamed at the moon's reflected light, made the nose of the vehicle turn round until it received the maximum light from the moon, and operated the shutters. After forty minutes, when all the film had been shot, the vehicle was made to spin again so that the heat from the sun would not melt the instruments on the side turned towards the sun. After automatic developing and fixing, the pictures were transferred to the transmission unit from where, on radio 'orders' from earth stations, the negatives were scanned and the light values translated into electric signals. These were then beamed towards the earth over a distance of up to 290,000 miles, and reassembled into complete images in photo-telegraphic receivers.

Goethe may be called one of the fathers of colour photography; in his 'Theory of Colour' (1812) he discusses the effect of coloured light on silver chloride. A few years earlier the English scientist, Thomas Young, had proved his theory that all colours may be produced by mixing in various proportions three elementary colours. The German physicist, Hermann von Helmholtz, defined these colours in the 1860's as blue, green, and red, and in 1869 the Frenchman, Charles Cros, took the first colour photographs based on the Young-Helmholtz theory. He took three negatives in the elementary colours of the same object by using coloured filters, and superimposed three coloured positive pictures on one another.

Charles Cros's collaborator, Ducos du Hauron, suggested another method: it also works with three filters in the elementary colours, but the negatives are dyed in the complementary colours (green is a complementary colour to red, orange to blue, etc.). These negatives are then used to produce a print or transparent picture, again with colours reversed, by superimposition.

This subtractive system, as it is called, has been brought to perfection in various ways and for various purposes. In amateur photography 'reversal' films—first marketed in America, Germany, Britain, Italy, and Belgium in the 1940's—make it possible to take coloured photographs with ordinary cameras and without the use of filters, the result being positive transparencies which are difficult to copy or enlarge. These films have three layers of emulsion, one of which is sensitive only to blue light, the second only to green, and the third only to red. Developing is, of course, much more complicated than with black-and-white film; different developers have to be used for each of the three layers.

Some subtractive processes produce prints on paper: three emulsions on the negative film correspond to three emulsions on the paper; but the processing is expensive, and the prints do not always represent the original colours faithfully. In magazine and book printing and in art reproduction, however, subtractive systems have been brought to great perfection, but these, too, are rather costly.

The incentive for inventors of a colour system suitable for cinematography was especially high because of the rapid pace at which the film became 'big business'. In 1926, after many years of experimenting, three scientists—D. F. Comstock, H. T. Kalmus, and W. B. Westcott—shot the first test films with the colour system they had developed at the Massachusetts Institute of Technology, Boston; they perfected it during the following seven years. In 1933 Walt Disney produced the first 'Technicolor' cartoon, *Flowers and Trees*. Although by no means a simple or cheap system, Technicolor was soon adopted by film companies in America and Europe.

The system needs a special camera in which the light beam entering the lens is split up so that three films, running synchronously, are exposed; one records the green elements of the light beam, another the red, and the third the blue ones. A 'matrix', a relief film in gelatine, is made of each of them and dyed in complementary colours. From these three matrices a fourth one, the 'key picture', is made in black and white. Then, in four consecutive processes, these four films are printed on a single one, which now contains all the colours.

The first 'monopack' system, using three colour-sensitive layers on a single film, was the American 'Kodachrome', developed by two music students from New York, Leo Godowsky and Leopold Mannes, in a crude form as early as 1923, and marketed eventually in 1935. Then came the German Agfacolor process, completed in 1936; since that time numerous other monopack processes have come into use (but they have not succeeded in ousting Technicolor completely). They do not require special cameras. Most of them have four layers: sensitive to blue, green, red, and between the first two a thin yellow filter layer to shut out the blue light from the two bottom layers. The developing process turns the layers into their complementary colours—blue becomes orange, green purple, and red green.

This is the negative, from which positive prints in the proper colours can be made through colour filters.

But this is already part of the technical history of the cinema. We shall anticipate no more of it, but begin at the beginning.

Few inventions have been attempted by so many inventors as that of the moving pictures, the film. There seems to have been an old and vivid desire in Man to make images appear on walls as though by magic. At any rate, all the nineteenth-century inventors who grappled with the problem knew exactly what effect they were aiming at. For this reason it is not easy to decide which of them really created cinematography: they found the elements of the invention already lying about like loose ends, waiting to be tied together.

One of these elements was the magic lantern. Invented in the seventeenth century by one Athanasius Kircher, a German Jesuit, as a development of the camera obscura, it was used as an amusing toy for a long time, and lecturers employed it to illustrate their talks with projected drawings. Sometimes charlatans scared the superstitious by making ghosts appear with it—Schiller told the story of one of them in the only serial thriller he ever wrote. The invention of photography provided the second basic element because the camera made it possible to project lifelike images instead of drawings; all that remained to be done was to make them move.

But this was not as simple as it sounds. An important scientific discovery had to come to the aid of the inventors. The man who made it paid heavily for the pleasures which the cinema offers to our eyes—with the loss of his own sight. His name, Joseph Plateau, is little known outside the annals of Science.

Plateau, a Belgian university professor, began in 1829, at the age of 28, with his research into the mechanism of human sight by staring into the sun for increasing lengths of time in order to observe the effect on the retina of his eyes. At 42 the sun had completely destroyed his vision and he remained blind until he died forty years later. What he had discovered was the 'inertia' of the eye—the fact that the retina does not part immediately with what it has seen, but retains the image for a fraction of a second after it has already disappeared. That means that if we see a succession of separate images, they 'overlap' in our brain, and if they show consecutive phases of movement that movement will appear to us continuous.

The first practical applications of this discovery took the form of Victorian nursery toys. Sir John Herschel, the astronomer, made one of them: a cardboard disc with a bird (or a dog) on one side and a cage (or a kennel) on the other; when the disc was turned round rapidly by means of a pair of strings the bird was seen sitting in its cage (or the dog in its kennel). An Austrian officer who later rose to the rank of field marshal, Franz von Uchatius, was probably the first man to project—in 1852— drawings by means of a magic lantern, making them apparently move on the wall by letting one succeed the other rapidly. Other inventors made 'magic' wheels and drums based on the same principle.

An Englishman, Edward Muybridge, who had made his name as an excellent landscape photographer in America, was asked in 1872 to help the Governor of California settle a dispute which the latter had had with his friends: whether a galloping horse did, or did not, lift all four feet off the ground at some stage of the gallop. Muybridge set up twenty-four cameras in a row on the racecourse of Palo Alto, and attached threads to the shutters; as the horse galloped past the row of cameras it broke one thread after another, thus operating the shutters. The experiment cost the governor a fortune, but it proved that he was right—the photographs showed that the horse did indeed lift all its feet off the ground during its gallop.

Muybridge published his pictures in a book, *The Horse in Motion*, which created a sensation among all those who were busy experimenting with photography of motion. Henry Heyl in Philadelphia, Janssen in Germany, Professor E. J. Marey in France, improved Muybridge's system by inventing cameras for taking serial pictures—'photographic revolvers', 'photographic guns'—and also projectors for showing their pictures in rapid succession. Marey especially carried on where Muybridge had left off by analysing photographically the movements of men and animals and the flight of birds. All these pictures were, of course, taken on glass plates.

It was only to be expected that Edison, America's most fertile inventive brain, would try to get to grips with the problem of the moving pictures, but if Americans today hail him as the inventor of the cinema they are prompted more by national pride than by historical facts. Edison was looking for some way of reawakening the interest in his fun-fair phonographs, which did not make as much money as they used to do. If people could look at moving pictures while listening to the phonograph, he thought, they might be tempted to spend their nickels more freely. The result was his 'kinetoscope', a peep-show machine with an eyepiece for the viewer. The first scene he shot was photographed on 158 glass plates in an office at Menlo Park; the 'stars' of this little love scene, two of his employees, had to endure eight hours' agony while the photographs were taken one after the other, with slight changes of position in each interval. In the kinetoscope, cardboard prints of the pictures flicked past the viewer's eyes, thus creating the effect of continuous motion. The machine was ready in October 1889, and proved an immediate success.

Only then did Edison think of trying out the new photographic material, Eastman and Goodwin's roll film. He ordered a 50-foot reel and built a camera around it so that the scenes for his kinetoscope could be taken in continuous movement. One day a showman who had bought some kinetoscopes asked one of Edison's assistants why the inventor did not try to make a machine for showing his moving pictures to more than one person at a time—perhaps an adaptation of the magic lantern? But Edison did not take up the idea.

Meanwhile events had moved more quickly in Europe. An English photographer, William Friese-Greene from Bristol, experimented with moving pictures in the early 1880's. At first he used glass plates, then paper strips soaked in castor oil to make them transparent, and eventually, without having heard of Eastman's invention, celluloid coated with a sensitive emulsion. It was Friese-Greene's great failing that he was not a good mechanic—he had to have his camera and projector built by a firm of instrument-makers; neither was he a good business man. He got into debt again and again, unable to find a financial backer. Nor did he have enough stamina to stick to one idea and carry it out in the best possible form.

However, he patented his invention in 1889 and went out into Hyde Park to shoot a few feet of film. That night, in his workshop, he developed and printed the film and put it in his projector. And the miracle happened—there were the people, the children and horses, all moving almost as in real life! Friese-Greene was so excited that he had to share his joy with some other human being. The story goes that he ran into the street—it was after midnight —and persuaded a reluctant policeman to come up with him and witness the new wonder.

It was the only high light in the poor inventor's life. He was disappointed when he could not at once find money to exploit his invention, and turned his mind to some other idea. Unpaid bills were piling up, and he went a few times to jail. He pawned his patent and never bothered to renew it. He was penniless when he died in 1921.

Another inventor might have made the grade had not his life been cut short by a mysterious accident. Augustin Le Prince, a French artist who had settled in Leeds, saw Muybridge's book, *The Horse in Motion*, during a visit in New York, and was so fascinated by the idea of photographing moving objects that he built a camera for use with Eastman's film. The first scene he shot, in 1888, was traffic moving across the bridge at Leeds. But before showing it to potential backers he wanted to get the advice of his brother, who lived in Dijon. He visited him and boarded the train back from Dijon to Paris in September 1890. From that moment there has been no trace of Augustin Le Prince, nor of his luggage, which must have contained drawings or models of his camera and projector.

Then there was Robert W. Paul, a London instrument-maker, who was visited by two Greek showmen in 1894; they brought him a kinetoscope and asked him to build a number of these machines, which promised to make a lot of money. But Paul thought it would be a better idea to project these little film scenes to a larger audience. He designed a projector and a camera, built a little studio in a London suburb, and began to produce his own films. On 20 February 1896—the date is important, as we shall see—he showed the first of them to an invited audience in London. Paul made the first 'feature' films in Britain and pioneered the newsreel; one of the earliest was shot at the Derby of 1896, and the Prince of Wales was able to see his horse win again—on the screen of a music-hall on the evening after the race.

Robert W. Paul rose to be England's first film industrialist. He made a fortune out of his films, but one day in 1910 he put his

entire film stock on a heap and set fire to it. He was disgusted with
the bad taste which the early filmgoers showed, and wanted to
have no more part in the development of the new medium in
whose future he did not believe. He thought it would never be
more than cheap entertainment for the uneducated.

In the early 1890's a former United States Treasury stenographer, C. Francis Jenkins, and two German inventors, the
brothers Skladanowsky, were among those who succeeded in
building cameras and projectors, and making short films. But
history credits two French brothers, Louis and Auguste Lumière,
with the perfection of an invention that was so much 'in the air'
at the time.

The Lumières owned a factory for photographic equipment in
Lyons. They knew, of course, about Edison's kinetoscope, and
discussed the idea of projecting these moving pictures. One night
Louis, unable to find sleep, worked out the technical details of a
camera and projector. The brothers had them built by their
mechanics, and shot an experimental film lasting only a few
seconds: workers leaving the Lumière factory for their lunch
break.

On 22 March 1895 they showed this short scene to a group of
Paris business men, who were most impressed. During the
following months they shot a large number of short films for their
first programme, and on 28 December 1895 they opened a show
which they called 'Cinématographie Lumière' in the basement
hall of the Grand Café in the Boulevard des Capucines, Paris.
The programme, lasting for altogether twenty minutes, contained such items as *Baby's Supper*, *A Boat in the Surf*, *Demolition
of a Wall*, a funny scene with a gardener being teased by a boy
with the water hose, and *Arrival of a Train in a Station*. The
pictures were shaky, the projector noisy, the flickering screen
unkind to the eyes—but the first cinema show was a sensational
success, and there were queues at the entrance from morning till
night.

Eight weeks later, on 20 February 1896, London was given its
first taste of the new medium of entertainment—on the same day
when Robert W. Paul gave his own demonstration. The
Lumières had been invited by the Polytechnic in Regent Street
to arrange public showings of their invention. The programme
was the same as that shown in Paris, and the *Arrival of a Train*

made the greatest impression; every time the audience saw the engine coming straight towards them there were people who panicked and rushed for the doors. Ladies fainted, and the management had to engage a nurse to deal with the casualties.

The Lumière camera and projector, designed and built expertly, established themselves easily against the various rival machines. Despite the vast strides made by cinematography in the decades that followed, they can still be regarded as the prototypes of present-day equipment. The Lumières fixed the standard width of the film at 35 mm.; the sprocket holes for transporting it through camera and projector are still the same, except in certain wide-screen and sub-standard systems. The speed of shooting the pictures remained 16 'frames' per second throughout the whole silent-film period so that each of them could be exposed for $\frac{1}{32}$ of a second, with a shutter—mounted on a horizontal axis —cutting off the light after each exposure for another $\frac{1}{32}$ of a second while a new frame was pulled into position behind the picture 'gate'. In the projector, this process was to some extent reversed: the light from a strong source, usually an arc lamp, housed in the 'magic lantern' body, penetrated the transparent positive film, but was also shut off by a revolving shutter while the film was moved behind the lens. The Lumières also devised efficient equipment for developing and printing their films automatically in a continuous process.

Rarely has a new invention been welcomed so enthusiastically in modern times as that of the moving pictures. Being a cheap form of entertainment, it fulfilled an urgent need for a relaxing and stimulating pastime among the masses of people who could not have afforded to go to the theatre or concert hall. It provided the possibility of an inexpensive outing after a long working day, of something to go to and to look at, of an escape to a glamorous dream world from a reality of drabness and worry. Naturally, the artistic standard of the films made for mass consumption—and as a rule by people who saw a chance of making money easily and quickly—was at first rather low and gave the 'flicks' a bad name. It took some twenty years until inspired and serious artists, directors as well as writers and actors, attempted to use the film as a new medium of expressing their ideas, thus showing that it could be an art in its own right. Only when that stage was reached did the technicians find it worth while to give the benefit of their skill and inventiveness to introduce a great number of improvements.

The logical development seemed the addition of sound. In fact, there were as many attempts at giving the film a voice as there had been at inventing cinematography itself. Scientists were working on systems of recording sound by photographic means even before the first cinema opened. Around the turn of the century the German physicist, Ernst Ruhmer, succeeded in recording sound waves in all details by photography, but the application to the cinema never occurred to him. In 1902 an English inventor, W. D. B. Duddell, took out a patent with this specification: 'A microphone is used to convert sounds into a phonic electric current, and this . . . is recorded by means of an oscillograph. The record is made on a moving film in such a way that the width of the part . . . is determined by the deflection of the oscillograph. From the original record copies may be made by photography or other means. To reconvert the record into sounds, a beam of light is passed through the moving record and is made to illuminate a selenium cell (or photo-electric cell), the variations of which are reconverted into sounds.'

There, in a nutshell, was the basic principle of the sound-on-film system. In 1906 another Englishman, Eugene A. Lauste, took out a patent for the simultaneous recording of picture and sound on the same film; he used half of the film width for the picture and the other half for the sound. But he found it rather difficult to solve the problem of reconverting the sound 'track' back into sound. Duddell had given an answer in principle, but it would not yet work in practice because electronic developments were still in their infancy. Without proper amplification by thermionic valves and accurate reproduction by loudspeaker there was little hope of introducing the system in the cinemas.

That was the reason why Lauste, after he had spent a fortune on his invention and ruined his health, had to give up, and why other and more primitive ways of adding sound to the silent screen were tried out. Edison had already combined his phonograph with the kinetoscope, and so the idea of coupling a disc record to a cinema projector was an obvious one. This was done again and again, but never with spectacular success. It was difficult to achieve complete synchronization of picture and sound—and to keep it up for any length of time. When one was ahead of the other, as usually happened after a while, the effect made for unintentional humour; and there was no way of retaining synchronization if the film broke or got damaged and a few frames had to be cut out, which is the rule rather than the exception in the projectionist's booth. If, on the other hand, one of the large records broke (which also happened during performances), the show had to stop altogether. In short, the sound-on-disc system was not much good.

After the First World War technical developments had reached a stage where the recording of sound on film, and even more so the all-important reproduction in the cinema, seemed within the inventors' grasp. In Germany three young engineers—Engl, Massolle, and Vogt—got together and produced, after three years of experimenting, a system which they called 'Triergon', the 'work of the Three'. A feature film on a Hans Andersen tale was made by UFA, Germany's leading film company, and shown in 1922. It had to be put off after two days; the sound was not good enough.

A year later Lee de Forest, the inventor of the amplifier valve, demonstrated his own 'Phonofilm' system at the New York Rivoli theatre. It was a success with the audience, but now the Hollywood producers and the cinema owners grew frightened— if people began to clamour for sound, studios and theatres would have to buy the equipment, which was still forbiddingly expensive. A 'conspiracy of silence' retarded the inevitable coming of sound for a few years, but eventually Warner Brothers decided to jump the gun and come out with the first sound-on-film feature for general release.

This was *The Jazz Singer*, shown in 1928, with Al Jolson in the leading part. It was an immediate success. The ultimate triumph of the 'talkies' was no longer in doubt, and the film industry realized that there was no time to lose in putting the entire business of making and showing films on a new basis.

Within a few years the revolution was complete. More capital had to be invested in the industry. Studios had to be rebuilt, new equipment bought and installed, specialists hired and trained. Most of the little 'flea-pit' cinemas disappeared, making way for the picture palaces. The film industry grew into an enormous business, playing an increasing part in the economic and social life of many countries. Now that two senses, sight and hearing, were occupied in the cinema, its impact was all the stronger.

Basically, the technique of recording and reproducing sound-on-film has remained the same. The microphone current is made to increase or decrease the light of a small electric lamp in the sound camera, and the fluctuations of the lamp are photographed on a narrow 'track' along the edge of the film. There are two systems: 'variable area' and 'variable density'; as these terms indicate, the first system works by varying the space filled by the track while in the other the track has constant width but its transparency varies from light grey to black according to the impulses coming from the microphone. However, both kinds of track can be reconverted into sound by the same appliance in the projector. The positive print of the film, which combines picture and sound track so that they are inseparably 'married' to each other, runs through the projector at a constant speed of 24 frames per second (as compared with the 16 frames of the silent days). The sound track at the edge of the film is scanned by a small lamp; the light penetrating the track falls on a photo-electric cell, which modulates an electric current passing through it according to the amount of light it receives. This modulated current is amplified and goes into the loudspeakers in the cinema, which convert it back into sound.

The development of the tape recorder in the 1950's made it possible to dispense with the heavy and costly sound camera, and record sound on tape; these magnetic recordings can then be converted into the usual sound track on the film. But the film can also be coated with a ferrous emulsion and the sound recorded magnetically on it; this is done when 'stereophonic' sound, with several separate 'channels' for as many loudspeakers distributed in the cinema, is required. Magnetic sound is also frequently used on sub-standard (16 mm.) film for showing in clubs and lecture halls.

The increasing popularity of television prompted the film-makers in the early 1950's to look for special attractions to lure their customers back to the cinema. They tried to give the public what it could not yet get from the little screens at home—vast expanses of screen space, stereoscopic sound, and, of course, colour (see the foregoing part of this chapter). A number of 'wide-screen' systems made their appearance as well as—for a brief period—the 'Three-D' system, which is based on the fact that our two eyes look at objects from a slightly different angle, which makes them 'stand out'. The most practical three-dimensional, or stereoscopic, system, invented by Raymond and Nigel Spottiswoode in England, works with two differently polarized

The stereoscope, invented by Sir Charles Wheatstone (c. 1855)

lenses through which the picture is photographed on two films, which are then projected simultaneously on the same screen; the audience has to use spectacles whose lenses are also differently polarized so that each eye sees only one image on the screen. Probably because cinema audiences found the use of these spectacles too inconvenient, the 3-D film disappeared after two or three years. Other systems of stereoscopic viewing, including one developed by Semyon P. Ivanov in Russia in 1947, have tried to achieve the desired effect by using 'rippled' or 'noduled' screens on to which the two images are projected, but they create the impression of depth only to those viewers seated in the centre before the screen while those at the sides see a blurred picture. Still, 3-D inventors are incessantly at work, and we might yet get the ideal system.

The wide screen in its various forms, however, has come to stay. Most of these systems use a slightly curved screen on which a picture of greater width but less height than formerly is projected. The width of the film itself remains 35 mm. (except with a few systems which use 55 mm. or even larger widths, one or two requiring projectors in which the film moves horizontally instead of vertically). Normal camera and projector lenses could not achieve a wide image; instead, 'anamorphic' lenses, invented by the French scientist, Dr Henri Chrétien, are used to 'squeeze' the picture to be photographed on to the film in the camera and expand it again in the projector.

One system, Cinerama, developed from 1937 to 1952 by a self-taught American inventor, Fred Waller, works with three synchronized cameras and projectors, and partly surrounds the audience with a semicircular screen of huge dimensions. A Russian system, Circorama, and a German one, the Cinetarium, both first shown in 1959, go the whole hog by enclosing the viewer completely with a screen of about 750 square yards' projection space, which includes the curved ceiling. The spectators walk around or sit on revolving seats; the German system provides loudspeakers under each. Its Hamburg inventor, Adalbert Baltes, uses a reflecting sphere suspended about three feet above the camera, which photographs vertically upwards. The image on the film is distorted, but by projecting it upwards on another reflecting sphere above the audience Baltes achieves a change back to normal proportions.

It may seem that the cinema, in its frantic efforts at holding its own against that powerful rival and ally, television, has overreached itself and will have to climb down a peg or two if it wants to survive at all in coming decades. Some critics even said that the introduction of sound was a basic mistake because the film is a visual art, and because voluntarily accepted restriction can serve as an incentive to greater artistic achievement. Be that as it may, the film is certainly on its way to becoming a 'minority medium', a form of art for a restricted public of devotees, perhaps even more restricted than the theatre public. After a glorious, glamorous, and expansive past, after a hectic period of trying to become twice as natural as life, it must find its modest niche in our civilization. Whether we like it or not, the mass medium of entertainment in the second half of our century is television.

L

# 6

❖◇❖◇❖◇❖◇❖◇❖◇❖◇❖◇❖◇❖◇❖◇❖

# Television

OF ALL the secret human desires which are echoed in the old
fairy-tales, and which modern Science has now turned into
reality, television seemed the most fantastic idea, the most
unlikely one ever to become a fact, to people only a generation or
two ago. Wicked queens, crafty sorcerers, adepts in the black art
—they knew, in the old fables, how to conjure up the pictures of
people at faraway places in their magic mirrors and crystals; but
who would have believed that we ordinary mortals might one day
have the power of summoning such images, at the turn of a knob,
into our parlours?

Yet the idea of transmitting pictures by electricity is about as
old as the electric telegraph. Alexander Bain, a young Scottish
psychologist, devised in 1842 a machine—developed five years
later by Bakewell—for transmitting drawings by the electric wire.
It bears an astonishing similarity to modern photo-telegraphic
equipment: two cylinders, one in the transmitter and one in the
receiver, revolve at synchronous speed, driven by clockwork; in
the transmitter, a thin sheet of metal foil is wrapped around the
cylinder, with the drawings to be transmitted applied in non-
conducting ink. As the cylinder revolves, a metal needle on a
short arm, not unlike a gramophone pick-up, touches the metal
sheet very lightly, moving along its length by means of a rotating
spindle. The needle is wired to an earth plate, the cylinder via a
battery to the receiver; whenever the needle touches the non-
conducting ink the circuit is interrupted. In the receiver, a sheet
of paper is wrapped around the cylinder; it is chemically treated
and moist so that the needle moving over it effects a colouring of

the paper by electrolytic action, except the lines of the drawing, because at these points the circuit is interrupted. The picture thus appears white on the coloured paper.

Over half a century later the German physicist Arthur Korn modernized that system by substituting photo-electric action for the electro-chemical: the transmitter needle was replaced by a photo-electric cell, which modulates by its varying resistance a current sent through it according to the amount of light which it receives; as the picture to be transmitted is scanned, pin-point by pin-point, by a sharp light beam, the resistance of the photo-electric cell varies and these modulations are sent to the receiver, where they modulate the light of a small lamp, which falls on a sheet of photographic paper on the revolving cylinder, exposing it more or less according to the lighter or darker shades of the original in the transmitter.

This system of photo-telegraphy, by wire or wireless, is still widely in use for the transmission of photographs, documents, and so on for the Press, in private business, for the police, in legal and personal affairs, and every postal and cable network in the world offers facilities for picture transmission. Since 1950 American radio companies have been experimentally transmitting entire newspapers by a high-speed photo-telegraphic process: a copy of the paper is scanned electronically in the newspaper office, and the impulses sent by very short (micro-) waves to the subscriber, in whose house a receiving set reproduces the copy, sheet by sheet, on sensitized paper. In this way the subscriber receives his paper within a few seconds after it has been produced; only one copy has to be printed for any number of subscribers, and there is no need for transport and delivery of the copies. British engineers believe that they could also pass the printed word simply over the telephone wire without disturbing its normal use; or the facsimile newspaper could be transmitted during 'idle time' over the television channels early in the morning while the subscriber is still asleep. It is, of course, an expensive way of bringing the morning paper to the reader's breakfast table, and unlikely to supersede conventional delivery unless ways can be found to mass produce cheap, small-size receivers. In 1959 the United States post started experiments with its 'Fax Mail' system by which letters written on standardized notepaper can be transmitted over long distances at a speed of 1,800 words per minute; as in facsimile newspaper transmission, the pages are converted into electric impulses and sent as micro-waves to their destinations, where they are changed back into their original form. It is claimed that 'Fax Mail' costs only a quarter as much as sending letters by airmail, and that the secrecy of their contents is guaranteed. These facsimile high-speed transmission systems are based on television techniques.

Once photo-telegraphy had become a fact in the early years of this century, the idea of transmitting 'living' instead of still pictures no longer seemed quite so fantastic. It was, in fact, merely a problem of speed—of scanning the scene to be transmitted, of sending the impulses to the receiver, and of assembling them there so quickly that the eye would accept them as the image of a real-life scene. As in the cinema, the inertia of the human eye was expected to be of great help in this process of reproduction.

A practical solution—sound in principle, though a rather crude one—of the scanning problem had been found as far back as 1883 by a student at Berlin University, Paul Nipkow. Two developments had stimulated his technical imagination, the invention of the telephone and the discovery that the element selenium allows an electric current to pass much more freely when the sun is shining on it—the discovery which later led to the invention of the photo-electric cell. Sitting under the Christmas-tree in 1883, Paul Nipkow realized that these variations of electric resistance according to the amount of light falling on selenium pointed to the possibility of transmitting a scene by electricity.

To achieve this it had to be divided into very small points; these points had to be 'scanned' quickly and their relative brightness or dimness turned into stronger or weaker electrical impulses. At the receiving end these impulses had to be turned back into light values so that the original scene could be built up from them.

The way in which that scanning and reassembling could be done occurred to Nipkow on that Christmas Eve. He designed a cardboard disc with a line of small holes arranged in the form of a spiral near its edge. A kind of camera with the disc in it, turned by a motor, would have to be set up in front of the scene to be transmitted. A strong lamp would then shoot a beam of light through the holes of the rotating disc at the object to be transmitted; thus it would be scanned—divided up into many brighter or dimmer spots. The spiral arrangement of the holes would make sure that the whole scene would be scanned with one revolution of the disc. A light-sensitive cell connected to a battery and to the receiver would then transmit the scene continually in the form of electric impulses which would make a lamp flicker accordingly, and with the help of another disc with spiral holes the scene would be built up again from innumerable brighter or dimmer points of light.

Nipkow patented his invention under the name of 'Electrical Telescope'. But that was as far as he could get; the technical difficulties were so enormous that he had to resign himself to wait until developments caught up with his idea. As it happened, he never returned to it but took up the career of a railway engineer.

The beginnings of electronics prompted other inventors to approach the problem of television from a different angle. Crookes's cathode-ray tube had been improved by Professor Ferdinand Braun, of Strasbourg University, who made the stream of electrons issuing from the cathode visible by coating the inside of the wide opposite end of his conically shaped tube with some fluorescent emulsion. Braun's tube, which he used as an oscilloscope for scientific research, was available from 1897, and in 1905 two scientists at Wolfenbüttel in Germany, Julius Elster and Hans Geitel, invented a rapidly reacting photo-electric cell (selenium reacts much too slowly for the purpose of television): two basic elements of any system of electronic television.

Boris Rosing, of the St Petersburg Technological Institute, seems to have been the first physicist who thought of using Braun's tube for the reception of images. As early as 1907 he suggested a system of remote electric vision, with a Nipkow disc for scanning the scene to be transmitted and a cathode-ray tube as the receiver. At about the same time the English inventor, A. A. Campbell-Swinton, also proposed a system of electronic television, but with cathode-ray tubes for transmission as well as for reception. He published his ideas in the scientific magazine *Nature* in 1908, and elaborated them again in 1911 and 1920, explaining that the image transmitted in this way could be split up into, and reassembled from, about 40,000 points of different light value within $\frac{1}{25}$ of a second. In 1909 a Munich engineer, Max Dieckmann, also published a theoretically sound system of television by cathode-ray tube in the German science magazine *Prometheus*, and even built a small model which could transmit silhouettes. 'It appears that the remaining problems of image-transmission might be solved more easily with the use of wireless telegraphy than by wire telegraphy', wrote Dieckmann.

The first practical—though, as it turned out, not the ideal—solution of the problem of television came, however, from a totally unexpected quarter. John Logie Baird, the son of a Scottish clergyman, had been unable to continue his engineering career, which he had begun before the First World War, because of ill health. He tried his hand at all kinds of business ventures, from making marmalade in Trinidad to selling French soap in London. Recuperating from malaria in Hastings in 1922, he pondered whether he should take up sales promotion for a new type of razor blade or try to invent television. He decided to do the latter.

Technical history knows few examples of the doggedness with which that intrepid Scotsman began to tackle one of the most difficult inventions of our century. Without any financial means, in poor health, and with next to no knowledge of previous work in this field, he began to experiment in his dingy garret. His wash-stand became the foundation of his apparatus; other parts were an old tea-chest, an electric motor picked up from a second-hand dealer in electrical equipment, a Nipkow disc cut from a piece of cardboard, some lenses bought at 4d. apiece from a bicycle shop, an ancient wireless telegraph invalided out of the Army, some torch batteries, darning needles, and pieces of wood—all of it held together with glue, sealing-wax, and lengths of string. A maze of electric wires extended throughout the garret.

After two years' incessant work, Baird succeeded in trans-mitting some shadowy shapes by wire over a distance of three yards. He moved to No. 22 Frith Street, Soho, and here the owner of London's largest department store saw the new world wonder. He engaged Baird to demonstrate it three times a day to customers in the electrical department. Baird accepted because he was in desperate need of money to keep body and soul together, but soon he realized that the demonstration of his imperfect invention would do him only harm and keep him from developing it. He therefore resigned and returned to Frith Street.

It was there that, on 2 October 1925, Baird succeeded for the first time in transmitting the features of a human face from one room to the next. An office boy from a firm below Baird's laboratory was the first person ever to be televised. A few months later he showed his system to the members of a scientific society and newspapermen. They were duly impressed, and a company was formed to exploit Baird's system.

Being a 'mechanical' system of scanning and reassembling the image, it was crude and full of pitfalls. Baird used the Nipkow disc for scanning the scene in the transmitter; a photo-electric cell modulated the current sent to the receiver first by wire and a year or two later by wireless. In the receiver, a light beam, modulated in intensity by the incoming signals, passed over a ground-glass screen via another Nipkow disc which was supposed to rotate synchronously with the one in the transmitter. A special synchronization signal was transmitted at the end of each of the thirty lines from which the whole picture was built up on the screen. Baird concentrated on giving his pictures a better 'definition' so as to show more details, and on increasing the range of transmission by wireless; he naturally expected the B.B.C. to start experimenting with his system. But there were many influential circles which did not like either the Baird system or the whole idea of television, and the B.B.C. had more or less to be forced by Parliament to start experimental transmissions in 1929.

While these were going on, the electronics system of television made great strides in American laboratories, where two men did outstanding work, Philo T. Farnsworth and his rival, Dr V. K. Zworykin. Vladimir Zworykin had studied in his native Russia under Boris Rosing in St Petersburg, and worked with him on his cathode-ray receiver from 1910; but they dropped their experiments two years later when they realized that mechanical scanning with the Nipkow disc and electronic reception with the Braun tube could not be combined into one system, and that a completely electronic method would have to be devised—but with the limited development at the time that was still too difficult. Only when Zworykin went to America in 1919 did he take up that problem again, and in 1928 he filed his patent application on what he called the 'iconoscope', a revolutionary device for transmitting television images quickly and efficiently. It has remained the basic device of the electronic television camera ever since.

The camera developed by Zworykin, who had the benefit of the great resources of the R.C.A. (Radio Corporation of

America), is something like an electronic replica of the human eye. The lens casts the image of what it sees on a plate inside a vacuum tube, covered with tiny photo-sensitive silver nodules, very close together but each insulated from its neighbours. As the image from the lens falls on this 'mosaic' the nodules become electrically charged, the charges varying with the amount of light which falls on the nodules; thus the mosaic represents an electrical 'picture' of the image to be televised. From the cathode of the tube, a thin beam of electrons is shot at the mosaic, scanning it about two dozen times per second nodule by nodule, line by line. As the beam passes over each nodule it carries away the electric charge from it—an action comparable to that of a weightless brush. The charges from the nodules can then be used to modulate the transmitter wave, which carries the image in the form of wireless impulses to the receiver.

The heart of the receiving set, as we know, is a large cathode-ray tube whose wide end, with a fluorescent zinc-sulphide coating on its inside, becomes the screen on which the picture is formed. The incoming impulses steer an electron beam which, coming from the cathode, moves across the screen at the same speed as that in the camera. Synchronization is achieved, as in the Baird system, by transmission of a special signal after each line. British television uses a 405-line system, but American and continental systems have up to 805 lines.

Philo T. Farnsworth, working as an individual inventor, developed a somewhat different system of image 'dissection' in 1928, and in the 1930's two other American inventors, Rose and Iam, invented the 'image orthicon', which makes the television camera so sensitive that it can operate by candlelight. Meanwhile, transmission of very high frequencies for conveying the video (picture) and sound impulses for television had been developed, and co-axial cables (q.v.) were available to carry them from one station to another over a television network so that nation-wide transmission became possible despite the fact that each transmitter had only a range of a few dozen miles.

The first regular television programmes were sent out from London's Alexandra Palace on 2 November 1936. It had been decided to use Baird's and Zworykin's systems on alternate weeks to see which of them would prove the best. But Baird could not achieve a better definition than 240 lines, and after a few weeks his system was abandoned in favour of the electronic one. When the Second World War began, Britain's television service closed down (the waves might have helped to guide enemy aircraft to London), to be reopened in June 1946. John Logie Baird died a few days later, only 58 years old; after getting over his disappointment that his system had been dropped he resumed work on colour television which, as he foresaw, would one day be wanted by the viewers.

In America television made a tentative start during the war, but only after its end did it develop by leaps and bounds when the big electrical firms began to mass-produce receivers. By 1960 it was reckoned that a major television programme, transmitted by 'hook-up' from the regional stations, would be seen by about two-thirds of the population. And as the eye conveys more lasting impressions than the ear, the power of television is much greater than that of sound-only radio: a power for good or evil influencing a whole people, potentially an excellent tool in a modern democracy. It brings the men and women who are responsible for the destinies of a nation into the family drawing-room, it shows the politicians seeking election in close-up, and it has a special knack of betraying insincerity. It can make us participate in the world's events, and convey to us the masterpieces of the theatrical and visual arts—including those of its rival, the cinema. It can also, of course, make us waste our time on meaningless cops-and-robbers stuff or stale jokes, and send us rushing to buy some brand of goods advertised on the screen: a far cry from the magnificent vision of a magic mirror for mankind, that promise which lasted only as long as television was but a dream. Few other inventions have so drastically demonstrated the inadequacy and backwardness of the human spirit in contrast to our technological achievements.

And they are indeed awe-inspiring in this field. In 1952 the first 'pocket-size' television equipment—a small hand camera, with a short-range transmitter strapped on the operator's back—was tried out in America and France; it has since come into widespread use as an independent reporting instrument which allows the cameraman to transmit from almost anywhere; micro-wave (centimetre-wave) links carry the signals to the regional transmitter from where they are relayed to the viewers. The 'zoom'

*L

lens, a fascinating piece of optical equipment—the mathematical calculations on which it is based took two and a half years to work out—can widen or narrow the camera's field of vision in a second's time; this gives to the viewer the effect of receding rapidly with the camera to get a general view of the scene, or 'zooming' forward to a close-up. It is extremely effective with outside telecastings of sports events, street scenes, and similar actualities.

Film transmissions are a most important part of television. Special cathode-ray tubes and scanners, different from those used to transmit 'live' scenes, work with 'flying spots' which build up the moving picture on the screen of the tube.

The technical problems of colour television have been solved long ago—a German patent for the transmission of images in colour was taken out by the physicist, Otto von Bronk, as far back as 1902—but the high cost of the equipment, especially receivers, has held up its general introduction. In America, television programmes in colour have been transmitted since the early 1950's to a limited number of viewers who can afford the extra cost, and an experimental service began in Britain in 1955. Japan started its regular colour service in the autumn of 1960; a year later there were already 15,000 receiving sets in operation, although the price of a colour set was still eight times as much as that of a black-and-white receiver. The Soviet Union, too, has introduced a colour television service.

There are various systems. Baird's 'Telechrome' works with two cathode-ray beams in a single tube with a transparent double-sided screen, the front being coloured blue-green and the back red so that the two images blend to give a picture in natural colour; this system was shown by Baird for the first time in 1928, and improved by him during the war.

Another system, using 'mechanical' scanning, was demonstrated in 1949. Developed by half a dozen engineers at the Pye laboratory in Cambridge, it works with a disc fitted with sets of red, blue, and green filters, which rotates at 750 r.p.m. behind the lens, and a similar disc in the receiver, running synchronously with it and producing twenty-five colour pictures a second. The principle of building up images in natural colours from the three primary colours is thus the same as in colour photography and cinematography, but the complications lie in the necessity of scanning and transmitting three separate sets of signals to the receiver.

An American system, developed by the British E.M.I. laboratories, separates the three colour elements by means of lenses, mirrors, and filters, and scans the three images electronically.

No doubt colour television will eventually supersede black-and-white transmissions. But there are other revolutionary developments to come, such as the 'flat' screen—it will replace the conventional receiver box with its cathode-ray tube. American and British engineers have been working on it since the end of the Second World War, particularly at the R.C.A. laboratories and at the Imperial College, London, where Dr D. Gabor demonstrated a prototype in 1958. The flat screen, which can be hung on the wall like a picture, may be no more than 2 to 3 inches thick. It has a fluorescent coating like conventional tubes, but the electrons from the cathode move almost parallel with it instead of striking it at a right angle. They start their journey from an electronic 'gun' at the top behind the screen, shooting downwards; at the bottom they are reflected by a 'reversing lens' to travel vertically upwards along the screen, which they eventually hit by the influence of a grid of conductors which accumulate electric charges from the electron beam and give them off to the screen. This device has some resemblance to that used in the iconoscope camera. The flat screen will be especially suitable for colour reception.

A major technical achievement in television (which can also be used in cinematography) has been introduced unnoticed by the average viewer. It is the recording of television programmes on magnetic tape. Ever since the tape machine for the recording of sound had come into general use (see Chapter 4), technicians experimented with that idea, and in December 1953 the research workers of the R.C.A. were able to demonstrate such a system for recording colour and black-and-white television programmes.

Previously, the usual way to preserve a 'live' television programme for repeat performances or for the archives was to make a 'tele-recording' or 'kinescope recording', a film taken at the end of a television receiver tube during the performance. The quality was never nearly as good as that of the original transmission. Another, more complicated and expensive, way was the simultaneous shooting of a film of the programme in the studio. It was clear that tele-recordings on inexpensive, easy-to-handle magnetic tape would solve many problems of preservation, repetition, editing, storing, and distribution of television programmes.

Although to the electrical engineer there is no basic difference between sound and vision impulses, the problems of recording the latter were quite formidable. Sound of very high quality can be recorded on tape at up to 16,000 cycles per second; but three to five million cycles are required to achieve good quality in vision—and twice as many for recording images in colour. This major difficulty was solved by increasing the sensitivity of the sound-head to the utmost and by using a tape of special width or speed—to provide room for all the signals. The 'translating' of the camera and microphone impulses into magnetic recording is a relatively simple process, carried out by an extra machine linked to the camera during transmission in the same way as the recording of sound alone; the same machine can later carry out the job of 'retranslating' the magnetic recording into vision and sound.

The first battery of 'video' tape recorders, a system called Ampex, was installed in the largest American television studios early in 1958. This system uses tape moving at a speed of 200 inches per second but only half an inch wide; the recording is done on three tracks, two for storing the video signals and one for sound. A special machine for the cutting and editing of the tape had to be devised as it cannot be edited visually like cine film; the editor presses a 'cue' key to mark the spot where he wants to cut while the tape moves through the machine at normal speed (which allows him to see the recording on a small screen), and when he replays it at a slow cutting speed the cue signal becomes audible in a loudspeaker.

The video recording system has also some advantages in film production because tape needs no developing and printing but can be played back straight away. The film director can, for instance, play back his 'rushes'—the unedited film—immediately after a 'take' or after a day's shooting to find out if they are satisfactory, or if re-takes are necessary. Even a whole feature film can be shot on tape, edited, and then translated into ordinary celluloid film; this reduces the costs of production considerably as the price of raw film stock represents a considerable item in the budget of a feature film. The tape can be 'wiped' and used over and over again. Eventually the video-tape replay machine may supersede the conventional film projector in the cinema, and even the cine amateur may be given a cheap video-tape camera for his holiday shots.

Television is far more than a means of cheap home entertainment in our time. It instructs schoolchildren; it is used in medical training where close-ups of operations in colour, transmitted over a closed circuit, help to instruct the medical student much more thoroughly than is possible in the operating theatre. In factories and research stations closed-circuit television is frequently used to control processes which cannot be watched directly either because they take place in inaccessible spots or because a human observer would be in danger if he approached too closely—for instance, in nuclear power stations or research reactors. Industrial television in '3-D' has become more and more necessary, especially where remote-handling operations or chemical experiments have to be watched. The stereo effect is achieved in the same way as with the 3-D films of the early 1950's—by using two cameras, representing the observer's right and left eyes respectively, and the two pictures, polarized on different planes by optical systems, are then superimposed on the screen and viewed through accordingly polarized glasses. The banks transmit the images of centrally stored account sheets to receiving sets in their branches; the railways have installed closed-circuit television in their sidings and marshalling yards, the airports in their control rooms, and the police in narrow town centres where the field of vision is restricted. The house of the future may have television cameras everywhere: the caller at the gate, the baby in its cot, the joint in the oven will then be watched through electronic eyes by the housewife on a central viewing panel. Underwater television cameras have transmitted pictures of ocean life and wrecks from depths which no human will ever penetrate except in a bathyscaphe, and space vehicles will show us the stars and planets as they look outside the earth's atmosphere by means of television. Science will no doubt recover some of the thrill and fascination that have been lost through the tawdriness and commercialization of the 'magic mirror'.

# 7

◇◇◇◇◇◇◇◇◇◇◇◇◇◇◇◇◇◇◇

## Everyday Electronics

Soon after the end of the First World War, a young meteorologist, Robert Watson-Watt, the son of a Scottish carpenter, entered the Royal Air Force Establishment at Farnborough with a particular problem on his mind. Civil aviation was developing quickly, but many accidents occurred because pilots often flew right into thunderstorms. Watson-Watt was trying to think of ways and means of warning them. As thunderstorms were electric phenomena whose crackling sounds could be heard in the headphones of a wireless receiver, there seemed to be an obvious way of investigating these noises, which were until that time merely regarded as a nuisance in wireless communications.

The young scientist had the idea of enlisting the help of radio listeners all over the Western hemisphere for his research. Broadcasting was just beginning to develop, and he persuaded the B.B.C. to co-operate in this scheme. Listeners who were prepared to help were sent in advance the texts of radio talks, and all they were asked to do was to mark those words in the scripts which, in their receivers, were accompanied by atmospheric crackling.

From Cairo to Bergen, from Madeira to Potsdam the marked scripts came back, and Watson-Watt went to work on them. He found that the movements of thunderstorms could be determined at distances of up to 4,500 miles. When he was transferred to the Radio Research Station at Slough, near London, he carried on his work by travelling to many parts of the world 'to make atmospherics sign the visitor's book', as he put it. As a result, thunderstorm warnings in air transport contributed a great deal to the safety of flying.

One day in 1934—he was working as a senior scientist at the

National Physical Laboratory in Teddington—he received a secret inquiry from a Government department asking him what he thought of the so-called 'death rays' which were then in the news, mainly as reports from Nazi Germany. Was there really a possibility of killing or paralysing people at a distance with some kind of rays, of setting off explosives, or stopping cars, tanks, and aircraft?

Watson-Watt's report said more or less that these stories were nonsense (they were, in fact, part of Hitler's psychological warfare of intimidation). There was, however, a more practical idea that had occurred to him during his work on atmospherics—a system by which aircraft or ships could be discovered through cloud, fog, and darkness. He called it 'radiolocation'. Would the Government be prepared to back some research work?

He was granted a modest sum to go ahead and collect a small team of scientists to carry out experiments. Radar—the name under which we have come to know the system, an abbreviation of 'Radio Detection and Ranging'—had its first test in a field ten miles from the powerful short-wave radio transmitter of Daventry, where Watson-Watt set up his equipment in a lorry in 1935. His theory proved correct: a wireless 'echo' from aircraft flying through the radio beam could be received on the ground, and its distance, speed, and direction determined. 'The wings of an aeroplane act like a kind of horizontal wire in the air', explained Watson-Watt. 'When you aim a powerful wireless beam at them they turn into a "secondary transmitter" and send the waves back at the angle of incidence, just as a mirror reflects light rays.'

This principle was, of course, no new discovery. As early as 1887 Heinrich Hertz had shown that electro-magnetic waves are reflected in a way similar to light rays, and already in 1904 a German engineer, Hülsmeyer, had taken out a patent on a radio-echo device. In 1922 Marconi said that he had noticed the reflection of wireless telegraphy waves and suggested that ships should use some such device to avoid collisions in fog. A few years later French radio technicians experimented with very short radio waves, which were sent out in 'pulses', or short bursts, with a view to saving lives at sea, and the liner *Normandie* was fitted with such an 'obstacle detector'. In Germany the firms of Telefunken and Lorenz began similar work in the early 1930's.

But it was left to Watson-Watt to develop a thorough system of aircraft detection. The clouds of war were gathering; air defence was important.

Apart from the problem of how to keep the work secret, the main difficulties were the design of a high-power transmitter capable of producing very short pulses (of one-millionth of a second duration), for the purpose of getting a strong 'echo', and the development of receivers which could be used by untrained personnel. Early research work was done by Watson-Watt's team in a remote part of the Suffolk coast, where inquisitive villagers were made to believe that these townsfolk were prospecting for oil. Already at the end of 1935 five radar stations were in experimental operation. By the spring of 1936 aircraft could be spotted by radar at distances up to 75 miles, and three years later, six months before the outbreak of the Second World War, a chain of radar stations from the Isle of Wight to Aberdeen formed an invisible, unbroken 'wall' which no enemy aircraft could penetrate without being identified long before reaching its target.

Radar was a decisive factor in the 'Battle of Britain' by helping British fighter pilots to beat back the massed assault of the German Luftwaffe, and it proved its enormous value in defending London against Goering's night bombers during the 'blitz'. When the tide of war turned in the Allies' favour, radar was ready with a number of new devices to guide and safeguard aircraft and ships on all their operations. The general public knew nothing of these inventions until the end of the war—Watson-Watt was knighted in 1942, but his achievements were not disclosed at the time.

Radar and its related techniques of electronic guidance and remote control have since found innumerable peace-time applications. Most ships and many harbours have installed radar more or less in its original form, as a reliable instrument for 'seeing' in all light and weather conditions. We are all familiar with the rotating radar aerial, which usually looks like a layer cake cut in half. As a rule, scanners are 'double-deckers': the upper section is used for transmission, the lower for reception of signals. The scanner rotates at a speed of 10 to 25 revolutions per minute, and frequently the transmitter and receiver are built in and rotate with it.

The transmitter sends its very short bursts of energy in the centimetre wave-band—about 1,000 bursts per second; they are concentrated in a narrow beam. A 'modulator' in the transmitter controls these bursts, which are produced by the 'magnetron', a small valve capable of sending out very short pulses with great precision. As soon as one burst has gone out, the receiver is connected to the aerial and 'listens' for the echo to come back. Any obstacle in the path of a wave, whether another ship, a hill, a coastline, or even a shoal of fish, reflects the pulse energy so that

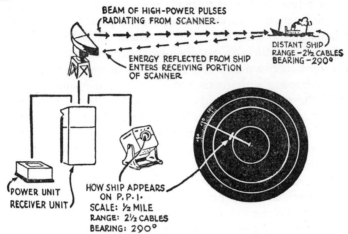

Radar installation for ship or harbour; P.P.I., Plan Position Indicator

some of it comes back as an 'echo', which is picked up by the scanner, amplified, and fed to a cathode-ray tube. The wide end of this tube, comparable to the screen of a television set, reproduces the image of what the echoes have brought back.

This is done by placing around the narrow neck of the tube two coils which act on the beam of electrons emitted by the cathode. They do more or less what optical lenses do to a light beam: the 'focus coil' determines the sharpness of the picture on the radar screen, and the 'deflection coil' controls the trace of bright, greenish 'blobs' on the screen. As this coil rotates in step with the scanner, the blobs are renewed 10 to 25 times per minute, and if the position of one or the other of them—representing, for instance, a ship—is changing this means that the real position of that object in relation to the scanner is changing too.

The most ingenious part of this process of 'painting' a map by electrons is the automatic measurement of the distance of an obstacle. This is done by determining the time—only a very small fraction of a second, of course—between the emitting of the radar pulse and the return of the echo. The blob made by the echo appears on the screen at a certain distance from the centre, which corresponds to the real distance of the obstacle. If, however, the 'True Motion' radar system is used, the operator's own ship is shown moving across the screen, other ships are seen proceeding with their true velocities instead of their relative ones, and all fixed objects such as a coastline appear stationary.

In aircraft, the scanner may be mounted on the underside (here the speed of rotation is usually once every second) so that the screen reproduces a map of the ground below through darkness or cloud—complete with towns, woods, rivers, hills, lakes, and so on —or in the nose to provide 'cloud and collision warning' by reporting obstacles in the air. These include not only solid objects such as other aircraft, but also clouds, e.g. of the cumulo-nimbus type, which can create serious turbulence and should be avoided by airliners. Airborne radar can pick up echoes from such clouds at a range of fifty or more miles, and of course echoes from mountains which might present a danger to the aircraft. The air-borne transmitter-receiver is combined with a gyro-stabilizer which maintains the instrument in its correct position irrespective of the movement of the aircraft—whether it is ascending, descending, banking, or even flying on its back!

Large harbours and airports depend to a great extent on radar for traffic control and safety; ferries use it to maintain their service even in dense fog; whaling ships mark the killed whales with radar reflectors so that they can be picked up later; polar expedition ships and icebreakers can distinguish between pack ice, sheet ice, and icebergs ahead—even tracks cut in the ice by ships can be seen on the radar screen; charting and surveying work is greatly helped by airborne and ground-stationed radar; in meteorology, 'radio sondes'—gas-balloons carrying a radar reflector, instruments for recording weather conditions, and frequently also radio transmitters—are sent up in the air and tracked by ground stations . . . to mention only a few of the innumerable peace-time applications of the radar echo technique. Policemen can trap speeding motorists with it, geologists discover mineral deposits, trawlermen locate their catch. The altitude of an aircraft can be seen on the dial of the radar altimeter, and marine echo-sounding to determine the depth of the sea bed is now usually carried out also with radar waves; previously, this was done with ultrasonic waves—sound waves of a high frequency which cannot be heard by human ears (they can be produced by applying an electric current to certain crystals, e.g., quartz). In Nature, ultrasonic 'radar' has been used for some millions of years by bats; flying at night, they utter short cries of high frequencies (around 50,000 cycles per second), and the returning echoes, which they can hear as sounds, tell them what obstacles there are in their path of flight, and at what distance. In using present-day radar systems we are, therefore, emulating the bats.

Navigational aids, especially in air transport, have been developed from radar and radio techniques in bewildering variety. Most of them work by sending out radio beams from ground stations, which tell the navigator where he happens to be and what course he must take; they use a 'master' and one or two 'slave' transmitters at one or both ends of the route to lay an invisible triangular pattern which shows the navigator his position on a screen or some other registering device. The DECCA system, developed in Britain during the Second World War and internationally regarded as the best, indicates the position of an aircraft in flight in three dimensions—latitude, longitude, and altitude—with the use of four transmitters, which create two hyperbolae of radio beams; the result can be seen at a glance on dials in the cockpit, with an accuracy of a few yards. Two young technicians, Harvey Schwarz and William O'Brian, developed this system in London and Hollywood during the Second World War; it had its crucial test on D-Day during the allied landing operations in Normandy.

A post-war system, produced by Marconi and R.C.A. engineers, is the Doppler navigational aid, which needs no ground stations. It uses a well-known principle discovered by the nineteenth-century Austrian physicist, Christian Doppler. We can observe it any time a locomotive whistles or a motorist sounds his horn, while passing us: as long as the source of the sound approaches us the pitch seems higher than when it moves away from us. Electro-magnetic waves such as those of light and radio are subject to this effect just as much as sound waves; their frequency seems to be higher while the source approaches an observer, and lower while it recedes from him. This effect is exploited in the Doppler system of aircraft navigation: two beams of radio waves are aimed at the ground from transmitters under the fuselage, the forward beam striking the ground slightly ahead of the aircraft and the back beam slightly astern; both alternate twice each second from port to starboard. The forward-beam signals reflected back to the aircraft are increased in frequency in proportion to its speed over the ground, the back-beam signals decreased. This difference in frequency is measured automatically

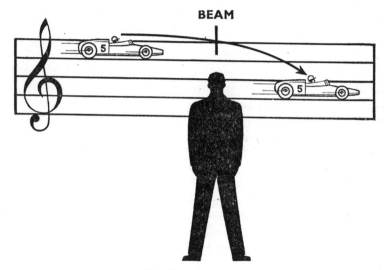

The Doppler Effect

to give the navigator an accurate indication of the speed of the aircraft and of the drift angle so that the course can be corrected accordingly.

The VLF (very low frequency) system, developed at the Royal Aircraft Establishment, Farnborough, works with extremely long radio waves whose crests are ten miles apart. An instrument in the aircraft counts the number of waves per second automatically and enables the pilot to pinpoint his position. Six VLF stations, spaced around the world so that pilots could at any time receive at least three of them, would provide complete international coverage.

Automatic flying and landing devices, which aim at eliminating the 'human error' factor that may defeat even the best pilots and navigators occasionally, have been tried out and introduced in several forms since the end of the war. The first 'pilotless' aircraft, a four-engined Skymaster, flew the Atlantic in 1947; throughout its flight over 2,400 miles no human hand touched the controls—after a push-button had been pressed, a self-controlled, pre-set 'brain' took over, making the machine take off, climb, level out, throttle down, and land, including the putting on of the brakes after touching down.

Today many military and civil aircraft types are equipped with automatic pilots, though they are never used on the whole length of a journey. 'Blind' landing devices have also been well developed and may one day replace the 'talking-down' system based on radio communication between the control tower of the airport and the cockpit. Among the safest of these blind-landing systems is that developed by the Royal Aircraft Establishment, Bedford, which can bring any aircraft securely down without the pilot's intervention. A pair of cables is laid down on either side of the runway and fed with electric current, which is picked up by receivers in the aircraft. This enables the automatic control gear to navigate it to the centre of the runway. A radio altimeter controls the descent to an accuracy of two feet, which is considered fairly good for the human pilot of a large airliner. During the last 250 feet of its descent, the aircraft is brought down by a complex system of servo-mechanisms which are constantly fed with information on altitude and runway approach produced by the instruments in the aircraft.

The internationally approved ILS (Instrument Landing System)—since 1961 in general use in Europe and the Near East—works with a radio beam from the ground, which operates an indicator in the aircraft or the auto-pilot directly. The indicator provides the pilot with precise information about the position of his aircraft in relation to the centre of the runway where he wants to land, and about the correctness or otherwise of his angle of descent so that he will come safely into view of the runway. This information is displayed on a crossed-pointer meter in the cockpit. The pilot also gets audible and visible signals when the aircraft is on the correct course at specified distances from the touch-down point on the runway. As soon as he sees the runway —the so-called 'critical height' is not less than 250 feet—he takes no more notice of his ILS; if he fails to see it he must either make another approach or be diverted to another airfield. In cases where the ILS acts directly on the auto-pilot the pilot takes over from it at the critical height.

But the aim of the inventors, engineers, and traffic controllers is, of course, the fully automatic landing—the complete elimination of the 'human element'—which they regard as a good thing, at least in flying. Since the Atlantic flight of the famous Skymaster in 1947 great advances have been made, and thousands of fully automatic experimental landings have been carried out at Bedford and American research centres. The Britannic R.A.F. freighter was equipped with this system in 1961. But there is some understandable hesitation in entrusting the lives of a hundred or more airliner passengers entirely to a machine. Sooner or later, however, complete automation will come.

The general introduction of blind landing would relieve not only the pilot and navigator of the most difficult jobs in aviation, but also take a great burden off the minds of the traffic controllers at the airport. They will be able to follow the descent of the aircraft exclusively on their various radar screens without having to do the strenuous work of 'talking-down' as well. Radar will then play an even more vital part in air traffic control than it has done so far.

It will also do so in urban traffic control on land. London Transport has developed a radar scanner which identifies buses at a series of points along their routes. The radar beams are reflected by special coded number-plates on the sides of the passing buses, whose numbers and positions are then recorded on an illuminated chart at headquarters. This makes it possible to telephone instructions to inspectors so that they can speed the buses up, slow them down, or let them turn round according to the over-all traffic situation.

In ocean-going ships the 'automatic helmsman' can steer a much more accurate course than the human one. It is coupled to the modern gyro-compass, which is no bigger than a portable typewriter, completely impervious to vibration and ship movement, and suitable for vessels of every size. Responding to 'slave' radar repeaters on shore or to pre-set instructions, the automatic helmsman will keep to its course unfailingly, but it will also make allowance for the state of the sea—in fact, the rougher the weather the better it works by comparison with the human helmsman.

No longer does the skipper have to give his instructions to the engine-room by telegraph or word of mouth, but the machine acts instantly and directly. Thus it avoids delays which, in an emergency, could lead to danger or even disaster.

Ever since Man had to leave the Garden of Eden under unfortunate circumstances, and was forced to work for his upkeep, he wished he could have his most arduous and strenuous tasks done by something or someone else—a genie, a willing giant, a Golem, a homunculus, a robot. The slave system gave at least some people a chance of letting others work for them; the accumulation of money, too, was found to be a great help in this matter—but the idle rich have always been a very narrow sector of society, and the great mass of the people were poor and had to work hard. We have seen how, since the dawn of civilization, Man's reluctance to do back-breaking jobs has been the mother of his inventiveness. Progress, though, was slow, and it was only in the eighteenth century that the age of mechanization began to dawn.

Until a few decades ago technologists believed that mechanization would be complete when as many jobs as possible had been taken over by machines operated by workers. Now we realize that a human operator performing a monotonous task at some machine is no less a slave than an oarsman in an ancient galley, though his exertion may not always be a physical one. The tendency in our time is to turn the machine operator into a machine-minder, a technician, and to let the machine look after itself as much as possible.

Only the development of automation has made this second industrial revolution feasible. It may still cause hardship and social unrest, just as the appearance of the railways did among the coachmen and horse-dealers. But every such upheaval brings eventually new and easier jobs, shorter working hours, higher standards of living, and the present revolution has already begun to do this.

Automation is no mysterious technical Mumbo Jumbo; it is no more and no less than the ability of a mechanical device to control itself. When Denis Papin invented his 'bone-digester' (see Part I) he prevented this early pressure cooker from blowing itself up by giving it a safety-valve, a weighted little stopper which *automatically* opened a small hole in the pot to let some steam out when the pressure increased too much, and which closed the hole again when the pressure had gone back to normal. James Watt invented a device to keep his steam-engine from going too fast—the 'governor', another automatic contrivance: two fly-balls on levers which rotated with the engine mechanism; as the speed increased the balls moved outwards and upwards by centrifugal force, pulling up the levers which were connected to the steam valve. The valve thus gradually closed, the speed of the engine decreased, the fly-balls moved down again, and the steam valve reopened.

Even from these early examples of automatic control we can see the principle of automation—measurement, control, correction. The measuring device replaces one or the other of the human senses: the watchful eye, the listening ear, the nose that detects a suspicious smell, the skin that feels if something grows too hot or too cold, the finger that discerns the thickness and smoothness of things. Aids to measure these sensations have been developed over the centuries: measuring rods, gauges, thermometers, chronometers and the like; but they still need the human senses to perceive what they measure, the human brain to decide what to do, and the human hand to act accordingly.

Automation, therefore, aims at making these devices self-operating. A thermostat, for instance, determines the temperature in a refrigerator or a hot-water tank, and when a pre-set upper or lower limit is reached it switches the electric current which operates the cooling mechanism or the immersion heater on or off. Thus it ensures that the temperature remains more or less constant. Another automation device, the photo-electric cell, which offers greater or smaller resistance to an electric current according to the amount of light falling on it, may be used to open a door automatically when someone approaches it and thus interrupts a beam of light, or it may watch a glowing furnace and switch off the current of the electric heater when the glow grows too bright.

The use of radio-active isotopes in measuring devices is of increasing importance. The United States oil industry alone estimates that they save more than 200 million dollars per year in oil-well stimulation and logging, refining and pipeline flow; here the 'tracer' technique—adding isotopes in small quantities to the oil or to chemical fluids to measure their rate of absorption or discover leakages—is widely employed. Isotopes can 'look' into closed packages of cigarettes, detergents, and so on to check if they are properly filled. For this purpose, beta particles—fast electrons which pass through thin sheets of cardboard or metal— are the most suitable type of radiation; in passing through a thickness of material the number of beta particles in a beam is steadily reduced as some of them are absorbed, and the amount of radiation that gets through indicates the thickness. A simple arrangement of a radiation source on one side of a moving belt with the packets on it, and a detector, an adaptation of the Geiger counter, on the other side carries out a continuous automatic control of the goods in the packets. A feedback device throws out the packets which are not properly filled. The control of liquids in tins or bottles works on the same principle. Isotopes are also used for the continuous measurement of the thickness of moving material such as metal sheeting, paper, plastics, rubber, etc., without any physical contact with the material. Here again, the radiation source is placed on one side of the moving product, often in form of a tube extending over the whole width of the machinery, and the detector on the other; the latter is, of course, connected with a feedback device for continuous adjustment of the thickness of the material while in production.

Another thickness gauge is based on the reflection or 'back-scattering' of beta particles; the rate of reflection, too, depends on its thickness. This method is particularly useful where a coat of paint, zinc, tin, or some other material on the surface of steel or plastic has to be measured. Gamma rays, which are similar to X-rays, are also reflected by matter; they are often used to check the thickness of hot rolled steel strip and of closed tube and tank walls.

These are comparatively simple instruments, but there are many others which consist of complicated assemblies of devices for measuring, controlling, and correcting this or that process. We have already mentioned the automatic pilot for aircraft. It has, among other instruments, an altimeter for determining and maintaining the cruising height by acting on the elevation rudders. It has a gyroscope—a spinning-top suspended in such a manner that its own inertia keeps it pointing in the same direction— to adjust the position of the machine in the air. The automatic pilot has receivers picking up the guiding radio beams from the ground stations, and if the aircraft strays from its path the steering mechanism is set in motion to correct the mistake. It has control devices which react if the aircraft falls into an air pocket or is rocked by a gust of wind. And it has an extra robot instrument, the monitor, which keeps watch over all these devices and sounds an alarm if one of them stops working properly. Then, however, the human pilot or navigator will have to take over. In fact, most automation systems have such emergency devices calling their human masters to help, for there may always be a situation with which even the cleverest machines cannot deal. After all, they have all been conceived by the human brain, which is still a good deal cleverer.

You can introduce some new automatic device in a household or let an automatic pilot take over the controls of an aircraft at a moment's notice once these devices are available, but you cannot convert a factory to automation overnight. That revolution has, in fact, been going on since the beginning of our century, with automatic machines and systems advancing slowly from industry to industry, from production process to production process. Machine tools can be made to carry out many different operations on the principle of the music box, in which little prongs on a rotating cylinder strike the tone-producing blades in a certain order so that we hear a tune. An electrically powered lathe, for instance, can be made 'semi-automatic' by incorporating such a music-box device, with cams or curved discs bringing one tool after another into operation. But the human worker was still required to place the workpiece in the machine, fasten it, and transfer it to another machine after the operation. This business of transferring products from one process to another seemed especially time-wasting to the engineers; one solution of the problem was the conveyor-belt system, which brings the product to the worker instead of making him go and fetch it. But it is frequently unsuitable where heavy pieces have to be transferred and lengthy operations carried out.

So the missing link in a chain of more or less automatic operations was the transfer of workpieces. Many devices had to be created to replace the hands and eyes of the human worker: moving bands, chutes, trolleys, cranes, mechanical arms, and so on, all of them working automatically. Now the machines received the product, which was fixed by mechanical hands and fingers, operated on, released, and sent on to the next stage. Still the machines were not yet completely self-regulating; this perfection was achieved by the 'feedback' and 'servo-mechanism' systems. The automation experts go so far as saying that they are the heart of the matter, the decisive elements in automatic production.

To understand them in simple terms, let us have a look at the 'oldest' type of automatic plant, a modern oil refinery. Into one end go distillates of crude oil; a catalytic 'cracker' applies high temperature and pressure to it, and after a series of chemical processes the product comes out as petrol. Half a dozen men are quite sufficient to supervise the operation of the oil refinery, for it is controlled by built-in instruments. If, for instance, the temperature of the fluids and gases in a certain unit rises above normal, a thermostat 'feeds back' the information to the automatic control centre, from where electrical 'orders' go out to the heating appliances to reduce their output. In the same way, pressure, quantity, rate of flow are controlled. Where the correction cannot be made merely by opening or closing an electric circuit, 'servo-mechanisms' come into play. Acting on orders from the control centre, these pneumatic, hydraulic, or mechanical devices, frequently operated by electric 'servo-motors', reduce or increase valve openings, slow down or step up the flow of chemicals, start or stop this or that operation.

In a steel-rolling mill a red-hot billet emerging from the furnace is caught by giant rollers which whip it back and forth a few times, pressing it into a long slab a few inches thick. The slab moves on to the machines that trim and cut it while another billet comes down from the furnace. The electric motors driving the rollers develop thousands of horse-power, but they can brake the movement of the slab to a standstill within a second. A feedback system with servo-mechanisms controls the operation. A tachometer (speed gauge) observes the speed of rolling, which has been set previously by the engineers; the required thickness and length of the slab are measured by gauges. The slightest deviation from these standards is fed back to the control centre as an electric signal, and out go the orders, also by electric signals, to adjust the roller speed, the pressure on the slab, or the cutting stops. This is done by the servo-mechanisms—more quickly than it could have been done by human hands.

These are comparatively simple examples, but they may show the principle on which automatic production is based. The first factory unit combining a whole series of automatic operations in car manufacture was built by the Ford company in Cleveland, Ohio, in 1952. Here finished and tested six-cylinder engine blocks were made from rough castings without being touched by human

Automatically controlled facing and drilling machine

hand. Forty-two automatic machines carried out five hundred different operations, including assembly and final testing of the blocks; any piece that was found faulty by the mechanical hands and eyes of the testing instruments was thrown out of the assembly line by a servo-mechanism, a hydraulic arm. In this way a cylinder block which used to be completed in nine hours was finished in fifteen minutes.

We have mentioned the semi-automatic machine tools. A fully automatic machine cannot, of course, work on the basis of the music-box system; it requires a control mechanism which gets its orders from punched cards, punched tape, or magnetic tape. This principle, too, is not as new as it might seem; at the beginning of the last century, the French mechanic, Joseph Marie Jacquard, invented a mechanical silk loom for mass production, controlled not by hand but by punched cards. We also know that Sir Charles Wheatstone used punched tape as far back as 1867 to speed up the transmission of telegrams (see Chapter 2). Only the control by magnetic tape is of recent origin; the first machine tools with this type of control were demonstrated in the early 1950's.

### ELECTRONIC CONTROL OF MACHINE TOOLS

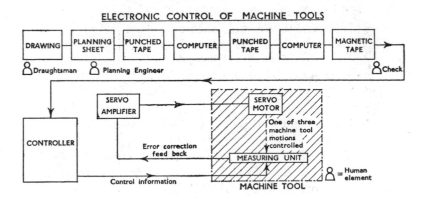

Automatic control by punched card, punched tape, or magnetic tape works by giving its orders to the machine in the form of numbers. The medium of information is prepared by translating the impulse numbers which determine the eventual form of the workpiece into punch-holes or electro-magnetic signals. All the operator has then to do is to insert the card or tape in the machine and press the start button; the machine does the rest.

It is, of course, uneconomical to rebuild for automatic control a machine originally designed for hand control. It has to be built for it right from the start (and the designer can save himself the trouble of incorporating hand-operated controls). An essential characteristic of automatically controlled machine tools is that they must have feedback devices informing the control section of the actual operations carried out; these are then automatically compared with the pre-set standards, and any deviation is corrected at once automatically. The transfer of raw materials and components, too, can be controlled by tape; one of the most advanced conveyor systems, developed in Britain, permits the automatic control of a programme of collecting, holding, storing, transporting, and presenting workpieces up to a week ahead.

A whole chain of machine tools can be controlled by one or more of these automatic devices. As the workpiece is transferred from one machine to the next, control also switches the punched or magnetic tape orders to the next machine. It is possible to make two machines work on one piece at the same time; it is even possible to detail to the automatic control system the job of selecting the tools for each machine operation, and of exchanging tools which have become useless for new ones.

This system, which has since been introduced in many countries and factories and adapted for a large number of products, cannot work without some guiding 'brain' supervising operations. That brain is the electronic computer.

Mechanical aids to 'doing sums' have been in use for thousands of years, beginning with the abacus. The first calculating machine, however, was invented in the seventeenth century by the French mathematician, Blaise Pascal; it could carry out multiplications and divisions by means of wheels bearing the numbers o to 9. The German philosopher, Gottfried Wilhelm von Leibniz, designed a machine that could multiply. These simple instruments were the ancestors of the mechanical calculating machine for industrial and office use developed in the first half of our century and still in great demand; many of these models are electrically operated. But they cannot compare with the electronic computer, whose operation depends on the thermionic valve or the transistor, and which works on an entirely different mathematical principle.

It is a machine that can solve calculating problems at very high speed and can be 'programmed' or 'conditioned' to carry out lengthy series of jobs in a given sequence; it can also be arranged to change its own programme under certain conditions. It can make decisions—but it cannot really *think*. For this reason, the popular term 'electronic brain' is somewhat misleading. But it can store facts and instructions in an electronic memory, and use that information whenever necessary.

The computer works very fast; it adds or subtracts in a few millionths of a second, and multiplies or divides in a few thousandths of a second. But this is only part of the job it has to do in automation; here, the main importance of the electronic computer is its ability to analyse, marshal, record, and report information in various forms from given data. This is called 'data processing', the special field of the 'digital' computer. Its principles were established a century ago by an English professor of mathematics, Charles Babbage, but the first modern machine of this type was invented by an American, Howard Aiken, in 1937; seven years later, Harvard had its 'Mark I' digital computer, the grandmother of many thousands of hard-working electronic computing machines which have been installed in laboratories and factories, universities and offices, in research establishments and in transport, to say nothing of military installations.

The computer consists mainly of innumerable valves or transistors and other small electrical parts grouped in units. The language of electricity is laconic; it knows only two words: 'Yes' and 'No', that is: 'Pulse' and 'No Pulse', or, in layman's language: 'Current' and 'No Current'. The mathematics of the computer have, therefore, to be translated into a system of communication with only two figures instead of the usual ten of our decimal system. This dual notation, an invention of our century (though the ancient Chinese had something similar), is called the 'binary' system. Its two numbers are 1 and 0, meaning 'Pulse' and 'No Pulse'. In it, the decimal notation 0 remains 0 and 1 is still 1, but 2 becomes 10, 3 = 11, 4 = 100, 5 = 101, 6 = 110, 7 = 111, 8 = 1000, 9 = 1001, and 10 = 1010. The binary system is simple but would be too longwinded for everyday use; 99, for instance, is 1100011—seven figures instead of two! For the electronic computer with its 'trains' of pulses, however, the system is ideal.

How are these figures represented in the computer? We know that it is an assembly of valve or transistor units, acting like relays. A partnership of two such units may therefore operate as a switch which opens and closes a circuit. If the circuit is in an 'off' position, the arrival of a pulse switches it on; if it is in an 'on' position, the next pulse will change it to 'off'—with a pulse being emitted. The figure 0 is represented by the 'off' and 1 by the 'on' position; thus a system of thousands of such circuits can be expected to cope with binary numbers of almost any magnitude. A computer at work has an incessant train of pulses flowing through it, usually generated by an electrically excited crystal which vibrates with a frequency of thousands of millions of cycles per second. By the incessant opening and closing of circuits at very great speed the computer does its 'sums'.

Whatever a computer is asked to do must therefore take the form of a mathematical problem to be solved. Specialists in 'programming' computers—i.e., translating its tasks into the mathematical language of binary numbers—are indispensable wherever these machines go into action. An 'order code', or basic list of instructions, is the first thing that has to be worked out; it is a code which lays down the rules according to which the computer must attack its tasks—approximately in the way an automatic telephone exchange has been 'conditioned' to connect us when we dial a number.

The actual 'programme' which the machine has to carry out according to its basic instructions is fed into its 'memory'. There are various memory systems; one has the shape of a metal drum whose sectors can be magnetized to represent either 0 or 1. Another system works with magnetic tape of the type used in a tape recorder, a third one with a cathode-ray tube in which the electron beam sweeps across the wide end as in a television receiver, but the picture assembled from innumerable tiny points on the 'screen' consists of 0's and 1's.

The tasks which the machine is asked to do within this programme are usually conveyed to it by means of punched cards or a punched tape like the roll of a pianola, with the holes representing 0's and 1's, or by magnetic tape with the number code 'inscribed' on it in the form of recorded impulses. As the tape unwinds in a special console the computer works according to its instructions, referring back to the programme in its memory during every operation.

The results may be put out in various forms. Some computers can type them out on electric typewriters, store them as impulses on magnetic film, or punch them as holes in paper tape or cards; others, for instance those controlling automatic production processes, send their instructions out in the form of electric impulses to the machine tools.

Some computers have been taught to read much faster than we can; an electronic scanner similar to that in a television camera distinguishes letters, figures, and signs, and a photo-cell translates them into impulses. Others respond to the human voice: they can take down a dictation and write on a typewriter what they hear —in simple phonetic spelling, of course, because even the smartest electronic computer cannot be expected to master the vagaries of English orthography. Translation machines have been developed to a remarkable degree; although they may not be able to render, say, Russian poetry in Shakespeare's language they can translate correctly factual texts. Since 1960 an American computer has been doing its daily job of translating the more important articles from *Pravda* into primitive but intelligible English at the rate of several dozen words per minute, and with a vocabulary of

Part of the 'dictionary' (magnified 300 times) of a translation machine: the tracks represent Russian words

several tens of thousands of words. Translating computers must still be fed with punched or magnetic tape from a separate machine on which a human operator types out the words, but prototype computers which read the printed text at a speed of hundreds of letters per second and type out the completed translation are already in operation.

Here the main difficulty is that in every language many words have more than one meaning, depending on the context and the subject. The 'memory' of the machine contains all the various meanings of these words, and the computer has to use its faculty of selecting one of several possibilities—of making a decision; it arrives at the correct decision by comparing other words of the text which have only one distinct meaning, and by referring back to them and counting their frequency the machine establishes the context, whether it is politics or medicine, farming or nuclear energy. Thus it is possible to avoid mistakes such as the one made by an early translating computer which rendered 'hydraulic ram'

M

as 'aquatic male sheep'. The job of establishing the context with the help of the 'memory' is done within the fraction of a second.

That faculty of arriving at the correct decision seems almost human, but we must never forget that computers can only 'think' what they have been told to think by their human creators, and their 'thoughts' have been programmed into them in elaborate and tedious detail. They have no mental powers of learning from past successes or failures, and they cannot cope with unexpected difficulties—except blow a fuse or sound an alarm that summons their human operators to help. They cannot solve problems for which the mathematicians who have 'programmed' and 'instructed' them see no method of solution. It has been said that intellectually they are just stupid, and that an earthworm is a good deal cleverer. In every sense, they were 'born yesterday'.

But it is precisely their capability of making decisions that gives these computers their importance in industrial automation. Here they can replace the machine-minder and foreman, the operator and inspector. At the lowest level, they can control and supervise individual operations. When, in a canning factory, an electronic eye sorts hundreds of millions of peas per day according to their colour, eliminating the yellowish ones and letting only the ripe, green ones pass for processing, the job of making decisions is not very difficult, and you don't need a full-scale electronic computer for it. But if, for instance, an automatic drill has to be watched, things become more complicated. Although the machine may be conditioned by purely mechanical means to drill holes of a certain depth into, say, motor-car pistons, it cannot be left entirely on its own to do so. What if the 'bit' of the drill breaks, if a piston cracks, or the hole is too deep or too shallow? An electronic 'robot' able to make decisions would then come into play. It can test the workpiece and find out if it is in good order; if not, it can have the piston thrown out. It could either renew a broken bit by setting some appropriate device in motion, or summon an engineer to do it. If a number of pistons are found to be faulty the robot could stop the machine altogether.

The electronic robot could do more than that. It could set the drilling-machine to start a different series of operations. It may not be able to read an ordinary blueprint like a human operator, but it can carry out blueprint instructions if these have first been 'translated' into the language of electro-magnetic impulses which it understands. How does the human operator make himself understood to the computer? He types out a message on a keyboard, say: 'ON KUL ON SPN GO RGT TL LFT CIR/CTR+2+3 RAD +5.' This message, in the form of a pattern of holes or magnetic impulses on tape, is understood by the computer according to the basic instructions that have been fed into it: 'Turn on coolant, turn on spindle, go right with tool on left side along a circle with a centre at $x = +2$, $y = +3$ and a radius of $+5$.' These instructions may come from another electronic computer, one which controls a whole section of the factory with a number of machine tools. Such a controller can be made to issue orders to, and supervise, not only a number of machines of the same type but a whole variety of them: production machines, transfer machines, assembly machines, inspection machines, packaging machines. These machines 'report back' continuously to the controller what they are doing; if something goes wrong, the controller would 'know' what to do to put it right, or summon human assistance if it doesn't.

The completely automatic factory would have a 'master controller', a computer to supervise computers, as its nerve centre. It would not only keep an eye on the whole production process, co-ordinating the various sections (for instance, to make sure that the speed at which one of them works does not outpace the others, which may result in lack of materials or even in complete chaos); it could also work out the best strategy for the entire factory and make changes in production if necessary. We know that a computer can only make a choice between two alternatives (o and 1), but it works its way through whole chains of them, going from one decision to the next. (This working method has made it possible to build chess-playing computers.)

Other computers in industry are employed to work out which product would be the most profitable one to make, on the basis of facts supplied by 'market analysis'; to carry out calculations in aerodynamics, which determine the shapes and performances of aircraft wings, engines, rudders, fuselages, and so on; to discover precisely how much strain a certain material or component can stand before it breaks up—and a thousand more tasks. Smaller computers are doing a variety of office jobs; they work out the wages of thousands of employees; they read, tot up, and analyse the sales figures; they carry out current-account book-keeping in banks; they translate ordinary language into Braille so that the blind can read it; they forecast the weather from meteorological information, carry out 'break downs' in a population census, and select at random the winning numbers in State lotteries.

When we hear that in America every worker produces already 400 times as much as his ancestors, it is small wonder that in the face of this invasion of the electronic robots many industrial and 'white-collar' workers fear for their livelihood. These anxieties are no doubt justified, but only in as much as the new machines threaten to revolutionize the old social system. The unskilled or semi-skilled labourer will find less and less to do, but the demand for people who understand the new machines is bound to increase so much that education will have to catch up with it. For some time the number of employees in non-manual jobs requiring a certain standard of education has been growing annually much faster than that of ordinary workers in industry. Older people will therefore find it more difficult to adapt themselves to the new techniques, and teenagers who can do not much more than read, write, and do simple sums will discover that their career chances are dwindling. An automatized factory needs only one-fifth or one-sixth of the labour force of an old-type plant, but it needs mathematicians who can speak the computer language. Some countries are taking account of these requirements; at Moscow University alone, for instance, over a hundred computer mathematicians are being trained every year.

In automation, as in many other fields, Russia and America are keen competitors, in the style of 'anything you can do I can do better'. When the Americans announce that they have an automatic factory in Los Angeles entirely run by miniature circuits using transistors and working twenty times faster than human operators, the Russians reply with a claim that their giant hydro-electric power station, Dnieproges, which required a permanent staff of 290 technicians in 1940, needs only six per shift today, thanks to automation. In at least one sector the Russians are one up on their rivals, that of cutting down the 'idle' time of transfer. They have invented a system by which components are being machined *during* transfer from one operation to the next; the components are gripped by rotating drums with varying speeds according to the time the operation requires, and machined while they revolve.

But to return to our computers—how are they likely to develop, and what will their effect on our society be? The first question can easily be answered. The trend is to make them as self-sufficient as possible. The 'reading' computer, the electronic eye which can scan ordinary type, will be developed to perfection. One line this trend may take is indicated by the invention of the 'visible record computer', which needs neither punched nor magnetic tape but works with magnetic-ink characters which both the computer and its human operator can read. Another development may be towards the 'do-it-yourself' computer, which can be assembled, dismantled, and reassembled in a different way by the works engineers; it has exchangeable printed circuits on flat plates no bigger than postcards.

Computers will become smaller and smaller because space is valuable. One method, the 'cryogenic' one, is to make their circuits of thin films of lead or tin and keep them at a temperature of minus 269° C. in a bath of liquid helium; at that temperature the metals become 'super-conductive', i.e. they lose all electric resistance, and if a current is set up in them it goes on circling indefinitely. At least 2,000 'cryotrons', as these circuits are called, can be accommodated in the space of a cubic inch. Other microcircuits have been printed on glass slips, for instance for computers—no larger than an orange—in research rockets and space satellites. Servo-mechanisms for industry also tend to become smaller and smaller; there are, for instance, hydraulic servo-valves weighing only 5–6 lb. which can operate the controls of an aeroplane or a lifting-jack with 1,500 lb. thrust.

Just about discernible on the technical horizon is an entirely new development which may grow into a full-scale revolution: the replacement of electricity in many electronic systems by liquids and gases so as to make them simpler, stronger, cheaper, and more reliable. Valves and transistors may be superseded by streams of fluid and small plastic blocks pierced by tiny tunnels in all kinds of appliances, from automatic washing-machines to rocket guidance systems and automatic machine tools in factories. This new concept of electronics without electricity, called PFA (pure fluid amplifiers), has been developed in the ordnance laboratories of the U.S. Army, although ordinary fluid amplifiers are already widely used in hydraulic and pneumatic machine control; but these require moving parts such as valves and pistons while there are none in 'pure' fluid amplification. It is all done by the principle of 'momentum'. When, for example, a powerful water jet from a fire hose is hit by a lighter jet coming from one side, it is deflected to the other side—the lighter jet 'controls' the stronger one. Many feedback devices could therefore be controlled by PFA instead of electronically.

Eventually automation may cause the extension of compulsory schooling for a few more years to get a better educated labour force (and to reduce the number of young unskilled workers looking for jobs). It will also, no doubt, bring a thirty-hour or four-day week at an increased level of real wages as production per man and man-hour rises to new peaks. It may also clear away the relics of the nineteenth-century tug-of-war system of industrial relations with employers and employees as opposing teams, and create new forms of common management and ownership. And if we ask ourselves what should be done with all the goods which automation will produce at an ever-increasing rate, we only have to remember that two-thirds of mankind are still hungry, and living in most primitive conditions.

This is an especially important point when we consider the future of food production. Agriculture, too, benefits from electronic techniques. After many thousands of years during which agriculture, in the Western as well as in the Eastern world, developed hardly at all beyond the primitive early stage, motorization began to replace animal and human muscles only slowly in our own century, and only in industrialized countries. First came the tractor for hauling farm implements over the fields, and as a general fetch-and-carry machine for the farmer. Ford in America and Ferguson in Britain introduced, in the time between the two world wars, tractors that were in effect power units for the operation of specially designed field machines, with a new system of linking the two. At the same time the combine harvester— which cuts the crops, threshes them, and puts the grain into sacks or storage tanks—made its first appearance as a self-propelled machine. Mechanization began to extend to livestock husbandry; it brought egg production in 'cafeteria batteries' (with the hens living in small compartments and being fed from a moving belt), milking machines, and even indoor rearing of cattle with the help of various machines.

From these beginnings, automation on the farm developed in

the 1950's, simultaneously in America and Russia. It began with the driverless tractor which was made to respond to remote control either by cable or by radio signals; these signals can be transmitted either by an operator or completely automatically by electronic control, ordering the tractor to attach itself to, or detach itself from, various implements, and to carry out a whole sequence of operations. There is no technological reason why every field operation—ploughing, cultivating, drilling, rolling, spraying, harvesting—should not be carried out by remote control from an observation room with radar or television screens and computers; but there is, of course, an economic one for the west European farmer, because complete automation pays only in wide spaces.

Many farmers in the American mid-West operate a system of semi-automation which future agricultural technicians may regard as somewhat crude; still, to most European farmers it must look like Utopian fantasy. By pushing buttons and pulling switches the operators control the machines that plough, sow, fertilize, pick and shell the corn, and empty it into glass-lined storage tanks. Another button is pressed at feeding-time, and a scientifically measured amount of corn goes down an elevator shaft and into a self-unloading wagon which automatically shunts it into the cattle troughs, mixed with supplementary vitamins, antibiotics, and hormones which help to fatten the cattle much faster and protect them against diseases. The cattle never graze in the fields —a motorist can drive for hundreds of miles through cultivated land in Illinois, Indiana, Missouri, Iowa, Kansas, and Nebraska without seeing much of the millions of head of cattle being reared in that vast area. They are kept in metal buildings where climate and feeding is strictly controlled. On an average, four times as many head of cattle can be reared by this system with only half the labour as compared with the old methods. But these farm-hands have to be mechanics and electricians as well, with a smattering of biological knowledge.

Two hundred head of cattle can be fed in five minutes. The hogs have troughs whose lids open mechanically at feeding-time. Cows, which must be 'exercised', have their own 'loafing areas' and special 'maternity stalls' for calving; milking, of course, is done mechanically, and the milk flows down a glass pipe-line cooler from where it is pumped into 3,000-gallon trucks which take it to market. A small electronic computer selects the mates for the chickens. They are killed, plucked, cleaned, and packaged by automatic machines.

England may not be ready yet for automation in agriculture, but the Farm Mechanization Department at the University of Reading has developed an automatic tractor which can carry the biggest part of the load of farm work. This machine has a self-navigational system enabling it to steer itself through any of the travel patterns required in field work. 'Sensing', signalling, and servo-mechanisms operate the clutches, brakes, steering, and accelerator, as well as any attached implement or machine.

The tractor will also be equipped with registering instruments. At Reading University it is believed that many of the farmer's decisions are too subjective, and that measurements of lengths, weights, temperatures, colours, and so on can be made with greater accuracy by instruments indicating the rates of growth and state of ripeness of plants, the maturity of animals, or the fertility levels of soils. Equipped with all these faculties, the Reading tractor and the computer which processes the data can almost release the farmer from his customary jobs in crop production; it can also be adapted to look after the livestock with a minimum of human supervision.

Another scientist at Reading University, specializing in horticulture, has designed a glasshouse of transparent plastic, into which air is blown automatically, conditioned to the right temperature, humidity, and carbon dioxide content. The plants are grown in artificial 'soil' with automatic control of their water and nutrient supply and, of course, temperature. Natural daylight is supplemented by artificial light whose spectral composition can be controlled. Harvesting and packaging of the fruit is done by automatic machines. The horticultural worker of the future will therefore have to be not just a gardener but a highly specialized technician.

Mining, the other of the two 'basic' industries on which civilization has been built, was just as slow in introducing mechanization. But as the demand for coal and ore rose steeply in the nineteenth century, mines grew deeper, the workings more widespread, and galleries and shafts longer. Harder rock had to be worked, more air circulated, more water pumped—all of which required power and mechanization. In our century, 'hand-holing' has been entirely replaced by machines and pit ponies largely by mechanical transport—electric locomotives, conveyors, power loaders. In the short space from 1954 to 1960, mechanized output in the British pits rose from 16 to 55 per cent. The second stage of this revolution has been reached with the application of a number of automatic machines which can hew and load mineral by themselves in one operation, some working rather like moles, making their own tunnels in the rock as they advance. Human attendants are still required to accompany and control most of them, but there are already models which are completely automatic.

One such machine, installed in Nottinghamshire in 1962, has a control unit with a 'sensing head' containing a radio-active isotope which emits gamma rays. The rays, reflected off the coal face, steer the coal-cutting machine by means of an electro-hydraulic linkage system. This ensures that the machine remains in the mineral 'bed'. Behind the 'shearer' automatic hydraulic-powered pit props are marching forward while a conveyor carries the coal back. The whole process is controlled by one man from a console 60 yards away. And nuclear power will also play some part; atomic explosions underground can be used to break up the rock in this way, thus giving access to seams which would be too difficult and uneconomical to work by conventional tunnelling.

No doubt the tendency in coal-mining is towards complete automation, towards the unmanned 'face'. Tomorrow's miner will have to be an electrical and electronic engineer, trained to control his machines from a switchboard by means of dials, gauges, television screens, knobs, and switches. The job of cutting the coal may then be done by gigantic hydraulic jets (the Russians have pioneered this system in the Donbas region, and Australian engineers have subsequently tried it out). Hydraulic mining needs very little manpower and lends itself greatly to remote and automatic control, and it entails no risk of fire as no chemical explosives are used.

Electronic devices which can do the most surprising things keep appearing in many industries. High-frequency heating, for instance, is used in smelting, plastic welding, wood glueing, and biscuit-making. The heat can be generated in three ways: by induction, by micro-wave irradiation, or dielectrically (i.e. by placing a non-conducting body between two electrodes, which creates heat in it). Electronic valves are required in this process.

* M

Transistors control driverless trolleys in factories, replacing expensive conveyor-belt or overhead crane installations. A number of these unmanned vehicles can be controlled from a central point; over the routes on which they are required to operate a normal wire is laid—either taped to the factory floor or fixed beneath the flooring—and an alternating current passed through it. Two 'sensing' coils in the front of the trolley pick up the signal currents from the magnetic field of the wire, and keep the truck on its path. As soon as it encounters an obstacle it stops, and when the obstacle is removed it starts again by itself.

On the roads, electronic traffic control is essential where large numbers of vehicles must be kept moving. The introduction of coloured traffic lights, operated manually by a policeman or in fixed time cycles, was sufficient to speed up urban traffic in the 1920's and 1930's. In the big cities of today, however, a more sensitive system is necessary; it uses an electronic device which adjusts the red-amber-green cycle to the speed and density of traffic. It calculates the speed of the vehicles approaching, say, a busy junction, and the length of time during which they will need the green light. If a cyclist approaches with a row of fast-moving cars, the control mechanism will disregard the speed of the cars and give him enough time to cross in safety.

Fire engines, ambulances, and police cars can be given a special right of way where a system first tested at Coventry in 1959 is used: the vehicles are equipped with small, short-range, very-high-frequency transmitters which send ahead a special signal; this is picked up by receivers built into traffic lights, changes them at once to 'green', and holds them at this phase just long enough to let the fire engine, ambulance, or police car pass through.

Electronic, automatic teaching machines which can instruct anyone on practically any subject, from playing bridge to piloting an aircraft, have been introduced by industrial firms, educational institutions, and the services, The 'auto-tutor' presents certain questions to the student; if he answers correctly, the machine congratulates him and sets a further task. If the student is wrong, the machine tells him how and why and encourages him to have another try. It records the student's rate of progress (or otherwise) in a 'report' which is later read by the supervising human teacher. The machine has a screen on which appear questions, images, and instructions projected from a microfilm; the student answers by pressing one or several of forty buttons.

We know that electronics, and especially computers, will develop in the general direction of higher speed and smaller size. Already now their fantastic speed has made it necessary to coin a new term, the 'milli-microsecond'—one-thousandth of a millionth of a second. Semi-conductors will play an increasing part; the 'parametron', invented by the German scientist von Neumann, and the 'paramagnetic amplifier' use radar techniques and semi-conductors such as germanium or silicon to increase the computer speed tenfold over the present one. Are these incredible speeds really necessary? They may be tomorrow in fast air travel, in traffic control, in industrial automation. The completely automatic production plant will do everything almost without human control, from accepting the customer's order to delivering the finished, packaged product together with the bill. The future will show if Man, in his turn, will develop the faculty of using this enormous capacity for production to a good purpose. An age of leisure coupled with plenty has been made possible by electronics; but so far human wisdom and kindness have lagged far behind scientific progress. Will we use it to make the 'haves' still richer, or to help the 'have-nots', and increase the sum total of human happiness on earth?

Few research instruments have helped the scientists so much during the last three centuries and a half as the microscope. Invented by two lens-grinders, the brothers Hans and Zacharias Janssen, of Middelburg, Holland, around 1590, it is essentially a combination of two magnifying glasses. It consists of two converging lenses, or systems of lenses: the 'objective', which is nearer to the viewed object, forming a magnified image of it; and the 'eyepiece', through which this image is observed, magnifying it still further. Daylight or artificial light is reflected on to the object, usually contained on a glass slide, by an illuminating mirror.

A modern optical microscope is a highly complex device; it owes much to the ingenuity of the German nineteenth-century physicist, Ernst Abbe, the founder of the Zeiss works at Jena. In forming an enlarged image, the microscope bends the light rays, and this process has its natural limits; therefore even the best optical microscope cannot magnify objects more than about 2,000 times. But does the microscope have to restrict itself to using only light rays? In 1924 Louis de Broglie, the French physicist, formulated his theory that electrons, like light, move in waves. Two years later Dr Hans Busch, of the university at Jena, discovered that when a beam of electrons passes through a wire coil —which acts as a magnet—the beam can be focused just as a light beam can be focused by a lens.

In 1932 Max Knoll and Dr Ernst Ruska in Berlin began to translate these discoveries into practice by building the first electron microscope. It renounced the elements which until then had seemed indispensable in optical instruments—light, glass, and air. Knoll-Ruska's first model was, of course, rather crude; they would succeed in catching a fleeting glimpse of some microbe or other, then the image would become blurred, and they had to adjust the knobs of the instrument for hours before getting their object into focus again.

But they established the principle of 'seeing with electrons' instead of light, and a few years later the television pioneer, V. K. Zworykin, demonstrated in America his own electron microscope with which he achieved magnifications up to five times greater than with the best optical microscopes. In 1941 the influenza virus was photographed for the first time.

The electron microscope is based on the fact that electrons have a much shorter wavelength than light rays, and therefore smaller particles can be made visible; a whole new microcosm of infinitely small things, living and dead, has been revealed by the new instrument. The 'lenses' are wire coils; the electrostatic and magnetic fields created by the coils serve as objective and focusing lens. Thus the electron beam emitted by a heated filament in a vacuum can be made to enlarge the image of a small object, such as a microbe, on a thin celluloid sheet. The electrons hitting the hard parts of the microbe are stopped, but the rest go through until they arrive at a fluorescent screen, where they are made visible like a television picture, or at a photographic plate where they can be recorded. The whole path of the electrons is kept free of air because they can travel only in a vacuum; neither is there any glass, which they cannot penetrate.

Today electron microscopes can achieve 'useful' magnifications of 1 : 1,500,000; this means that the detail shown is as small as five to ten atom diameters. We can already distinguish some molecules, and perhaps one day we shall see that elusive particle, the atom, and photograph it—though probably not its nucleus, which is a great deal smaller still. Much depends on the preparation of the specimen because the electrons have to go through it and are not reflected from it like the light rays in an optical microscope. Specimens must, therefore, be extremely thin; the thicker they are the cruder is the enlargement. Thicknesses of less than two-millionths of an inch produce the best results. The specimens must also be thermally, mechanically, and electrically stable to withstand the onslaught of the electrons without deterioration.

The instrument has found extensive use in metallurgy, where the technique used in specimen preparation is that of making thin metal foils by rolling and electrolytic polishing. In biological research, 'ultra-microtomes' are produced—slices of organic matter which are so thin that the full power of the electron microscope can come into play.

Less powerful, but somewhat more practical to handle, is the ultra-violet television microscope. It uses the short wavelengths between the visible-light spectrum and the X-rays, and the image is electronically magnified and projected directly on to the screen of a television receiver. This instrument holds much promise as a research tool.

There are other modern ways of making the invisible perceptible. In scientific research, the 'image intensifier', developed at the Imperial College, London, can magnify and record photographically very faint images. The instrument, which looks like a small telescope stuck through one or two dozen wire coils, works by converting photons—quanta of light—into electrons. Another exciting possibility, still waiting to be developed, is the 'maser' (micro-wave amplification of stimulated emission of radiation). The principle was first conceived by Dr Charles H. Townes of Columbia University, who believed that electromagnetic radiation could be magnified by taking advantage of its interactions with matter. Very high frequency radio waves and light waves can be amplified by means of a ruby coated with silver except for a small hole at each end; when light amplification is required, it is first exposed to green light, which pumps energy into the electrons in its crystal structure; this whirls them about in a highly energetic state and makes them unstable. Now red light is shone on the ruby, which makes the electrons 'jump' to lower energy levels. As they do so they give off their excess energy as a pure beam of light emanating from the holes in the ruby—red light in the form of a narrow, very intense beam. Similarly, V.H.F. radio waves can be amplified by the ruby maser. It is hoped that this system can be made to play an important part in the new science of radio astronomy.

Electronics has given us the key to the world of the smallest things; it has also opened the door to the distant depths of the universe for us, and it will probably, in the near future, answer those fundamental questions about the origin and development of the celestial spaces which Man has been asking since he first raised his eyes to the heavens.

Until the beginning of the seventeenth century the forces of spiritual darkness in Europe managed to restrain the scientists from finding out, and pronouncing, the truth about the world around us; and there were no instruments for a closer investigation of the stars and planets. In 1609 the great Italian astronomer, Galileo Galilei, heard a rumour that a Dutchman had invented a glass that could magnify distant objects. Using his optical knowledge, he built such a glass himself—a telescope. Among the first surprising discoveries he made with it were the facts that the moon did not have a smooth surface but that the patches we see consist of many rugged mountains and valleys; that the Milky Way was a vast mass of stars; and that the planet Jupiter had four satellites. All these discoveries, and the general ideas about the universe which Galileo deduced from them, were most disturbing to the Church. He was summoned to Rome, where the Inquisition forced him to renounce his 'heresies', and for the rest of his life he remained virtually a prisoner, forbidden to say what he had found to be true.

Galileo's telescope and that of Johannes Kepler, invented around the same time, are the prototypes of our present-day binoculars, while most modern astronomical models are based on the reflecting telescope invented by Isaac Newton around 1670. A large concave mirror reflects the object, and this image is then magnified by the eyepiece. The picture thus obtained is inverted, which does not matter in astronomical research. Instruments with mirrors of diameters up to 200 inches (Mount Palomar, California) have been built, with powers of magnification up to 1 : 1,000,000.

Telescopes can only see what emits or reflects light, and until a few decades ago no astronomer suspected that there might also be stars emitting other rays than light rays. In 1932, however, Dr Karl Jansky, working at the Bell Telephone Laboratories, received radio waves which seemed to him to emanate from the 'empty' interstellar space. For a decade and a half this discovery was not appreciated, and it could not have been studied without the highly sensitive radio instruments developed during the Second World War. Electronic engineering made it possible to build 'radio telescopes' of such precision that they can receive, identify, and locate waves from the most distant parts of the universe. The first of these instruments found in 1948 that the most powerful sources of these radio emissions were in two distinct spots in the constellations of Cygnus and Cassiopeia: the first 'radio stars' to be discovered. Since then many thousands of them have been found, making up an entirely new map of the heavens. One of the most sensational scientific discoveries of our time was the fact that our nearest neighbouring galaxy, the Andromeda nebula, contains a great many of these invisible suns. Andromeda is 'broadcasting' on a wavelength of 1·89 metres, but other sources emit waves of lengths between a few centimetres and about 20 metres. Not only individual stars emit them; the Cygnus source, for instance, has been identified with a collision of two vast nebulae at a distance of 200 million light-years—near the limit from which light can be received by the 200-inch Mount Palomar telescope.

In 1951 another type of emission on a constant wavelength of 21 centimetres was discovered, coming from clouds of hydrogen gas in interstellar space. When received on earth, however, the wavelength is shifted because of the Doppler effect—it decreases in frequency as the source of emission moves away. This means that we can now measure the speed at which such cosmic bodies recede from us, a fact which, as we shall see, may help us to find an answer to the question of the nature and age of the universe.

The man who developed radio astronomy from chance observations to a new branch of science on a par with optical astronomy within the short space of ten years was Professor Sir Bernard Lovell, of Manchester University. After working under

Sir Robert Watson-Watt on radar, he acquired some unwanted army equipment and moved with a small team into Jodrell Bank, Cheshire, where Manchester University had its Botany Department. The original idea was to use war-time radar techniques—shooting off pulses and catching the echoes—to track down showers of cosmic rays, a field of research in which Lovell's colleague, Professor P. M. S. Blackett, was the leading authority in the world.

The results were curious. There were 'echoes' far beyond the expected ones; they turned out to be trails of meteors—invisible ones, whose existence the astronomers had never suspected. But there were many more 'galactic noises' which kept coming in, tempting investigation; Jansky's fifteen-year-old discovery seemed to fit in with these phenomena. Also, the American Army Signal Corps had succeeded in getting radar echoes from the moon in 1946. Lovell wanted to take up these experiments, and shoot pulses also to the sun and Venus. So he built his first 'radio telescope', 130 feet high, with a large bowl of steel lattice for transmission and reception of waves from space. It was with this instrument that the first 'radio stars' were discovered.

Ten years later, in 1957, Professor Lovell's new, gigantic radio telescope was ready for operation at Jodrell Bank—just in time to track the first Russian *sputnik* which went into its orbit, 560 miles above the earth, in October of that year. The reflector bowl, 80 yards in diameter, over an acre in surface, is suspended from two lattice towers which run on bogies around a circular track 350 feet in diameter. The reflector, itself geared to move up and down, can therefore be pointed at any part of the sky.

The new science of radio astronomy has so far only scratched the surface of its immense field of research. Fascinating prospects have opened up before the astronomers, whose work of observation, by the way, is no longer restricted to the hours of darkness and cloudlessness. There is the still unsolved riddle of the radio stars. Are they very hot bodies, so hot that the visible light is absent from their spectra? Or is their light hidden by vast depths of gases surrounding them? A good deal of the electro-magnetic emission we receive seems to be the result of collisions between galaxies somewhere in the depths of the universe.

And there is the age-old question: is there any intelligent life on planets in other solar systems? Astronomers have not much hope that they will discover man-like beings on some planet in our own solar system; but why should there not be conditions favouring organic development on at least a few of the innumerable planets around the 100,000 million suns of our Milky Way? The Jodrell Bank telescope could try to establish contact with one or the other—surely there must be intelligent beings who have developed the technique of sending and receiving radio waves as we have. Chances are that one day the incoming signals might 'try to say something'. But how could we communicate with our unknown fellow-beings somewhere in space? Mathematics seems to be a possible cosmic language. One could start by exchanging decimal numbers, go on to transmit their powers, the mathematical equivalent of the Pythagorean theorem, logarithms —and eventually find a common idiom. But it will be a somewhat drawn-out conversation; for our closest neighbouring sun, Alpha Centauri, is five light-years away, and the next closest constellations, Epsilon Eridani and Tau Ceoi, twelve light-years. Even if we could generate sufficient energy to penetrate these enormous spaces we would have to wait for at least ten years for an answer to our signals. But it will be tried—Man will try anything to satisfy his undying curiosity.

He also wants to know how the universe began, and when. Within a few years radio astronomy will be able to answer that question. While the 200-inch telescope on Mount Palomar has a range of $4\frac{1}{2}$ thousand million light-years, the radio telescope gropes for sources of waves perhaps ten thousand or more millions of light-years away, eventually penetrating to the ends of time and space— there is no difference between these two concepts.

Two conflicting theories on the nature of the universe have been developed in our generation. One, the evolutionist theory, says that the universe was created in the form of an immense lump of matter of such density that a cubic inch of it must have weighed (in earthly terms) several millions of tons; this 'primeval atom' began to disintegrate many thousands of millions of years ago, and has been expanding ever since, forming galaxies, stars, and solar systems.

The other theory is that of the 'steady state'. According to it, the universe does not alter with time in its general appearance, for matter is being continuously created throughout it, thus compensating for the 'disappearance' of matter owing to expansion.

This means that the universe never had a beginning and will never have an end, and if there had been people to look at it from our earth thousands of millions of years ago it would have appeared to them little different from what it is now.

How can radio astronomy help to decide which theory is correct? We have already at least one radio telescope which is

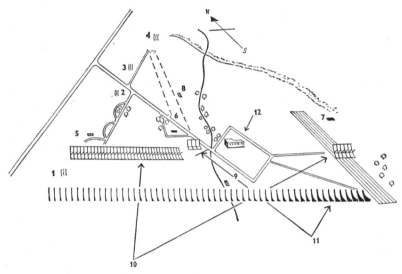

Map of the Radio Astronomy Observatory, University of Cambridge

*Key:* 1–4. Interferometers for measuring diameters of radio sources. 5–9. Interferometers for sunspot investigations. 10. Radio star interferometer. 11. 'Pencil Beam' instrument for investigating galactic radio emission on a wavelength of 8 metres. 12. Main observatory building

able to 'look' at corners of the universe some 9,000 million light-years away, that is, 'see' it as it was 9,000 million years ago. It has been tracking the galaxies speeding away from us by means of the famous Doppler effect. If the 'steady-state' theory is right, then the density of matter and its speed will be found to be about the same as they are, or were, at much shorter time-space distances. If the evolutionists are right, then there will be much greater density because at that time the expansion of the universe was still in a much earlier phase.

That instrument is one of a group of radio telescopes built for the famous Cavendish Laboratory, University of Cambridge, in

1955–7—the 'Mullard Radio Astronomy Observatory'. It is basically different from the bowl-shaped Jodrell Bank telescope and consists of two structures, 2,300 feet apart, each in the form of a cylindrical paraboloid. One is 1,450 feet long in an east–west direction and 65 feet wide; it is fixed to the ground, while the other, 190 by 65 feet, can be moved along a 1,000-foot railway track laid along a north–south line. These structures have 'reflecting surfaces' of steel wires stretched over the parabolic frames.

The telescope is a 'transit' instrument and uses the rotation of the earth for scanning the sky. When, for instance, a sector of the sky is to be surveyed, the movable aerial is set at one end of the rails, and the signals received from the universe are recorded automatically for twenty-four hours. Day after day, the aerial is moved to a new position along the track until, after thirty days' observations, it has reached the other end of the rails. By that time all the signals received from a strip of sky 4° wide in declination have been recorded. Each strip of sky yields about 200,000 'readings'; they are recorded on teleprinter tape in a form which can be fed directly into an electronic computer at the Cambridge University mathematical laboratory.

The guiding spirit behind this work is Professor Martin Ryle of the Cavendish Laboratory. Early in 1961 he had come to the conclusion that the steady-state theory of the universe was wrong because he had observed, in the farthest depths of space about 9,000 million light-years away, a much greater number of radio stars than the steady-state theory had predicted. That means that 9,000 million years ago the universe was much more tightly packed with matter, which would point to the correctness of the expansion theory: that at some point in the past all the matter of the universe was concentrated in the 'primeval atom', and that an explosion took place—we might call it 'creation'—which made that lump of matter undergo rapid changes, and dispersed it so that it has been expanding ever since. Of course, the steady-state cosmologists, with Professor Fred Hoyle in the forefront, have not given up yet. They believe that much further evidence has to be collected in the years to come before we shall have solved the mystery of creation beyond any doubt.

Thus it is invention and engineering which will deeply

influence our philosophy, our way of thinking, as they have influenced our way of living in the past. They are of our own creation, and it is up to us whether we want to use them to satisfy our greed, our folly, our craving for power, and our lust of destruction—or, in Albert Einstein's words, 'to open the way to a new paradise'.

# Index

Abbe, Ernst: microscope, 361
Adams, W., 89
Ader, Clément: aeroplane, 213
Aeronautics, Leonardo da Vinci's ideas, 191
Aeroplane: predicted by Marquis of Worcester, 29; aerodynamics, 209–10; the father of the modern aeroplane, 210–211; earliest models, 210–14; Wright brothers, 214–17; development, and Blériot crosses Channel, 217–18; passenger aircraft, 219; military uses, 219–220; first Atlantic crossings, 220; jet-engined, 220–3; breaking the sound barrier, 223–4; turbo-jet system, 224; the ram-jet, 225–6; helicopters, 226–232; gliders, 232–3; nuclear-powered bombers, 233–4; problem of airborne reactor, 234; the rocket, 235–6; difficulties and possibilities of rocket propulsion, 236–7
Agfacolor process, 308
Agriculture, electronic techniques in, 356–358
Aiken, Howard: computer, 349
Aileron, 218
Air-cushion principle, 144, 188–90
Air pump, 47
Aircraft detection, by radar, 334
Airships: Gusmão's, 193; early dirigibles, 203–6; rigid and semi-rigid, 206–7; military uses, 207; first Atlantic crossing, 207–8; disasters, 208
*Akron* (airship), 208
Akroyd-Stuart, Herbert: heavy-oil engine, 158
Alchemists, 28, 72
Alcock, Capt. John, 220
Alexander the Great, 209
Alexander I, Tsar, 260
Alexandria, library of, 243
Alweg railway, 143–4
American Civil War: balloons used, 202; photography in, 302
American Locomotive Company, 139
Ammann, O. H.: Hudson Bridge, 111
Ampère, André-Marie: electro-magnet, 53, 262
Ampex recording system, 330
Amplitude modulation, 287
Anamorphic lenses, 318
Andromeda nebula, 365
Arago, François, 300
Archimedes: principle of the lever, 17, 18; fundamental law of hydrostatics, 21

*Archimedes* (screw-propelled ship), 180–1
Archytas of Tarentum: kite, 209
Arco, Count George: wireless, 281
Arkwright, Richard: 'water frame', 41
Arlandes, Count d': balloon, 199
Arles, Roman 'power-station' at, 19
Armstrong, Edwin H.: short-wave broadcasting, 287
Atom, term coined by Democritus, 72
Atomic energy: the atom, 72–3; radium and X-rays, 73; matter into energy, 73; nature of atom, 73–4; neutrons, 74; isotopes, 74–5; chain reaction in uranium, 75; first atomic bombs, 75, 77; first atomic reactor, 77; for peaceful uses, 77–9, 85–6; types of reactor, 78–81; nuclear fusion, 81–4; atomic battery, 84–5; radio-activity, 85–6
Atomic Energy Commission (U.S.), 85, 240
Augustus, Emperor, 104–5
'Autogyro', 228, 229
Automatic landing, 340
Automatic pilots, 339, 343–4
Automatic pistol, 29
Automatic spit, 30
Automation: development, 341–2; principle of, 342–6; machine tools, 346–8; computers, 348–55; replacement of electricity, 355–6; agriculture, 356–8; mining, 358–9; other industries, 359–360; teaching machines, 360–1
Autotype process, 302
Aveling, Thomas: road-roller, 107

Babbage, Charles: principle of the computer, 349
Bacon, Francis T.: fuel cell, 162–3
Bacon, Roger, 28
Bain, Alexander: photo-telegraphy, 320
Baird, John Logie: television, 324–7
Baker, Benjamin: Forth bridge, 112
Baker-Nunn satellite-tracking camera, 305
Bakewell: photo-telegraphy, 320
Balloons, 193–202
Baltes, Adalbert: Cinetarium, 319
Baltic–White Sea Canal, 122
Bardeen, John: transistor, 289
Barium, 75
Barry, Sir J. Wolfe: Tower Bridge, 116
Bats, and ultrasonic radar, 337
Battery, electrical, 50–1
Baudot: multiplex telegraphy, 268
Bauer, Friedrich: printing, 248, 250